# Proceedings of the XIV International Ornithological Congress

# PROCEEDINGS OF THE XIV INTERNATIONAL ORNITHOLOGICAL CONGRESS

Oxford 24-30 July 1966

Edited by

## D.W.SNOW

Blackwell Scientific Publications

Oxford and Edinburgh

*Printed in Great Britain in the City of Oxford at*
THE ALDEN PRESS
*and bound by*
THE KEMP HALL BINDERY, OXFORD

# Contents

# Contents

# Preface by the President

The success of the XIV Congress at Oxford (and reports indicate that it was a success) is due primarily to one man, the Secretary-General, Dr N.Tinbergen. He had many helpers, who are acknowledged in the Secretary-General's report, but the main responsibility and the main burden were his, and I take this opportunity to thank him, on behalf of the whole Congress, for the distinction which he brought to his task and for the extremely hard work which he so ably undertook. Indeed at one time the burden seemed so heavy that I wondered whether it could be right for us, once every four years, to use a leading scientist for this post, to the detriment of his own research and hence of ornithological progress. But I have now changed this view because I see that the authority of a distinguished and respected scientist is needed to make the responsible decisions involved, to gain acceptance for them, and to obtain the many facilities, such as we enjoyed at Oxford, from other persons and organizations.

There is no doubt that the burden of organization would have been much less heavy if the Congress membership had been smaller, and we should all be exercised about the big increase in our numbers at each successive meeting. I believe, and so do many others, that the Congress is already too large, and that, unless numbers can be reduced, (a) we will lose further specialist groups in the way that, sadly, we have already lost almost all the ethologists (and among those who will not think it worth their while to come may be some of our most distinguished scientists), (b) potential host countries will be even more reluctant to invite a future Congress than they were this time (while many do not even possess the necessary accommodation), and (c) no distinguished scientist will be willing to act as Secretary-General. Hence I seriously suggest that, unless drastic steps can be taken, the Congress may destroy itself, at least as a gathering to discuss progress in our science at the highest levels, and valuable as the social side of the Congress is, the scientific side must come first. Any steps to reduce numbers will mean a reduction, perhaps a big one, in the subsidiary facilities and attractions of our Congress; but unless such steps are taken we may, instead, lose its essence. This may seem a sombre note on which to end, but recognition of a problem is the first step towards finding its solution.

On behalf of all our members, I thank most warmly all who helped at the Oxford meeting, and send best wishes to our Dutch hosts for 1970.

David Lack

# Report by the Secretary-General

The ornithologists of Great Britain consider it a great honour to have been selected for the third time to act as hosts to the International Ornithological Congress. The Fourth Congress met in London in 1905 with 250 members under the Presidency of Dr R.Bowdler Sharpe; Dr E.J.O.Hartert and Mr J.L.Bonhote acted as Secretaries. Many of us still remember the Eighth Congress in 1934 when 350 members met in Oxford, with Dr E.Stresemann as President and the Rev. F.C.R.Jourdain as Secretary. Since then numbers have almost trebled—if this present trend continues the organization of future Congresses will become a major task which may well be beyond the powers of non-professional organizers, and in addition may put great demands on accommodation and lecture halls.

At the XIII Congress in Ithaca, Dr David Lack was elected President. Vice-Presidents for 1962–66 were:

| | |
|---|---|
| Dr Salim Ali | Dr Alden H. Miller (deceased) |
| Dr F.Bernis | Dr F.Salomonsen |

The British members of the International Ornithological Committee formed the core of the British Executive Committee, and Dr N.Tinbergen was elected Secretary-General. The full composition of the British Executive Committee, supplemented by a few co-opted members, was as follows:

| | |
|---|---|
| The President | Mr G.Mountfort |
| The Secretary-General | Mr C.A.Norris |
| Miss P.Barclay-Smith | Dr I.D.Pennie |
| Mr S.Cramp, Treasurer | Col. H.M.Salmon |
| Dr J.M.Cullen, Local Secretary | Dr D.W.Snow, Editor |
| Sir Hugh Elliott, Bt. | Mr R.Spencer |
| Mr I.J.Ferguson-Lees | Sir Landsborough Thomson |
| Mr J.Fisher | Prof. W.H.Thorpe |
| Dr G.V.T.Matthews | Mr E.M.Nicholson |
| Mr J.D.Macdonald | Mr G.Waterston |
| Dr J.Monk | Prof. V.C.Wynne-Edwards |
| Mr R.E.Moreau | |

Miss J.M.Allard was appointed Assistant to the Secretary-General, who also had the services of Miss A.Freeman-Taylor. Dr C.Perrins acted as the Assistant to the President; and Dr R.Dawkins took on the task of organizing transport and signposting.

The preparations for the Oxford Congress began in the autumn of 1962. The British Executive Committee, bearing in mind the article by E.M.Nicholson in *British Birds*, Vol. 53, 1960, and proposals made by the President, considered carefully how the Congress could meet the growing and changing demands of our science and of international communication. The first task, the choice of a place of meeting, was difficult. While much was to be said for meeting once more in Oxford, the growing membership could be feared to impose too heavy demands on the limited facilities available. As the President explained in his foreword to the Programme, Oxford was selected partly because it is at present active in ornithological research (in the Edward Grey Institute and the Animal Behaviour Research Group), and partly because it presents a nearly unique feature of English life. Also, it has a large number of small lecture rooms, ample accommodation in colleges, and an excellent social centre in Rhodes House. Large rooms for plenary sessions might prove too small, and there was no hall large enough for a Congress dinner if the membership should be as large as or exceed that of Ithaca, but these difficulties were not considered insurmountable.

The British Executive Committee accepted the decision, taken in Ithaca by the International Ornithological Committee, that the Congress need not be held in the breeding season. It was about to accept another recommendation, viz. that it need not be preceded or followed by field excursions, when the Scottish Ornithologists' Club proposed that they should organize a single study cruise in a ship large enough to hold all the Congress members. We are extremely grateful to the Scottish Ornithologists' Club for this opportunity to see Britain's finest seabird colonies, and for thus both adding a unique feature to this Congress and simplifying the organization of the Congress week in Oxford. A report on the Scottish Bird-Islands Study Cruise appears elsewhere in this volume (p. xix).

It was agreed to retain the customary mid-week break and to set aside the Wednesday for whole-day excursions on which members could relax and meet each other informally. In addition, during the Congress short visits were to be organized for small groups to places of ornithological interest in or near Oxford. A Sub-Committee on Excursions, headed by Mr John Buxton, and with Mrs S.Cowdy and Mrs M.Campbell as members, made the necessary arrangements and also undertook the organization of entertainments and ladies' programmes.

The British Executive Committee further decided to increase the membership fee considerably. This was done as an experiment in order to see whether the

# Report by the Secretary-General

Congress could be made self-supporting, which would have the advantage that in future no small or poor country need fear that acting as host to the Congress would necessitate big outside grants or private gifts.

The large number of members expected made it further necessary to reconsider whether all offered papers should be accepted, which would of course increase the number of sections. The British Executive Committee decided to streamline the Congress in two ways:

(a) By authorizing its Programme Committee to be selective in the acceptance of offered papers. This was done by requiring would-be speakers to send in an abstract beforehand, a procedure to which many members submitted readily and which enabled us to print the abstracts before the Congress. It also had the advantage of leaving the authors free to publish their full accounts elsewhere.

(b) By inviting prominent workers to deliver, in Plenary Sessions, more comprehensive contributions dealing with fields of research which could be considered growing points of our science. It was hoped that such reports would stimulate future research. We are glad to be able to report that hardly any of the distinguished colleagues invited were unable to contribute.

This procedure had as a consequence a different publication policy. The British Executive Committee considered that the conventional Congress Proceedings were in danger of imposing too heavy a burden on the finances of the Congress since they often contained material that could justifiably be published in the normal ornithological journals, where it would also be more accessible. It was therefore decided not to publish any of the offered papers at all and instead to allow the invited speakers more space so that they could, if desired, print a more elaborate version of their actual lecture, which, owing to restrictions of time, might have to be too much condensed.

By thus reducing the total number of lectures it would be possible to make more time available for two other functions of the Congress which are gradually acquiring increased importance. All evenings were set aside for film shows, of which we had two running concurrently every evening; and the period from 1700 till 1900 hours was to be kept free for informal gatherings and for meetings of special committees.

The scientific programme was planned along these lines by a Sub-Committee on which the following members served:

| | |
|---|---|
| The President | Dr J.Monk |
| The Secretary-General | Mr R.E.Moreau |
| Mr J.Boswall (films) | Dr D.W.Snow |

# Report by the Secretary-General

Dr J.M.Cullen          Dr W.H.Thorpe
Dr G.V.T.Matthews

It screened the papers offered for the Sectional Sessions and allocated the task of organizing the Plenary Sessions to:

Dr David Lack          Population Ecology
Dr W.H.Thorpe          Vocal Communication
Mr R.E.Moreau          Systematics and Taxonomy
Dr G.V.T.Matthews      Orientation and Navigation
Dr N.Tinbergen         Aspects of Physiology

The British Executive Committee further decided that, as at previous Congresses, exhibits were to be organized. The exhibits would consist of photographs (to be selected by Mr Eric Hosking), bird art (to be organized by Dr E.A.R.Ennion and Mr R.Gillmor), and scientific exhibits (of which Dr C.Perrins would be in charge). For the selection of films we were fortunate to get the expert help of Mr J.Boswall of the Natural History Unit of the British Broadcasting Corporation.

The British Executive Committee accepted with gratitude the generous offers of the Hon. Mrs Lane and Mr Christopher Marler to organize private parties for large numbers of members at their homes in Elsfield and Weston Underwood respectively.

The Congress finally ended with a traditional Oxford Garden Party on the last afternoon of the Congress, instead of the conventional dinner, for which no hall could be found in Oxford which was large enough to hold the greatly increased membership.

Over 830 people attended the Congress in Oxford. The total membership was 687 Full and 203 Associates. This showed that the high membership fee had been no serious obstacle. A list of delegates representing scientific bodies is given on p. 375.

Registration for the Congress began on Sunday, July 24 at 1100 and members received, among other documents, the Volume which contained abstracts of all papers to be given at the Sectional meetings.

The Congress week opened on Sunday evening, July 24, with a formal meeting in the Sheldonian Theatre, designed by Sir Christopher Wren in 1664. Members were welcomed by 'ornithological music' played on the organ by Mr Martyn Parry of Brasenose College, who with the President had selected the following items:

Couperin   Le Rossignol en Amour
           Les Fauvêtes Plaintives

# Report by the Secretary-General

| | |
|---|---|
| Rameau | Le Rappel des Oiseaux |
| Grieg | Vöglein |
| Haydn | Song of the quail: minuet from 'The Musical Clocks' |
| Delius | On Hearing the First Cuckoo in Spring arranged for organ by Eric Fenby |
| Mozart | Der Vogelfänger from 'Die Zauberflöte' (The Magic Flute) |
| Handel | Concerto for organ No. 13 in F. major: The Cuckoo and the Nightingale |

Brief words of welcome in various Congress languages were given by Overseas Delegates: Dr Salim Ali (on behalf of the English speaking peoples), Dr Jean Dorst (for the French), Dr Lars von Haartman( for the Fenno-Scandians), Dr E. Stresemann (for the Germans), and Dr Charles Sibley (for the Americans). They were followed by brief addresses from the Pro-Vice-Chancellor of Oxford University, A.L.P.Norrington, and the Linacre Professor of Zoology, J.W.S. Pringle. The President then summarized the main objectives of the Congress: members should be able to meet each other and exchange views informally; they should have the opportunity for bringing themselves up to date in their science by hearing review papers as well as reports on new research, and for discussing any international problems that might arise. He further explained how the British Executive Committee had attempted to adapt the Congress to the ever-changing requirements, and urged all members to give thought to the future of the Congress.

The Plenary Sessions, held each morning except on Wednesday, had a large attendance throughout, without being overcrowded. The full texts of the lectures form the bulk of the contents of this volume. It was regretted by all that, owing to the absence of Drs Dementiev and Gladkov, their planned joint paper could not be presented.

The Sectional Sessions, held each afternoon except on the Wednesday, were also well attended. The fear of the organizers that some sessions might attract disproportionately large numbers and thus become overcrowded was not realized. A special word of thanks is due to the chairmen and the speakers of these sessions which almost without exception kept strictly to their time limits, thus making it possible for members to move from one session to another in time to hear the papers of their choice.

# Report by the Secretary-General

The following specialists' meetings were held:
European Ringing Committee.
 Chairman: R-D.Etchécopar.
Meeting on Sea-Bird Research.
 Chairman: V.C.Wynne-Edwards.
Ornithology of the Western Palaearctic—a new project.
 Chairman: E.M.Nicholson.
Report to the Congress by its Standing Committee on Nomenclature.
 Chairman: E.Eisenmann.
International Bird Ringing Committee.
 Chairman: R-D.Etchécopar.
Proposal by David Lack for an internationally agreed world list of birds.
 Chairman: Jean Dorst.
International Union of Applied Ornithology: Annual General Meeting.

The meeting on Sea-Bird Research resulted in the formal recognition of the Committee on Sea-Bird Research as an Official Standing Committee of the International Ornithological Congress. Its composition is printed on p. xviii.

A report on the proposal by Dr David Lack for an internationally agreed world list of birds is printed on p. 365.

In spite of the limitations on bar facilities imposed by British law, Rhodes House was of great value as a social centre. During coffee and tea breaks, and particularly from 1700 to 1900 hours, many members congregated in its rooms and corridors, and, when the weather permitted, on the lawn. Here Miss Allard and Miss Freeman-Taylor and their helpers manned the desk of the Congress Secretariat; they were untiring in their efforts to meet the wishes of members. The helpers at the desk of the Entertainments Committee were rarely idle, and the exhibits in Rhodes House were seen by a constant stream of visitors.

The Photographic Exhibit consisted of a selection of the National Collection of Nature Photographs, assembled and kindly lent by the Nature Conservancy. The Art Exhibit in the Ashmolean Museum contained a selection of paintings, drawings and illustrations by the leading British bird painters of the last three centuries, while the Bear Lane Gallery housed an exhibit by ten living British bird artists. Both exhibits were visited by many and provided an attractive 'side show' for the main Congress.

The Wednesday excursions were made to: The Wildfowl Trust, Slimbridge; Whipsnade Zoological Park, Bedfordshire; The Royal Society for the Protection of Birds, Sandy; The British Trust for Ornithology, Tring; the Grey-Roosevelt

Midweek Excursion to the Wildfowl Trust, Slimbridge. Peter Scott (just right of centre) with members of the Congress. (Eric Hosking)

Master and pupil. (Eric Hosking)

Midweek Excursion to the Wildfowl Trust, Slimbridge. Dr G.V.T.Matthews gives Professor L.Portenko a specimen of *Branta sandvicensis*. (Eric Hosking)

Ernst Mayr, Doctor Scientiae Honoris Causa, with the President.          (Gillman & Soame)

The Garden Party: Folk Dancers. (Gillman & Soame)

Congress members joining in. Foreground left of centre: J.Dorst and Mrs A.Schifferli.

(Eric Hosking)

walk in the New Forest; and a walk on the Berkshire Downs. All were favoured by good weather.

Dr Perrins and his helpers led numerous parties up the University Museum Tower to see the nesting Swifts, subjects of Dr D.Lack's book 'Swifts in a Tower'. Small parties were taken out to Wytham Woods, the estate belonging to Oxford University, where much of the work of the Edward Grey Institute is being carried out. Dr Glen W.Schaefer kindly demonstrated his radar tracking site near Lutterworth, Leicestershire, to parties of visitors.

Films were shown every evening except on Saturday, 30 July. In spite of critical selection, the number of worthwhile ornithological films was so large that two concurrent showings had to be laid on. Here again, our fears that the available rooms would be overcrowded proved to be without foundation.

The Hon. Mrs Lane opened her home at Elsfield to members throughout the week and many seized the opportunity to see the exhibits of photomicrographs, cameras, microscopes and field glasses and also the exhibition of bird sculpture by various artists. On Friday evening a private party held at Elsfield Manor continued until the early hours of the morning and was greatly enjoyed by all who attended.

On Tuesday evening Mr Christopher Marler kindly invited members to a private party at his home in Western Underwood, which was also much enjoyed.

A highlight of the Congress was the conferment of the Honorary Degree of Doctor of Science by Oxford University on Dr Ernst Mayr, President of the preceding Congress. A hundred members of the Congress were given seats in the Sheldonian Theatre and heard the University's Public Orator deliver the following oration:

Hector olim Polydamantem increpans 'nil curo' inquit 'genus alituum', quam vocem temerariam Nemesis exaudiit; hic vero hospes noster si quisquam avium scientiam pietate eximia prosecutus eventu fruitur felicissimo. in Germania natus eruditusque, mox, dum in Museo Zoologico Berolini laborat, usque ad Papuam insulasque Salamonias in expeditionem missus est. deinde mare Atlanticum transvectus studia Historiae Naturalis in Museo Novi Eboraci continuavit, unde ad Harvardianos abhinc tredecim annis migravit. in Oceani autem Pacifici insulis varias volucrum species diligenter scrutatus nova et gravia argumenta de formarum origine excogitata bello hoc altero nondum composito sollertissime protulit, ex quo tempore cum duobus collegis ingeniosissimis, quibus ambobus iam nos honores decrevimus, Georgio Simpson palaeontologo Theodosioque Dobzhansky in rebus geneticis exercitato investigationes perquam fructuosas communicabat. quid? nempe Ovidius scripsit mare et terras et caelum a deo naturaque esse e Chao evoluta; nos autem Carolum Darwin atque cetera magna aetatis Victorianae ingenia, qui quam late pateret haec ratio dilucide demonstraverunt, meritis laudibus extollimus: hic tamen eandem rationem perspicaci mente, laboribus assiduis ad multiplicatam huius saeculi doctrinam unus omnium maxime accommodavit. idem iamdiu ephemeridas 'Evolutio' nominatas edit nuperque alterum librum egregium eadem de re conscripsit: idem abhinc quattuor annis Congressioni Ornithologiae Studiosorum sagacissime praesedit; denuo hac Congressione idque apud nos convocata libentissime excipimus οἰωνοσκόπον praeclarissimum, Ernestum Walterum Mayr, inter Harvardianos Cathedram Zoologiae in memoriam Alexandri Agassiz constitutam summa omnium approbatione adeptum, quem praesento ut admittatur honoris causa ad gradum Doctoris in Scientia.

The official translation runs as follows:

In Homer Hector rebuked Polydamas, saying 'I care naught for birds', a rash remark overheard by Nemesis. But our guest has pursued ornithology with a success that matches his devotion. German-born and educated, while holding his first post at the Berlin Zoological Museum he was sent on expeditions to Papua and the Solomon Islands. He crossed the Atlantic to join the staff of the American Museum of Natural History in New York (1932–53) where he continued his researches. He moved to his present Chair at Harvard in 1953. His work on birds in the Pacific Islands led to the publication in 1942 of an important book in which he gave a fresh account of the origin of species. There followed a fruitful collaboration with the palae-ontologist George Simpson and the geneticist Theodosius Dobzhansky, both of whom already hold Oxford honorary doctorates. Ovid told how sea, land and sky 'evolved' from Chaos: we in our turn admire Darwin and other eminent Victorians for explaining scientifically the wide application of evolutionary doctrine. It is however Professor Mayr's synthesis which at the present time holds the field. He is founder-editor of the journal *Evolution* and was President of the International Ornithological Congress in 1962. The Congress is now meeting again and in this country, and we take the opportunity of cordially welcoming this prince of bird-watchers, Ernst Walter Mayr, Agassiz Professor of Zoology at Harvard, whom I now present for admission to the Honorary Degree of D.Sc.

The ceremony was followed immediately by a Garden Party in Trinity College. After a veritable cloudburst at 1400 hours, the sky miraculously cleared

# Report by the Secretary-General

and warm sunny weather put the pessimists to shame, and delighted the organizers and members who either knew or had heard of the fickleness of the English climate. Dancers from the Buckinghamshire District of the English Folk Dance and Song Society were a generally appreciated attraction and succeeded in drawing many members into joining them. The President announced the decisions reached by the International Ornithological Committee for the President and country of the next Congress in 1970, and Professor Mayr conveyed the thanks of the members to the Organizers of the Congress.

It is a pleasure to acknowledge the help of all those who contributed to the success of the Congress. We are particularly grateful to the Trustees of the Cecil Rhodes Trust for the use of Rhodes House; to the Heads and Fellows of those Colleges who kindly entertained groups of distinguished members at lunch; to the President and Fellows of Trinity College for hospitality for the Garden Party; to the Trustees of the Ashmolean Museum for the use of the Drapers' Gallery, and to the Assistant Keeper of the Department of Western Art, Mr Ian Lowe; to the Hon. Aylmer Tryon for his assistance in acquiring so many fine pictures and for printing the cover of the Catalogue; to the Directors of the Bear Lane Gallery; to the Heads of University Scientific Departments for permission to use lecture rooms; to the Wildfowl Trust and the Zoological Society of London for hospitality to the large numbers visiting the New Grounds and Whipsnade Zoological Park; to the British Trust for Ornithology and the Royal Society for the Protection of Birds for hospitality to members and, with the Scottish Ornithologists' Club and the Nature Conservancy, for exhibition material; to the Hon. Mrs Lane and Mr Christopher Marler for their generous hospitality to so many members of the Congress; to Shell Mex and B.P. Limited for calendars and the booklet *The Shell List of Birds*; to our hard working room stewards; and finally to those members who, by acting as College Representatives, did so much to make members feel at home in their temporary and in some respects unusual habitat.

As usual, the Permanent Executive Committee met twice, as did the International Ornithological Committee. It was decided that the XV International Ornithological Congress should be held in Holland in 1970 and Professor N.Tinbergen was elected as its President.

The various Committees for 1966–70 were constituted as follows.

### THE PERMANENT EXECUTIVE COMMITTEE

Prof. F.Bernis                                    Prof. Finn Salomonsen

# Report by the Secretary-General

Prof. Jean Dorst                     Dr Dominic Serventy
Dr David Lack                        Prof. Charles Sibley
Prof. Günther Niethammer             Marquess Yoshimaro Yamashina

## INTERNATIONAL ORNITHOLOGICAL COMMITTEE

See p. 369.

## STANDING COMMITTEE ON NOMENCLATURE

Mr Eugene Eisenmann, Secretary      Dr Charles Vaurie, Chairman
Prof. Jean Dorst                     Prof. Karel H.Voous
Prof. Finn Salomonsen

## STANDING COMMITTEE FOR THE COORDINATION OF SEA-BIRD RESEARCH

Prof. V.C.Wynne-Edwards (U.K.), Chairman
Dr W.R.P.Bourne (U.K.), Secretary
Mr R.A.Falla (N.Z.)
Dr F.Goethe (Germany)
Mr C.Jouanin (France)
Dr N.H.Kuroda (Japan)
Prof. Karel H.Voous (Netherlands)
Dr G.E.Watson (U.S.A.)

Professor Finn Salomonsen was elected Representative to the International Committee for the Protection of Birds 1966–70.

N.Tinbergen

The Permanent Executive Committee

Standing from left to right: G.Niethammer, J.Dorst, L.von Haartman, W.H.Thorpe, C.G.Sibley, Y.Yamashina.

Sitting from left to right: S.Ali, N.Tinbergen, D.Lack, F.Salomonsen, F.Bernis.

(Gillman & Soame)

Presidents

From left to right: D.Lack 1966, Sir Landsborough Thomson 1954, A.Wetmore 1950, J.Berlioz 1958, E.Mayr 1962, E.Stresemann 1934.                    (Gillman & Soame)

# The Scottish Bird–Islands Study Cruise

## REPORT BY A. LANDSBOROUGH THOMSON

This was the longest, most ambitious, and most imaginative excursion that has ever been provided for an International Ornithological Congress. Through a combination of superb organization, favourable weather and general goodwill it was an immense success. For these meetings, tending to increase in size with each quadrennium, it may indeed prove to be 'the main excursion to end all main excursions'. How else but on a big ship could one compactly transport several hundreds of people for over 1,000 miles, housing and feeding them for a week? And where else, in the readily accessible parts of the world, could a cruise offer a series of spectacular exhibits of bird-life on such a scale as around these Scottish islands? Moreover, to be able to let so many people see so many breeding birds without detriment to the latter was in itself a most important consideration.

When the XIV International Congress was allotted to the United Kingdom, Scottish ornithologists hoped that Edinburgh might this time be chosen for the meeting; and they early had the idea that a main excursion to the bird-islands could be part of the plan. When various reasons led the British Executive Committee of the Congress to decide in favour of Oxford, the members from Scotland (Dr Ian Pennie and George Waterston) urged that a Scottish cruise should still be included in the programme; and this was agreed in principle. The British Executive Committee in due course approved the general plan of the cruise and fixed dates for it and for the following meeting at Oxford; subsequently the International Council for Bird Preservation fitted its own Conference for 1966 into the time schedule by arranging to meet at Cambridge in the week before the cruise. From January 1964 the Scottish Ornithologists' Club took over full responsibility for the cruise, which was thenceforth organized separately from the Congress as an associated enterprise.

This was a big task for the Club, involving more than two years of hard work for its Secretary (Mrs Irene Waterston) and many of its members; these services were given with great willingness and effect. There was also an element of financial risk, as a vessel had not only to be provisionally chartered long beforehand, but the large fee (£26,000) was to be paid well in advance. To protect individuals,

# The Scottish bird-islands study cruise

a private company called 'Scottish Ornithological Cruise Limited' was formed; guarantors against loss were found, and insurance against risks of cancellation was effected. The Club appointed a Cruise Committee, and this set up subcommittees on such aspects as finance, land transport, films and lectures, and the final day in Edinburgh. An attractive brochure was provided (as a contribution from Oliver & Boyd Limited) for making the project known to all likely to be interested.

The vessel secured was the M.S. *Devonia* (12,796 tons), one of three ships of the British India Steam Navigation Company Limited that have been specially fitted out for educational cruises. In the event, it carried 910 passengers—732 accommodated in dormitories, at the low inclusive charge of £30 a head, with cafeteria meals in four relays; and the other 178 in cabins, at £54–75 a head, with meals in a dining saloon (two services). Apart from the sleeping and feeding arrangements, and one lounge reserved for cabin passengers, all had 'the run of the ship' and equal treatment in every respect. Of the total number of passengers, about 400 were Congress members; 330 of these were from overseas, including 199 from the United States.

Mostly arriving by special coaches from Edinburgh or Glasgow, the passengers embarked at Greenock on the morning of Saturday, July 16, and *Devonia* (Captain F.A.J.Downer D.S.C) sailed about noon. Dr W.J.Eggeling (Nature Conservancy) had been designated as Cruise Leader, with George Waterston (Scottish representative, Royal Society for the Protection of Birds) as Chief of Staff and Mrs Irene Waterston (Secretary, S.O.C.) as Cruise Secretary. C.K.Mylne (National Trust for Scotland and Scottish Wildlife Trust) was in charge of the daily programme of talks and films, the former given by a group of experts who also, at appropriate points, provided a multilingual running commentary over the ship's public-address system.

On that first morning, the Firth of Clyde was looking its best, with peaceful sunlit waters under a dappled sky and the lovely panorama of hills to the west. After lunch there was a close view of the mountains of the Isle of Arran to starboard; and late in the afternoon came the first ornithological spectacle when the ship 'circumnavigated'—a key word this!—the great granite cone of Ailsa Craig, rising sheer from the sea. There was a fine view of the Gannets *Sula bassana* and other seabirds nesting on the steep cliffs; and large numbers of birds were in the air or on the water about us. Thereafter, the ship rounded the Mull of Kintyre, with Northern Ireland visible on the port side, and for a while one was just conscious of a slight swell—remarkably, the only occasion of the whole voyage. As evening fell we were passing west of Islay.

# The Scottish bird-islands study cruise

The morning of Sunday, July 17, found us at anchor off Rhum, one of the Inner Hebrides and the largest island National Nature Reserve owned by the Nature Conservancy. Here, after breakfast, we were put ashore by the ship's launches. It was a beautiful day, and many were content to spend it lazily in the vicinity of Kinloch Castle, sometimes watching the female Eiders *Somateria mollissima* with their broods close inshore, or the Shags *Phalacrocorax aristotelis* swimming in parties further out. Others took part in the walking excursions arranged by the Conservancy, the hardiest making the rough ascent of Halival and Askival to the breeding-grounds of the Manx Shearwater *Puffinus puffinus* at 2,000–2,500 feet. In the early evening the ship cruised past the southern end of Skye, with the Cuillin Mountains as a background to Loch Scavaig.

By the morning of Monday, July 17, the ship had reached the most westerly point of its route, at St Kilda. Mist unfortunately shrouded the upper levels of the islands, concealing the great height of the cliffs—but at the same time lending additional awe to the scene. As the ship passed through and round about the group, even threading the quarter-mile gap between Stac Lee and Stac an Armin, nobody can have failed to form a lasting impression of this grim and remote habitat of myriads of seabirds—Gannets (the world's largest colony), Fulmars *Fulmarus glacialis*, Puffins *Fratercula arctica* and others. Later in the day our north-easterly course brought us to other lonely bird-islands; we passed close to the Flannan Islands and the stack of Sula Sgeir, with the gannetry that its name implies, and circumnavigated North Rona, "island of the seals".

Continuing in the same direction through the night, the morning of Tuesday, July 19, found us circumnavigating Foula, a south-westerly outlier of the Shetland Islands with a Norse name signifying that it is a haunt of birds; these include a large colony of Great Skuas *Catharacta skua*, and many of them came near the ship, some exhibiting their piratical behaviour against the Gannets. The rest of the day was spent coasting round the Shetland group; and in the afternoon we reached the northernmost point, the skerries of the Muckle Flugga, where our American friends were reminded—just to keep their relativities right!—that the latitude (60° 52′N) was approximately that of the northern tip of Labrador. By this time, however, the fog was closing in, and it had become dense by the time anchor was dropped off Lerwick. It had nevertheless been possible, before that, to send a boat to shore on Noss to reconnoitre a landing-place for the next day; and also for the Lord Lieutenant of Shetland and a concert party to come aboard for the evening.

On the morning of Wednesday, July 20, the majority of the passengers were landed at Lerwick by the ship's launches. These were taken by coach, half in the morning and half in the afternoon, to Sumburgh Head, the southernmost tip of the mainland of Shetland, where the remarkable prehistoric site of Jarlshof was inspected. The transference of so large a party to and from coaches and launches inevitably involved some queuing—endured by all with good-natured resignation! Meanwhile *Devonia* had returned to Noss with a minority who regarded themselves as 'physically fit and active'—actually, the sea was so calm that landing, on a specially constructed pontoon, presented no difficulty. There was a rich ornithological reward, as this party was right among the birds nesting on the slopes and summit of the hill, notably Great Skuas and Arctic Skuas (Parasitic Jaegers) *Stercorarius parasiticus*, and had good views from above of the species preferring the cliffs. The ship returned with this party in the afternoon and embarked the other at Lerwick in time to reach, and circumnavigate, Fair Isle in daylight. A group from the Bird Observatory had lit a bonfire and stood on the cliff-top as the ship passed; they were able to acknowledge, by flag, greetings spoken over the tannoy. The Principal Lightkeeper at the North Lighthouse, too, greeted us with some blasts on the foghorn as we passed. And so, overnight, to the Orkney Islands.

The passengers were put ashore at Kirkwall on the morning of Thursday, July 21; visits to the Cathedral of St Magnus and other sights occupied such time as was not spent on the excursion by coach, in two relays. The coaches visited various places, including the prehistoric site of Skara Brae and the Standing Stones of Stenness. Hen Harriers *Circus cyaneus* were seen on the way; and a nearly fledged young bird, found close to the road by Edward Balfour (Orkney representative, R.S.P.B.), was exhibited to the occupants of several coaches. At Marwick Head a short walk brought the parties within a close range of a section of cliff crowded with breeding Guillemots (Murres) *Uria aalge*, Razorbills *Alca torda*, Puffins, Kittiwakes *Larus tridactylus* and Fulmars. Return on board in the launches involved some tossing and splashing, as a strong wind had sprung up, but there was not enough sea to affect the ship itself on its overnight passage down the east coast of Scotland.

Friday, July 22, was the last day of the cruise. From the Isle of May, just after breakfast, we soon reached the Bass Rock; and it was in sunny weather and on a calm sea that the island was circumnavigated, so that its classical gannetry was seen to advantage. The ship then cruised up the Firth of Forth, past the lesser islands (one with a substantial ternery, including Roseate Terns *Sterna dougallii*) and under the old and new Forth Bridges. *Devonia* then came back under the

The Scottish Bird-Islands Study Cruise: Mrs Irene Waterston (organizer).     (J.A.MacGeoch)

The Scottish Bird-Islands Study Cruise. Above: Passing the Bass Rock (J.A.MacGeoch). Below:
M.S. Devonia (J.A.MacGeoch).

bridges and berthed at Leith in the late afternoon, when the majority of passengers disembarked.

Congress members were allowed to stay on board until early next morning. They then spent Saturday, July 23, in Edinburgh under the auspices of the Club. Various facilities were provided throughout at the Assembly Rooms in George Street; the morning was free for shopping and a sight-seeing tour of the city by bus had been arranged for the afternoon. Later, at the Assembly Rooms, a display of Highland Dancing was given by members of the Royal Scottish Country Dance Society. This was followed by an informal dinner, when 'Trinovid' binoculars were presented to both Irene and George Waterston on behalf of the very justly grateful participants in the cruise. Buses then transported the party to a reception given by the University of Edinburgh, at which the guests were received in the Library by Principal Michael Swann F.R.S., and by Dr Ian Pennie, President of the Scottish Ornithologists' Club; Professor Erwin Stresemann, senior surviving Past President of International Ornithological Congresses, expressed thanks. The buses thereafter took the members to Waverley Station for the special overnight train to Oxford; of that no more need now be recorded than that the allocation of sleeping-berths had unfortunately not been left in the efficient hands of the Club.

Altogether, the cruise was indeed a memorable event. It was full of ornithological and other interest; it was thoroughly enjoyable; and it was marked by great friendliness among all who took part. To those who made it possible, by their devoted and skilful labours, the best thanks of the XIV International Ornithological Congress are due.

Papers presented at Plenary Sessions

# Interrelationships in breeding adaptations as shown by marine birds

## DAVID LACK

### INTRODUCTION

The theme of this address is that the many adaptations for breeding in birds cannot be evaluated separately, but are closely interrelated with each other and with ecological factors such as food and predation. It has become recognized in recent years that the type of breeding dispersion, the timing of breeding, clutch-size, the size of the eggs, the lengths of the incubation and fledging periods, the age of maturity, and other features of breeding biology, are all subject to natural selection, and that each is closely linked with the others. The development of this theme represents a new and exciting development in ornithology which may well prove rewarding in other groups of animals also. In preparing this address, I have been particularly stimulated by the work of Tinbergen (1963, 1966), Ashmole (1963 a, b) and Crook (1965).

I will develop this theme through comparisons between different kinds of birds, but I would stress that this is only a first, though necessary, stage in such a study, and that the ideas to which it gives rise need testing, wherever possible, by experiment. I have chosen my examples from marine birds, for three reasons. First, there have in recent years been detailed breeding studies of a diversity of species. Secondly, marine birds include a number of distinctive families, which have evidently been in existence a long time, and have evolved a variety of specialized adaptations. Thirdly, though man has modified all natural environments, he has disturbed the sea less than the land or fresh waters, so that there is a better chance of studying marine than other birds in the habitat where their adaptations were evolved. Even so, human disturbance must not be ignored, the more so because much of it has occurred beneath the surface of the sea, and hence out of sight.

Marine birds are here defined as those which feed primarily on marine organisms. They include three subdivisions, (a) intertidal (or shore) feeders, which find their food on the mud, sand or rocks exposed at low tide or by wading in shallow water, (b) inshore (or neritic) feeders, those that feed on or under the water mainly in sight of land, and (c) offshore (or pelagic) feeders, those that feed in the open sea mainly out of sight of land. (Group (c) is sometimes subdivided into those that feed respectively on and beyond the Continental shelf, but I doubt if this can be sustained.) The principal marine birds, with certain features of their breeding biology, have been set out in Table 1. Of the twenty families there listed, twelve are exclusively marine, three others comprise chiefly marine species, and the others include a few marine species. In all, there are just under 270 species, about 3 per cent of all birds.

Omitted from Table 1 and from this address are further species that feed on marine organisms primarily outside the breeding season, notably many Scolo-pacidae on the shore, many diving ducks (Anatidae), some grebes (Podicipitidae) and the divers (Gaviidae) inshore, and phalaropes (Phalaropidae), skuas (Stercorariidae) and the gull *Xema sabini* offshore. This winter influx does not, so far as is known, coincide with any corresponding increase in the marine foods of the birds concerned, and is attributable to the unsuitability of fresh waters and marshes at high latitudes for feeding in winter (while in addition the far north probably provides terrain more suitable for the dispersed cryptic nests of species with nidifugous young than do the restricted shores further south).

For discussion later in this address, I have set out in Appendix 1 the weights of adults and eggs, the incubation and fledging periods and the main references to breeding biological studies of each marine species. To save space, these references have not always been repeated when the particular species is referred to in the text, though additional references are there cited in the standard way.

### TYPE OF YOUNG, NEST SITES AND DISPERSION

While the young of a few marine species are nidifugous and leave the nest soon after hatching, most are nidicolous and do not depart until fully fledged. In an intermediate group (denoted by ½ in Table 1), the young can move around actively after hatching but normally remain in the vicinity and do not leave the colony until fully fledged. Each of these types is linked with a certain type of nest site and a particular pattern of dispersion. The nidifugous species nest solitarily (except for the Eider *Somateria mollissima*, which usually nests in colonies on islets). In contrast, all the fully nidicolous species nest in colonies (usually large) in relatively inaccessible sites, often on cliffs or in holes, many on offshore islets, and others on oceanic islands or the antarctic mainland. Finally, most of the species with partly nidifugous young nest in small colonies on low-lying coasts, on islets where available, and otherwise on extensive beaches or remote headlands.

# Presidential Address

These features have evidently been evolved primarily in relation to predation on the eggs or young, especially by land mammals. Land mammals cannot get to islands but can hunt along the shore, though they are less likely to do so if there are extensive areas of sand or shingle otherwise devoid of food for them. Hence the nests of plovers, oystercatchers and ducks, which are on or near the shore and accessible to mammals, are widely dispersed to assist their concealment. The plovers and oystercatchers have evolved cryptic eggs and young, and the parent runs from them when a predator is still distant, while in ducks the eggs are probably too large and too numerous for cryptic colouring to be effective and most species have evolved cryptic females which sit tightly (and one species nests in holes).

In contrast, the eggs, young and parents of the fully nidicolous species are not cryptic, as they usually nest in inaccessible sites. But such sites are often restricted, and may be inadequate for all the birds that the feeding grounds would support, so that there may be intense competition for nesting places. Probably it is for this reason that, on Bear Island for instance, each of the six breeding species of Alcidae has a different nesting site, *Uria lomvia* on cliff ledges, *U. aalge* on the flat tops of stacks and on flat areas between the cliffs and the steep slopes above them, *Cepphus grylle* in clefts in the rocks, *Fratercula arctica* in larger and *Plautus alle* in smaller holes, and *Alca torda*, there rare, presumably in covered niches on cliffs as elsewhere (personal observation). Similarly on Whero Island, off New Zealand, each of five species of Procellariiformes burrows in a different layer of soil (Richdale, 1965). Such segregation of nesting sites recalls the segregation in habitat of many passerine species (Gause's hypothesis), and while both types of segregation must be brought about by behavioural responses, the latter were presumably evolved through the effects of competition.

It might be argued that the semi-nidicolous young of gulls, terns, skimmers and skuas are simply an intermediate stage in evolution from a nidifugous to a nidicolous condition owing to the recent adoption of colonial life. But the evidence suggests, instead, that they represent another well-adapted condition. As already mentioned, gulls and terns usually nest on low-lying coasts in more accessible places than the fully nidicolous species, so that it is advantageous for them to have cryptic eggs in somewhat dispersed nests and cryptic young which hide if a predator approaches. However, their sites are less accessible than those of the nidifugous species, and in addition, unlike other marine birds, the adults attack predators of their eggs and young, and such attacks are more effective when a number of pairs participate (Tinbergen, 1963, 1966). Hence it is also advantageous

5

TABLE I

Breeding of marine birds

| Family | Approx. no. of species | Usual nest dispersion | Type of young | Usual clutch | Length (in weeks) of Incubation period | Fledging period | Usual age (in years) of first breeding |
|---|---|---|---|---|---|---|---|
| **INTERTIDAL FEEDERS** | | | | | | | |
| Haematopodidae oystercatchers | 6 | Solitary | Nidifugous | 3 | 4 | $4\frac{1}{2}$ | 3 |
| Charadriidae shore plovers | 4 | Solitary | Nidifugous | 3, 4 | $3\frac{1}{2}$ | $3\frac{1}{2}$ | 1 |
| Dromadidae crab plover | 1 | Colonial | Nidicolous | 1 | ? | ? | ? |
| Chionidae sheathbills | 2 | Solitary | Intermediate | 2 | 4 | ? | ? |
| **INTERTIDAL OR INSHORE FEEDERS** | | | | | | | |
| Anatidae ducks | 6 | Solitary | Nidifugous | 5–12 | 4 | 8 | 3 |
| Stercorariidae skuas | 2 | Solitary or colonial | Intermediate | 2 | 4 | 8 | 3 |
| Laridae gulls | 35 | Colonial | Intermediate | 3 | 3 | 4 | (2)3 |
| Rynchopidae skimmers | 1 | Colonial | Intermediate | 3 | ? | ? | ? |

| INSHORE FEEDERS | | | | | | | |
|---|---|---|---|---|---|---|---|
| Spheniscidae penguins | 15 | Colonial | Nidicolous | 2 | 5–6 | 8–14 | 3(+) |
| Pelecanoididae diving petrels | 5 | Colonial | Nidicolous | 1 | — | 8 | 2 |
| Pelecanidae pelican | 1 | Colonial | Nidicolous | 3 | c. 4 | 9 | 2 |
| Phalacrocoracidae cormorants | 25 | Colonial | Nidicolous | 3–4 | 4 | 7–8 | 3 |
| Sternidae terns | 35 | Colonial | Intermediate | 2–3 | 3 | 4–5 | 3 |
| OFFSHORE FEEDERS | | | | | | | |
| Diomedeidae albatrosses | 14 | Colonial | Nidicolous | 1 | 9–11 | 21–29 | 8–11 |
| Procellariidae shearwaters, etc. | 50 | Colonial | Nidicolous | 1 | 7½ | 10–14 | 5–6 |
| Hydrobatidae storm petrels | 20 | Colonial | Nidicolous | 1 | 6 | 9 | 3+ |
| Phaethontidae tropic birds | 3 | Colonial | Nidicolous | 1 | 6 | 10–15 | — |
| Sulidae boobies | 9 | Colonial | Nidicolous | 1–2 | 6 | 13–19 | 5 |
| Fregatidae frigate birds | 5 | Colonial | Nidicolous | 1 | 6 | 26 | — |
| Alcidae auks | 20 | Colonial | Nidicolous (most) | 1(2) | 4–6 | 7 | 3 |

NOTES: (i) In the fully nidicolous groups, the young are dependent on their parents for several weeks after fledging in Pelecanidae, Phalacrocoracidae, Fregatidae and most Sulidae, and independent after fledging in Spheniscidae, Pelecanoididae, Diomedeidae, Procellariidae, Hydrobatidae, Phaethontidae, at least some Alcidae and *Sula bassana*.

(ii) Some of the above families also include fresh water or terrestrial species, which have been omitted. The grouping for feeding refers solely to the breeding season and is that usual for the marine species in each family. A few families also include species in another category, e.g. a few Laridae and Sternidae feed offshore. The number of species (given to the nearest five for totals over fourteen) is that in the feeding category in which the family has been placed, and does not include any exceptions. Hence the total number of marine species is a little greater than shown.

(iii) A few more families might have been included, e.g. the heron *Demigretta* (Ardeidae), some sea-eagles *Haliaetus* (Accipitridae), the Osprey (Pandionidae) and the thick-knee *Orthorhamplus* (Burhinidae). Groups that are marine solely in winter have been excluded.

for these species to nest in colonies, and for their young to stay in them. The breeding adaptations of gulls and terns therefore represent a compromise between the conflicting advantages of dispersed and grouped nests and of active and immobile young. It may be added that the size of the colonies and the proximity of the nests differ somewhat in different species, in accordance with their somewhat different requirements, as shown by Cullen (1960) for certain *Sterna* species.

In contrast to the intense competition for safe nesting sites in the marine species with fully nidicolous young, gulls and terns often nest where there are ample available sites, so that there is little or no competition for them and little or no segregation in breeding sites. For instance, through the kindness of Dr George Lowery, I was flown above the Mississippi delta, where the colonies of ground-nesting *Sterna maxima*, *S. sandvicensis*, *Larus atricilla* and *Rynchops nigra* are restricted to a few out of many similar sandy inlets. This type of distribution, also found in other types of colonial birds, is brought about, I suggest, because it is advantageous for pairs that have bred successfully to return to the same colony and for young birds seeking sites to join an established colony, as the latter's existence is the best indication that a site is safe (cf. Lack, 1954); but in many gulls and terns it is reinforced by the fact that the adults attack predators of their eggs and young.

BREEDING DISPERSION AND FEEDING HABITS

While the breeding dispersion of marine birds has evidently been evolved primarily to counteract predation of eggs and young, feeding habits have probably played some part, since solitary nesting is restricted to intertidal feeders, while the colonies of the inshore feeders tend to be smaller and at more frequent intervals than those of the offshore species. As intertidal feeders feed close to where they nest, each pair will usually be closer to suitable feeding grounds if the nests are dispersed at intervals along the shore than if they are grouped, and this might be particularly advantageous if they have nidifugous young that run to the shore to feed. At the other extreme, offshore feeders are almost inevitably distant from their feeding areas, so that the extra distance flown if they nest in colonies instead of singly is negligible, especially as most of them fly strongly. But the evolutionary trends here reinforce each other, since the long wings evolved by most species that feed in the open sea make them clumsy in taking off from level ground, thus increasing their need for inaccessible, and hence for restricted, nesting sites. The inshore feeders are intermediate between the intertidal and offshore feeders in their nesting dispersion and the distance of their feeding grounds.

8

# Presidential Address

In marine birds, the subadults normally frequent the colonies at least a year before they breed. As in other colonial species, the size and spacing of the colonies seem broadly related to the food supply, and as I argued earlier for the Heron *Ardea cinerea* (Lack, 1954), this will be achieved if birds which bred successfully in the previous year return to their former sites, and if young birds take up breeding stations for the first time without laying eggs and return to breed in the next year if they have found conditions satisfactory, but if not, move elsewhere. Hence this type of dispersion is explicable through natural selection, and there is no evidence to support Wynne-Edwards (1962) that it is due to epideictic behaviour and group selection (cf. Lack, 1966).

A few marine species may nest either solitarily or in colonies. In the Eider *Somateria mollissima* on Bear Island, this is linked with the risk of predation, nests on lake islets inaccessible to foxes *Alopex lagopus* being crowded together, whereas those on the mainland are solitary, presumably to assist concealment (personal observation). Again, the large gulls *Larus marinus* in Britain and *L. dominicanus* in New Zealand may nest solitarily or colonially, and as this cannot usually be correlated with their nesting sites, it is presumably related to food supplies.*

While in most of the marine species which have them, nidifugous young are obviously of advantage in reducing predation, this does not apply to certain auks (Alcidae). The young of guillemots (*Uria* spp.) and the Razorbill *Alca torda* leave for the sea when partly grown, and those of murrelets in the genera *Endomychura* and *Synthliborhamphus* when only 2 days old (Storer, 1960). All four genera often nest on islands, *Uria* and *Alca* on cliff ledges and the two murrelets in holes, so their nesting places are as safe from predators as those of the nidicolous Alcidae. Probably, therefore, the advantage to these species of nidifugous young is to enable the adults to take them to distant feeding areas instead of carrying food to them. But not enough is known about the food of Alcidae to say why these, but not the other species, should have evolved this habit. In the Emperor Penguin *Aptenodytes forsteri*, also, the young leave the nesting colonies as the sea ice breaks up and drifts north, though still only one-third of the adult weight, and thereafter they are independent (Prévost, 1961). That no very young penguins move with

---

* While relatively scarce shore birds like oystercatchers or shore plovers can disperse their nests sufficiently far apart to assist concealment, in places where gulls are really numerous, an equal spacing of their nests along the shore might mean that each was close enough to others to attract rather than reduce predation. Hence under some circumstances high numbers as such might perhaps favour colonial nesting. It may be added that one gull, *Larus fuliginosus* of the Galapagos, normally nests solitarily (Lévêque, 1964), but the possible reasons have not been studied.

their parents out to sea, as in the Alcidae, may be because, unlike the murrelets, their main predators are marine animals.

Table I shows that about 93 per cent of marine birds are colonial, as compared with about 13 per cent of all the birds in the world (Lack, in preparation, closely following Crook, 1965). Probably, the high proportion among marine birds is due mainly to the unusually safe sites provided by islands and cliffs.

### CLUTCH-SIZE, GROWTH-RATE AND AGE OF BREEDING

In most birds in which the parents feed their young, clutch-size almost certainly corresponds to that brood-size from which most young survive, the limit being set by the amount of food which the parents can collect for their brood (Lack, 1954). Further, in species in which the young hatch asynchronously, the last young usually die quickly if food is short, which I have interpreted as an adaptation to a somewhat unpredictable food supply, as it reduces the brood-size to the availability of food without jeopardizing the survival of the older young. I consider that these generalizations hold for the nidicolous marine species. In particular, this probably explains why, as shown in Table I, the average clutch is more than twice as large in intertidal and inshore feeders as in offshore feeders, nearly all of which lay only one egg. For the species which feed in the open sea bring food to their young much less frequently than those which feed inshore, both because their feeding areas are much farther away, and also because suitable food is presumably scarcer in the open sea than near to land, though the difference does not appear to have been measured. (Even if the offshore species bring more food on each journey than the inshore species, this could not compensate for the big difference in feeding frequency.)

In species in which the young feed themselves from hatching, clutch-size has obviously not been evolved in relation to the size of brood which the parents can feed. This may be why the marine ducks have larger clutches than any other marine species. But the shore plovers *Charadrius* lay only three or four eggs at high northern latitudes and only two or three eggs in the tropics (Mackworth-Praed & Grant, 1952), the possible reasons for which require study.

In some land birds the amount of food received has a marked direct effect on the rate of growth of the young, but in others not, and in the latter, hereditary factors are presumably much more important (Lack, 1954). Similarly, food has a marked direct effect on the growth-rate of terns such as *Anous tenuirostris* and *Sterna fuscata* (Ashmole, 1962, 1963a), but hardly any effect in shearwaters such as *Puffinus puffinus* and *P. griseus* in which both well nourished and poorly nourished young fledge at the same age (Richdale, 1963; Harris, 1966). In general it is presumably advantageous for a bird to evolve as rapid a growth-rate and as short a fledging period as possible, especially where there is great risk of predation in the nest, but an upper limit is set by the fact that if feather growth is too rapid, the young might be unduly weak. Hence the growth-rate of each species has presumably been evolved primarily in relation to the average amount of food which can be brought to the young in the time available.

In general, larger species grow more slowly than smaller ones, but there are many exceptions, particularly when species in different families are compared, and such differences have presumably been evolved mainly in relation to differences in the average availability of food for the young. As shown in Table 2, for instance, the shearwater *P. puffinus* is fully fledged in 70 days, but the Shag *Phalacrocorax aristotelis*, which is four times as heavy, in 55 days. This is one example of the tendency shown in Table 1 for the offshore species to have longer fledging periods than the inshore feeders, presumably because they feed their young less frequently.

The length of incubation must also be influenced by hereditary factors, and hence subject to natural selection, and in general it must be advantageous for it to be as short as possible, particularly if the eggs are liable to be taken by predators. Among related species, incubation takes a little longer with larger eggs. Much more important, quite apart from any influence of size, the length of incubation is correlated with the fledging period. This can be seen from Table 1; in particular, the incubation period, like the fledging period, is longer in offshore than inshore feeders. It is hard to see how a longer incubation period as such could be advantageous, but I have suggested (Lack, 1947-48) that perhaps the easiest way to evolve a slower rate of growth of the young (in species whose food is sparse) is to evolve a slower rate of development as a whole, including in the egg. It also seems possible that the egg may be more resistant to chilling if development is slower; this might be important in offshore feeders with a sparse or distant food supply, as a result of which the sitting parent has sometimes to depart to feed before its mate returns to relieve it.

Table 1 shows, further, that the age of first breeding is higher in offshore than in inshore or intertidal feeders, which I similarly link with the greater difficulties that offshore species have in finding food for their young, as such difficulties could well diminish with greater age and experience (Lack, 1954). Fitting with this view, there are a number of species (not marine ones) in which younger individuals are known to breed less efficiently than older ones, and others in which birds breed at an earlier age than usual when competition is relaxed (Lack, 1966). In opposition to this view, Wynne-Edwards (1955, 1962) argued that deferred maturity has been evolved in marine species to reduce productivity and prevent over-population in species with a low annual mortality, but there is no evidence for this.

TABLE 2

A comparison of breeding in two marine and two land birds

| | European Shag *Phalacrocorax aristotelis* | Manx Shearwater *Puffinus puffinus* | European Robin *Erithacus rubecula* | Common Swift *Apus apus* |
|---|---|---|---|---|
| Feeding habitat | Inshore | Offshore | Ground and vegetation | Air |
| Nesting dispersion | Small colonies | Large colonies | Solitary | Small colonies |
| Usual clutch | 3 | 1 | 5 | 2–3 |
| Stint on eggs | $3\frac{1}{2}$ hours | 6 days | $\frac{1}{2}$–1 hour | 2 hours |
| Feeding visits to older young | 11 per day | 1 in 2 days | 4 per hour | $\frac{1}{2}$–2 per hour |
| Incubation period in days | 31 | 51 | 14 | 19–20 |
| Fledging period in days | 55 | 70 | 14 | 41 |
| Post-fledging period of dependence in days | 21 | 0 | 14(–21) | 0 |
| Age of first breeding in years | (2) 3 | 5 | 1 | 2(+) |
| Annual mortality of adults | 15% | c. 5% | 57% | 18% |
| Weight of adults in grams | 1600 | 400 | 21 | 33 |

NOTES: Data on *Phalacrocorax aristotelis* from Snow (1960, 1963) and Potts (1966), on *Puffinus puffinus* from Harris (1966), on *Erithacus rubecula* from Lack (1965) and on *A. apus* from Lack (1956).

The various differences between inshore- and offshore-feeding species have been set out for a typical British species of each type, a cormorant and a shearwater respectively, in Table 2. Alongside them I have placed similar details for two British land birds, the Robin *Erithacus rubecula*, which obtains its food near the nest, and the Swift *A. apus*, which like an offshore-feeding seabird flies a long way from its nest to feed. It is interesting that the differences between the Robin and the Swift are in the same direction as those between the Shag and the Manx Shearwater respectively. (This comparison would have been more significant had it referred to species of the same size, but this was not possible.) In addition to the parallels shown in Table 2, there are parallels in the weight-curves of the young, as shown in Figure 1. The young Robin and Shag increase steadily to near the adult weight, but the young Swift and Manx Shearwater deposit fat, so that temporarily they weigh more than the adult. This fat is used during temporary fasts when food is sparse.

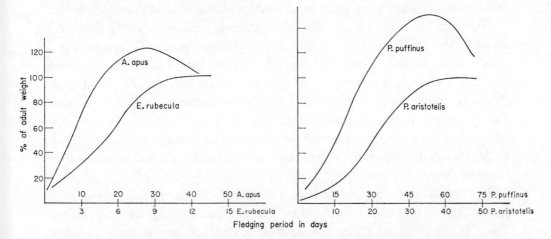

FIGURE I. Weight curves for young of *A. apus* compared with *Erithacus rubecula*, and *Puffinus puffinus* compared with *Phalacrocorax aristotelis*. Note that the time-scale is different for each species and that weight has been expressed as a percentage of the average adult weight.

### INSHORE AND OFFSHORE FEEDERS IN SAME FAMILY

That the differences between the families of inshore-feeding and offshore-feeding birds just discussed are genuinely related to the difference in feeding habits is corroborated by the fact that, where both inshore and offshore species occur in the same family, they differ in similar ways. As pointed out by Ashmole (1963 a, b), the various respects in which the tern *Sterna fuscata* resembles offshore feeders in other families and differs from inshore-feeding terns are presumably due to convergent evolution, and hence are adaptive. To illustrate this, I have in Table 3 compared an inshore- and offshore-feeding species in each of three different families. Ideally, such comparisons should be made between species of similar size breeding in the same area, but in practice one has to use the comparatively few species that have been well studied. The reader should therefore keep in mind that, apart from any differences in Table 3 correlated with feeding habits, clutch-size tends to be smaller at lower than at higher latitudes, while incubation and fledging periods tend to be longer in larger than smaller birds.

In each of the pairs in Table 3, the inshore feeder breeds in smaller colonies, lays a larger clutch, relieves its mate on the eggs more quickly, feeds its young more frequently, and has shorter incubation and fledging periods than the off-shore species, while in the two pairs for which figures are available, the inshore feeder starts breeding when younger and has a higher annual adult mortality.*

The data for various less well studied seabirds reinforce these findings. For instance, the offshore-feeding gull *Creagrus furcatus* of the Galapagos has a clutch of one instead of three and much longer incubation and fledging periods than the shore-feeding Herring Gull *Larus argentatus*, which is about the same size (Snow & Snow, 1967). Similarly the tern *Sterna anaethetus* feeds well offshore like *S. fuscata*, breeds in immense colonies and has a clutch of only one (Alexander, 1928). Again the booby *Sula dactylatra* is of similar size to *S. nebouxii*, feeds rather farther from the shore, but not so far as *S. sula*, and is intermediate between these two species in all the points mentioned in Table 3 (Dorward, 1962; Nelson, 1966). Yet again, while most auks (Alcidae) feed offshore, those in the genus *Cepphus* feed close inshore. In the North Atlantic, the Black Guillemot *C. grylle*, as compared with the offshore-feeding Puffin *Fratercula arctica*, breeds in much smaller colonies, has a clutch of two instead of one, and much shorter incubation and fledging periods (Kartaschew, 1960). In the North Pacific, a similar contrast is presented by the inshore-feeding *Cepphus columba* (Drent *et al*, 1964) and the offshore-feeding *Ptychoramphus aleutica* (Thorensen, 1964).

## REVERSALS OF TRENDS IN PELECANIFORMES

In most nidicolous birds, clutch-size is larger at higher latitudes (Moreau, 1944; Lack, 1947–8). But whereas most tropical boobies, including *Sula dactylatra*, *S. nebouxii*, *S. leucogaster* and *S. variegata*, usually lay two eggs (though *S. sula* and *S. abbotti* lay one), the species breeding at high latitudes, *S. (Morus) bassana*, *S. capensis* and *S. serrator*, lay only one egg. Yet except near cold upwellings, notably

---

* While all the rest are adaptations, I regard the higher mortality simply as a consequence of the higher reproductive rate, in populations that are limited by density-dependent mortality (Lack, 1954, pp. 103–5), and *contra* Wynne-Edwards (1955, 1962), who argued instead that longer-lived species evolve lower reproductive rates.

TABLE 3

Comparison between inshore and offshore feeding Laridae, Sternidae and Sulidae

| | GULLS | | TERNS | | BOOBIES | |
| | Black-headed Larus ridibundus | Kittiwake Rissa tridactyla | Common and Arctic Sterna hirundo and S. paradisaea | Wideawake S. fuscata | Blue-footed Sula nebouxii | Red-footed S. sula |
| --- | --- | --- | --- | --- | --- | --- |
| Feeding habitat | Shore, inshore | Offshore | Inshore | Offshore | Inshore | Offshore |
| Usual type of colony | Smaller | Larger | Smaller | Larger | Smaller | Larger |
| Usual clutch | 3 | 2 | 2 (3) | 1 | 2 | 1 |
| Incubation period in days | 23 | 27 | 21 | $29\frac{1}{2}$ | 41 | 45 |
| Fledging period in days | 30 | 43 | 30 | 60 | 100 | 130 |
| Incubation stint | $1-2\frac{1}{2}$ hours | 1-2 per day | 1/3-2 hours | $5\frac{1}{2}$ days | 18 hours | $4\frac{1}{2}$ days |
| Feeding visits to older young | 1 per hour | 1 per 4 hours | 3-4 per hour | 1 per day | 1.8 per day | 0.8 per day |
| Usual age of breeding in years | 2 | 3-4 | 2-4 | 6 | — | — |
| Adult mortality | 18% | 12% | 25% | 16-20% | — | — |
| Adult weight in grams | 250 | 350 | 135 | 175 | 1800 | 1070 |

NOTES: Information for *Larus ridibundus* from Ytreberg (1956) amplified by N.Tinbergen's research group (personal communication); for *Rissa tridactyla* from Coulson & White (1956–61) as summarized in Lack (1966), and amplified by Coulson (personal communication); for *Sterna hirundo* in Witherby *et al* (1938–41), Schönwetter (1960–66) and Austin (1956), supplemented for various points by data for *S. paradisaea* from J.M.Cullen (personal communication); for *S. fuscata* from Ashmole (1963a), supplemented for age of breeding and annual mortality from Robertson (1964) and O.L.Austin (personal communication); for *Sula nebouxii* and *S. sula* from J.B.Nelson (1966 and personal communication).

the Humboldt current (where *S. variegata* and *S. nebouxii* sometimes lay three eggs (Murphy, 1936)), tropical seas tend to be much poorer in food than seas at high latitudes in summer, and in addition the birds breeding at high latitudes have roughly half as long again each day in which to hunt for food. Hence one might have expected *Sula* species to be able to raise larger broods, and hence to have evolved larger clutches, at high than at low latitudes.

This unexpected reversal seems explicable through specific differences in growth-rate, the latter being linked with differences in the breeding season. *S. nebouxii*, *S. dactylatra* and *S. sula* are roughly half the size of *S. bassana*, yet their young take respectively 1½, 4 and 6 weeks longer to fledge (on average, 30 per cent longer). Further, they then depend for another 2 to 4 months on their parents for food, whereas the young of *S. bassana* are independent after fledging (Dorward, 1962; Nelson, 1964). Given the same quantity of food, a pair of birds could raise more young slowly or fewer young quickly. Tropical boobies can raise young in any month of the year, so that there is no urgent need for them to complete breeding by a given date, and under these circumstances natural selection has evidently favoured a larger clutch and brood with a resultant slower growth-rate. At high latitudes, on the other hand, it is presumably necessary for the young to be fully independent before the winter, and this is probably why natural selection has there favoured a much more rapid rate of growth, but this has been achieved only at the expense of a smaller brood.*

The egg of *S. bassana* is almost twice as large as those of *S. nebouxii*, *S. dactylatra* and *S. sula* (weights of 106, 65, 68 and 54 grams respectively), but incubation takes a similar time, i.e. it is shorter in *S. bassana* than would be expected from the size of the egg. Since the fledging period of *S. bassana* is also shorter than those of the other species, this accords with the general tendency, already noted, for the incubation period to vary in parallel with the fledging period in birds.

One of the rare exceptions to this last trend occurs in another family of Pelecaniformes, the tropicbirds (Phaethontidae). For instance, the young of *Phaethon aethereus* (Stonehouse, 1962) are fledged in 3⅓ months and are then independent,

---

* While I think that these are the main reasons for the observed differences in clutch-size, further study is needed, because on Ascension Island *Sula dactylatra* and *S. leucogaster* lay two eggs but raise one chick, while on the Bass Rock *S. bassana* lays one egg, but can raise two chicks if artificially provided with them (Dorward, 1962; Nelson, 1964, 1966; see also Lack, 1966). Another factor reducing the efficiency with which *S. bassana* can feed its young is that it moults its wing feathers while breeding, which the other species do not do—see Appendix 2.

whereas those of *Sula sula* take 4⅔ months and remain for a further 3 months in the care of their parents. Hence, even allowing for the fact that *S. sula* is 30 per cent larger, *Phaethon aethereus* grows much faster, and so one would have expected it to have evolved a much shorter incubation period. In fact, however, it is almost the same (43 compared with 45 days in *Sula sula*), but this is reasonable from another viewpoint as the eggs of these two species are fairly similar in size, 67 compared with 54 grams (and *S. dactylatra*, which has an egg of almost the same size as *Phaethon aethereus*, has an incubation period 1 day longer). Hence the unexpectedly long incubation period of *P. aethereus* is perhaps correlated with its having evolved a proportionately larger egg than the Sulidae, which presumably means that the embryo hatches at a later stage of its development, and so passes proportionately longer in the egg and less time as a nestling than in Sulidae.

### SIZE OF EGGS

This last point raises the problem of why the proportionate size of the egg differs markedly in different kinds of birds. As shown by Heinroth (1922), larger species tend to have larger eggs, but the proportionate size of the egg varies inversely with body-size and this means that body-weight must be allowed for when comparing different species. The averages for the various families of marine birds are shown in Figure 2 for the lighter species and in Figure 3 for the heavier species, based on data in Appendix 1.

Heinroth (1922) found that, though there are many exceptions, the eggs tend to be proportionately larger in nidifugous than nidicolous species, and in species with smaller than larger clutches. Considered separately, neither trend is obvious in marine birds, but many of the apparent discrepancies disappear when the two trends are considered together. Proportionately the largest eggs occur in the Crab Plover *Dromas* (nidicolous, c/1), nearly all Procellariiformes (nidicolous, c/1), a few tropical terns (Sternidae) (semi-nidifugous, c/1) and most auks (Alcidae) (nidicolous, c/1); all of these, it will be noted, have a clutch of one. Then follow the gulls (Laridae) together with most terns (semi-nidifugous, c/2–3) and, after them, the shore plovers (nidifugous, c/3–4); hence these groups are nidifugous or partly so. Next come the tropicbirds (Phaethontidae) (nidicolous, c/1), the marine ducks (nidifugous, c/5–12), and the oystercatchers (Haematopodidae) (nidifugous, c/3). Finally the groups (all nidicolous) with proportionately the smallest eggs are, in order, the diving petrels (Pelecanoididae) (c/1), penguins (Spheniscidae) (c/1–2), frigate birds (Fregatidae) (c/1), pelicans (Pelecanidae) (c/3), boobies (Sulidae) (c/1–2) and cormorants (Phalacrocoracidae) (c/3–4).

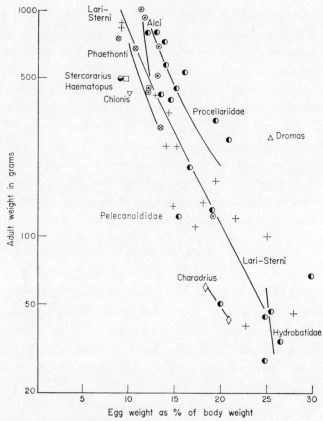

FIGURE 2.* Relationship of adult weight to proportionate egg-weight (expressed as a percentage of body-weight) for birds weighing up to 1 kilogram.

* Figures 2–7 show the relationship to each other of body-weight, egg-weight, incubation and fledging periods, based on the data in Appendix 1. The vertical axis is in each case on a logarithmic scale. Each point represents a single species, and the lines show mean positions (drawn by eye) for species in the same family. The symbols used, the same in all six figures, are for species in the same family or group of families, as follows:

| | | | |
|---|---|---|---|
| ⊕ | Spheniscidae | □ | Haematopodidae |
| ◑ | Procellariiformes | ◇ | Charadriidae |
| ⊗ | Phaethontidae | △ | Dromadidae |
| ◉ | Pelecanidae | ▽ | Chionidae |
| ● | Sulidae | ⊖ | Stercorariidae |
| × | Phalacrocoracidae | + | Laridae and Sternidae |
| ❂ | Fregatidae | ⊙ | Alcidae |
| ✻ | Anatidae | | |

18

## Presidential Address

Hence the proportionate size of the eggs is probably related both to the type of young and to clutch-size, but as neither relationship is very close, other factors are probably important as well. It may be added that among marine birds, the proportionate weight of the clutch in relation to body-weight is highest in the Shelduck *Tadorna tadorna* (c/12) and some shore plovers *Charadrius* (c/4) which

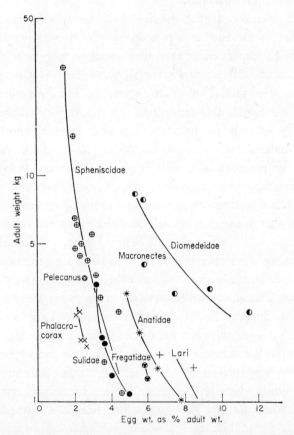

FIGURE 3. Relationship of adult weight to proportionate egg-weight (expressed as a percentage of body-weight) for birds weighing 1 kilogram and over.

lay almost their own weight in eggs, and is lowest in those boobies (*Sula*) and penguins (*Aptenodytes*) which lay one egg, the clutch comprising only 1.5 per cent of the body-weight in *A. forsteri*.

The clearest point in Figures 2 and 3 is that the proportionate size of the egg is characteristic for each family of birds, and to a lesser extent for each order.

The only marked exception to the latter occurs in the Pelecaniformes, in which the eggs are proportionately very small in the Fregatidae, Pelecanidae, Sulidae and Phalacrocoracidae, but fairly large in the Phaethontidae as already noted. That the proportionate size of the egg is characteristic for each family implies that, if conditions change, a bird is much less likely to evolve a change in egg-size than in other breeding adaptations.

As shown by Heinroth (1922), the size of the newly hatched chick is proportional to the size of the egg, and presumably the main advantage of a larger egg is that the chick hatches either at a more advanced stage or with a bigger food reserve, which could well assist its survival, particularly if it is nidifugous, or if very small young need special food that is sparse, or if feeding is intermittent, as in many Procellariiformes. In this connection it is suggestive that the heaviest losses of young usually occur in the first few days after hatching, both in nidifugous species like the Eider *Somateria mollissima* (Milne, 1965), and in nidicolous species like the Shag *Phalacrocorax aristotelis* (Snow, 1960; Potts, 1966). Under these conditions it is probably advantageous for the embryo to continue its development in the egg until it is as well grown as possible. On the other hand, the formation of a proportionately large egg might well be disadvantageous in imposing a strain on the food reserves of the female bird before laying, particularly in species in which it is advantageous to breed as early as possible after the time when food is short in winter (see later). In order to form their proportionately large eggs, the females of various Procellariiformes leave the colonies for some 2 weeks prior to laying (Marshall & Serventy, 1956 a; other references in Lack, 1966). But such an extended departure is possible only for species laying a single egg, and would not be possible between the successive eggs in a clutch. It is also suggestive that, even though they have proportionately very small eggs, those penguins (Spheniscidae) and boobies (Sulidae) which lay two eggs produce the second egg as long as 3 to 5 days or more after the first (Gwynne, 1953; Richdale, 1957; Sapin-Jaloustre, 1960; Dorward, 1962; Nelson, 1966 and personal communication). This is presumably because the females cannot obtain enough food to form the second egg any quicker; and this could well be the main reason for their evolving small eggs. If these arguments are sound, the proportionate size of egg evolved by each species and family of birds is presumably a compromise between conflicting advantages, especially relating to the food supplies available respectively for the laying female and for newly hatched young. But unfortunately these food supplies have not been measured, and hence the reasons for the size of egg evolved by each species remain speculative.

# Presidential Address

## LENGTH OF INCUBATION

The relationship between the size of the eggs and the length of incubation in marine birds has been set out in Figure 4. This shows that, within each family, larger eggs take slightly, but only slightly, longer to hatch, while there are marked

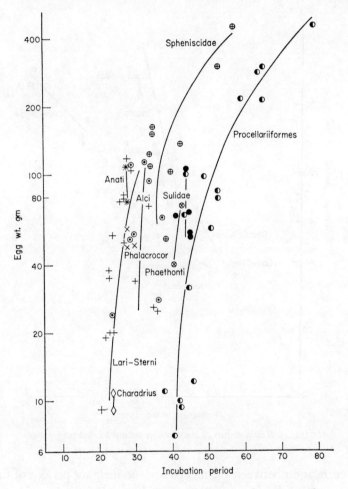

FIGURE 4. Relationship of egg-weight to incubation period.

differences between families that are independent of the size of the egg. For eggs of about 80 grams, for instance, incubation takes just under 4 weeks in the gull *Larus fuscus* but about twice as long in the petrels *Puffinus tenuirostris* and *Pterodroma macroptera*.

21

# David Lack

Larger species, as compared with smaller, tend to take longer to fledge, and also to lay larger eggs that take somewhat longer to hatch; for which reason alone, the lengths of the incubation and fledging periods tend to be correlated. But the latter correlation also holds independently of the influence of size (which in any case is small) and this accounts for many of the anomalies in Figure 4. Figure 5

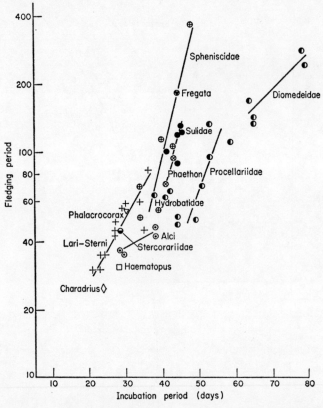

FIGURE 5. Relationship of incubation period to fledging period.

shows the correlation between the incubation and fledging periods of the different species of marine birds and also shows that this is characteristic for each family, though there are some discrepancies. For instance, as compared with other Procellariiformes, *Fulmarus* and *Daption* have longer incubation periods and *Pterodroma* a short one relative to the lengths of their fledging periods. Among marine species the shortest incubation periods, relative to both egg-weight and fledging period, are those of gulls and many terns, perhaps correlated with the fact that their eggs are more subject to predation than those of other species, so that there has been unusually strong selection for rapid incubation.

## GROWTH-RATE IN PROCELLARIIFORMES

In Procellariiformes every species has a clutch of one, though different species take very different foods, some breed in the tropics and others at high latitudes, and the largest species is nearly three hundred times as heavy as the smallest. It is not credible that the availability of food should be closely similar in all these species, and though any increase in clutch-size means doubling the number of young to be fed, there are other birds in which the clutch at high latitudes is more than double that in the tropics. A possible explanation is that in Procellariiformes (as in Sulidae) natural selection has favoured differences in the growth-rate rather than in clutch-size. This might be particularly advantageous since Procellariiformes lay such large eggs that even one may require a fortnight's preparation, as just mentioned.

The fledging periods of the different species of Procellariiformes, set out in Appendix 1, have in Figure 6 been plotted against body-size. This shows that there is little correlation with body-size; indeed if the points for the albatrosses (Diomedeidae) are omitted, there is none. To take the most striking examples, *Fulmarus glacialoides* weighs nearly thirty times as much as *Hydrobates pelagicus*, but the latter takes 26 per cent longer to fledge. Again *Pterodroma macroptera* weighs 25 per cent less than *Fulmarus glacialoides*, but takes two and a half times as long to fledge. Indeed, *Pterodroma macroptera* takes 3 weeks longer than *Macronectes giganteus*, which is seven times as large. However, the albatrosses (Diomedeidae), which are the largest species, take longer to fledge than any others.

The marked differences in the growth-rates of different species presumably depend at least partly on hereditary factors, and hence are adaptive, presumably to the usual availability of food for each species. As the sea is, in general, much poorer in food in warm than cold waters in summer, it is suggestive that relatively long fledging periods are found in two species of warmer waters, *Pterodroma macroptera* and *Diomedea immutabilis* (though not in two others *D. nigripes* or *Oceanodroma castro*), while relatively short fledging periods are found in those breeding at very high latitudes, such as the species of *Pagodroma*, *Fulmarus*, *Daption* and probably *Oceanites*. While there is presumably strong selection for rapid development at high latitudes, as the young must fledge before the winter, the young could not grow fast unless there were enough food for them, so it may be more meaningful to say that only those species of Procellariiformes which can find enough food for rapid growth breed successfully in the arctic and antarctic.

The Sooty Shearwater *Puffinus griseus* takes only 3 days longer to fledge than the Short-tailed Shearwater *P. tenuirostris*, though the latter is two-thirds the size. The observations of Richdale (1963) and Serventy (1966) suggest that in both species the young have only just time to complete their development before their

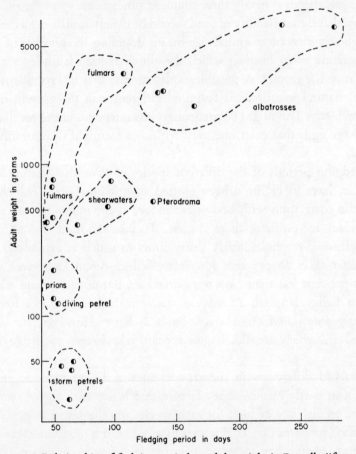

FIGURE 6. Relationship of fledging period to adult weight in Procellariiformes.

long autumn migration. But while the young of *P. tenuirostris*, like those of nearly all other Procellariiformes, have big temporary fat deposits and fledge at rather above the adult weight, in two seasons studied those of *P. griseus* fledged at an average of 622 grams, only four-fifths of the adult weight; indeed, in the second season about one-third of them were only half the adult weight, while many others starved before fledging. The importance for subsequent survival of a high weight at fledging is suggested by the fact that the six ringed fledglings of *P. griseus* later found breeding departed at weights ranging from 635 to 820 grams, hence all were above the average figure. This suggests that it might have been advantageous for the young to have grown more slowly and so to have had time to form bigger fat reserves, if it had not been for the need to migrate by a certain date, and that the latter has resulted in the evolution of a growth-rate so rapid in relation to the food supply that many die. In contrast, the young of *P. tenuirostris* have time to form big reserves, presumably helped by their smaller (adult) size and doubtless by more abundant food.

As already shown in Figures 4 and 5, in Procellariiformes, like other birds, the incubation period is positively correlated with egg-size and, independently, with the fledging period. But these two correlations do not explain all the observed variations. For instance, the incubation period of *P. tenuirostris* is 4 per cent longer than that of *P. puffinus* and similar to that of *Pterodroma macroptera*, but its fledging period is 34 per cent longer than that of *Puffinus puffinus* but 40 per cent shorter than that of *Pterodroma macroptera* (and for weights see Appendix 1). Again in *Puffinus puffinus* as compared with *Hydrobates pelagicus*, the incubation period is 20 per cent longer but the fledging period only 5 per cent longer, whereas in *Diomedea immutabilis* compared with *Puffinus puffinus*, the incubation period is again 20 per cent longer, but the fledging period is twice as long. Hence there are probably other as yet unknown factors influencing the duration of incubation. One of these might be that the chick hatches at an earlier stage of its development in some species than others.

### GROWTH-RATE IN OTHER SPECIES

As can be seen from Appendix 1, in most other families of marine birds the larger species tend to take longer to fledge, but there are striking exceptions. In particular, offshore feeders and tropical species take longer, relative to their size, than inshore feeders and species that breed at higher latitudes respectively. In the Sulidae, these other factors more than offset the influence of size, so that there is an inverse correlation with size, as shown in Figure 7. For reasons discussed earlier (p. 16), the shortest fledging period is that of the largest species, *Sula bassana*, which breeds at high latitudes, while the longest fledging period is that of the smallest species, *S. sula*, which feeds offshore in tropical waters poor in food. This difference also raises the problem of why the different species of *Sula* differ in size. But the factors influencing body-size come outside the subject of this address, except to remark

# David Lack

that, among other things, size is adapted to feeding habits, and hence is linked with the factors influencing breeding biology. I have added to Figure 7 the fledging period in relation to adult weight of those species in other families of Pelecaniformes for which both are known; again, there is no correlation with size.

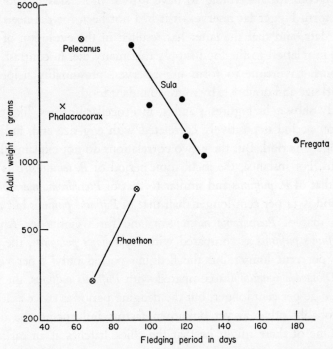

FIGURE 7. Relationship of fledging period to adult weight in Pelecaniformes.

## FAT STORES IN THE YOUNG

The young of many marine birds, like those of most other birds, grow gradually to almost the adult weight at fledging. But in Procellariiformes, tropicbirds (Phaethontidae), the Gannet *Sula bassana* (but not the tropical Sulidae), the Puffin *Fratercula arctica* (and presumably other nidicolous Alcidae) and the King Penguin *Aptenodytes patagonica*, the young form big temporary fat deposits, most of which they lose before fledging. The average peak weight of the young is below the adult weight in *Fratercula arctica* (Myrberget, 1962, 1963; Kartaschew, 1960), about equal (in two seasons) in *Puffinus griseus* (Richdale, 1963), 20 per cent above it in *Pelecanoides* (Richdale, 1943, 1945) and *Pachyptila* (Richdale, 1944; Tickell, 1962), about 50 per cent above it in nearly all other Procellariiformes, also in Phaethontidae and *Sula bassana*, 70 per cent above it in *Oceanodroma leucorrhoa* (Huntington

26

in Palmer, 1962) and *Daption capensis* (Prévost, 1953, 1958), and 80 per cent or more above it in *Puffinus tenuirostris* (Serventy, 1966) and *Oceanites oceanicus* (Roberts, 1940). In nearly all these species, the young fledge at an average weight a little above that of the adult, but in *Fratercula arctica* below it.

Marked differences have been recorded in the peak weight of individual young of the same species, presumably due to differences in the amount of food brought by particular parents. But the average differences in peak weight between different species are so marked that they presumably have a hereditary basis, and hence have been subject to natural selection. As already mentioned, the young of the shearwater *Puffinus griseus* have possibly evolved an unusually rapid growth-rate to enable them to migrate in time, but at the expense of their fat reserves. Again, the young of the diving petrel *Pelecanoides urinatrix* are probably fed more frequently and more regularly than those of most other Procellariiformes, so they probably have less need than others of big fat stores, which may be why they have evolved only small ones.

Probably the main function of fat deposits in the young is to enable them to survive temporary fasts, and subsidiarily perhaps in species at high latitudes, to insulate them from cold. It is therefore suggestive that, in marine birds, they are found almost entirely in offshore feeders, which feed and brood their young much less often and also more irregularly than inshore feeders. In shearwaters, in particular, the parents sometimes do not return with food for 1 to 3 weeks (Richdale, 1963; Serventy, 1966), while young Wilson's Petrels *Oceanites oceanicus* may be temporarily blocked in their burrows by snow (Roberts, 1940). As a special case, big fat stores enable the young King Penguin *Aptenodytes patagonica* to survive the winter, when it is fed only once in 5 or 6 weeks (Stonehouse, 1960). The only inshore feeders with fat deposits are the diving petrels *Pelecanoides*, but they are presumably descended from offshore-feeding Procellariiformes and anyway have smaller deposits than most other species. There are also two genera of offshore feeders, the frigate birds *Fregata* and the tropical boobies *Sula* (*sens. strict.*), whose young do not have big fat stores. They also differ from other offshore feeders in that the young depend on their parents for food for several weeks after fledging, whereas all the others are independent as soon as they fledge. This might be a coincidence, or alternatively might mean that another advantage of fat stores is to provide the fledglings with a food reserve for their first days of independence, when feeding may be difficult. The latter is probably important in the Gannet *S. bassana* but at most of minor importance in other seabirds in which, as already mentioned, the young lose almost all their surplus fat before fledging.

Fat stores perhaps have an additional function in certain long-distance migrants like the shearwaters *Puffinus tenuirostris*, *P. griseus*, *P. gravis* and *P. puffinus*, in which the young are fed rarely, if at all, during their last fortnight in the nest. They could not survive this 'starvation period' without big fat stores, and in one season many young *P. griseus* which did not form big stores died, as already mentioned. Since a starvation period could hardly be of advantage to the young, it may be wondered whether it is of advantage to the adults, in enabling them to migrate a fortnight earlier than they otherwise could. That an earlier departure favours survival in these species is suggested by three points, first that sub-adults without family cares leave well before parents with young, secondly that in *P. tenuirostris*, *P. gravis* and *P. griseus* the laying season is extremely restricted, and thirdly that in *P. puffinus*, in which the season is more extended, those young which leave earliest have the greatest chance of survival (Perrins, 1966). It there-fore seems possible that big fat stores in the young are of advantage in enabling the parents to migrate earlier, presumably because food is becoming scarce round the colonies. If true, it means that the young depart at a less favourable time than the adults, but this might be *faute de mieux*.

### TIMING OF BREEDING

Nearly all marine birds, like most others, breed each year at one regular and restricted season. Indeed *P. tenuirostris* is the most regular of all birds so far studied (Marshall & Serventy, 1965a). I formerly argued that in species which, like nearly all marine birds, raise only one brood in a year, the average date of laying will have been evolved so that the young are being fed when their food is most abundant (Lack, 1954). This view has to be seriously modified because Perrins (1966) found for *P. puffinus* (and also, 1965, for the Great Tit *Parus major*) that those individuals which lay their eggs earliest in the season are the most likely to leave surviving offspring. Hence it may be asked why all individuals do not breed as early as the earliest pairs (if not even earlier). Perrins suggested, and I agree, that this is probably because the females cannot normally obtain enough nourishment to form their eggs earlier, and in this connection it will be recalled that shearwaters lay proportionately very large eggs. Here, then, is another factor which may have influenced the evolution of egg-size, since if the bird had a smaller egg, it could presumably lay rather earlier, and hence could have young at what is probably a more favourable time for their survival; but a smaller egg would mean a smaller chick at hatching, which might be harder to feed and keep warm. Hence the size of egg evolved is probably a compromise between these conflicting advantages. But in tropical waters there may be no marked annual cycle of marine foods, and hence no such marked advantage in the egg being laid by a particular date, and that is perhaps why certain tropical petrels, such as *Puffinus nativitatis*, *Pterodroma alba* and *Nesofregetta albigularis* have larger eggs, proportionate to their weight, than comparable species at high latitudes.

In the Kittiwake *Rissa tridactyla*, as in *Puffinus puffinus*, the pairs which breed earliest tend to raise most young (Coulson & White, summarized in Lack, 1966). In this species, females paired with their former mates lay earlier than those with new mates (Coulson, 1966), so it is usually of survival value to retain the former mate, which is presumably why this and many other species of seabirds do it (cf. Richdale, 1957). In *Rissa tridactyla*, the position is complicated because the earliest pairs tend to lay larger clutches than the later ones, presumably as an adaptation to the feeding conditions for the chicks later. Hence in this species the timing of breeding also influences clutch-size.

While nearly all marine species breed regularly once a year, species in several different families breed at intervals shorter than a year on Ascension Island (Chapin, 1954; Stonehouse, 1962; Dorward, 1962), and in the Galapagos (Snow, 1965, 1966), while the frigate bird *Fregata minor* breeds at a longer than annual interval in the Galapagos (Nelson, in preparation). This would be possible only in environments where the food supplies show little or no regular seasonal fluctuation. A more unusual occurrence is that, in the Phoenix and Line archipelagos, the tern *Sterna fuscata* has a breeding season regularly every 6 months, those pairs that successfully raise a chick breeding only once a year, but those which fail doing so after 6 months (Gallagher, 1960; Ashmole, 1963c, 1965). Likewise the storm petrel *Oceanodroma castro* has a breeding season once every 6 months in the Galapagos (Snow, 1966). Another unusual variation occurs in the King Penguin *Aptenodytes patagonica*, which in South Georgia can raise two young every 3 years, those individuals which lay early in one season finishing in time to lay again rather late in the following season, but then not having time to lay again until the fourth season in this sequence (Stonehouse, 1960). Finally, the large albatrosses *Diomedea epomophora* and *D. exulans* can raise a chick only once in 2 years (Richdale, 1952; Tickell, 1960). The evidence suggests that all these species are breeding as fast as conditions permit.

## CONCLUSION

I have aimed in this address to show that the various adaptations for breeding in birds are closely interrelated with each other, so that the selective factors responsible for one cannot be properly evaluated in isolation from the rest. To recall only one example briefly, clutch-size has evidently been evolved in relation to the type of young, to whether the adults feed inshore or offshore, to the size of breeding colonies, to the growth-rate of the chick, to the size of the egg, and to the timing of breeding. Such interrelationships have arisen because the whole organism is an adapted unit.

The evidence for adaptations has here been derived from comparisons between species, which can usually be interpreted more clearly between closely than distantly related forms. Since such comparisons are more revealing the greater the number of species that have been studied, there is need for more life-history studies. But a greater need is for critical tests of the views put forward here by suitably designed field experiments carried out under as nearly natural conditions as possible. Already, broods have been supplemented to see whether a species can raise more young than its normal clutch (with discordant results, see Lack, 1966), while the rate of predation has been measured on eggs placed inside and outside gull colonies (Tinbergen, 1963, 1967), but this is only a start. The experiments on gulls bring me, however, to Dr Tinbergen's talk. It was the Programme Committee's intention that he should now replace me on the rostrum, but for administrative reasons his talk has had to be postponed to the session on behaviour and physiology. The two talks were, however, planned together and are intended to be read in conjunction.

SUMMARY

1. The many adaptations for breeding in birds are closely interrelated.

2. The type of nesting dispersion is related to the nesting site, the type of young and feeding habits. (i) Most intertidal feeders have nests accessible to predators but widely dispersed, with cryptic eggs and cryptic nidifugous young, (ii) most offshore and some inshore feeders have large colonies in inaccessible sites and nidicolous non-cryptic young, (iii) many inshore feeders have more accessible colonies, with cryptic eggs and cryptic young which, though active, stay in the colonies, where the adults attack intruders.

3. Clutch-size tends to be larger in nidifugous than nidicolous species, and larger in inshore than offshore feeders. Offshore feeders also have longer incubation and fledging periods and start breeding later in life than inshore feeders; these differences hold between different families, and also between species in the same family.

4. If clutch-size is adapted to the number of young that can be fed, it may also

be influenced by the growth-rate. The uniform clutch in Procellariiformes, and the smaller clutch at high than low latitudes in Sulidae, are linked with marked differences in the growth-rates of the young.

5. Irrespective of variations due to size, the length of incubation is correlated with the fledging period, except in Phaethontidae. The proportionate weight of the egg differs markedly in different families. A larger egg means that the chick is larger at hatching, but its production may impose a strain on the female.

6. The young of many offshore feeders form big temporary fat deposits, which probably help them to survive intermittent fasts. In some shearwaters they perhaps allow the parents to depart on migration before the young fledge.

7. Food is perhaps too sparse in spring for some species to be able to lay their eggs in time for the young to hatch at the best season for feeding them. Most marine birds breed annually, but some at a shorter or longer interval.

8. The possible adaptive relationships suggested in this address are based on comparisons between species and should be tested by field experiments.

### ACKNOWLEDGEMENTS

I am extremely grateful to the following for providing unpublished observations on particular species, or for supplementing what they have published: N.P.Ashmole, J.C.Coulson, J.M.Cullen, G.M.Dunnet, M.P.Harris, C.Huntington, G.P.Potts, U.Safriel, D.L.Serventy, D.W.Snow, B.Stonehouse and J.Warham. I am also extremely grateful to P.R.Evans, R.E.Moreau, I.Newton and C.M. Perrins for criticizing the manuscript before publication, and to Mrs Whittaker for preparing the graphs.

APPENDIX I

DATA ON BREEDING BIOLOGY USED IN TABLES AND GRAPHS

The species are listed in the sequence and nomenclature of Peters (1931, 1934)

| Species | Adult weight (grams) | Weight of egg (grams) | Incubation period (days) | Fledging period (days) | Main references (egg-weights in Schönwetter, 1960-66, if not in authors cited) |
|---|---|---|---|---|---|
| SPHENISCIDAE | | | | | |
| Aptenodytes patagonica | 15,000 | 300 | 53 | c. 360 | Stonehouse, 1960 |
| A. forsteri | 30,000 | 450 | 62 | (160+) | Prévost, 1961 |
| Pygoscelis papua | 6,200 | 136 | — | — | Stonehouse, pers. comm. |
| P. adeliae | 5,000 | 124 | 33 | 51 | Taylor, 1962 |
| P. antarctica | 4,500 | 110 | — | — | Stonehouse, pers. comm. |
| Eudyptes sclateri | 3,600 | 120 | — | — | Stonehouse, pers. comm. |
| E. crestatus | 2,500 | 110(2nd) | 34 | 70 | Gwynn, 1953; Warham, 1963 |
| E. schlegeli | 4,500 | 162(2nd) | 35 | — | Gwynn, 1953 |
| E. chrysolophus | (4,200) | 154(2nd) | 35 | (61) | Gwynn, 1953 |
| Megadyptes antipodes | 5,200 | 138 | 43 | 106 | Richdale, 1957 |
| Eudyptula minor | 1,100 | 52 | 39 | 55 | Stonehouse, pers. comm.; Richdale, 1940; Warham, 1958 |
| E. albosignata | 1,500 | 55 | — | — | Stonehouse, pers. comm. |
| Spheniscus demersus | 2,900 | 103 | 40 | 113 | Stonehouse, pers. comm.; Rand, 1960 |
| S. humboldti | 4,200 | 119 | — | — | Stonehouse, pers. comm. |
| S. magellanicus | 4,900 | 107 | — | — | Stonehouse, pers. comm. |

| | | | | | |
|---|---|---|---|---|---|
| **DIOMEDEIDAE** | | | | | |
| *Diomedea exulans* | 8,040 | 488 | 78 | 280 | Tickell, pers. comm. |
| *D. epomophora* | 8,290 | 445 | 79 | 236 | Richdale, 1952 |
| *D. nigripes* | 3,090 | 291 | 65 | c. 140 | Frings, 1961; Rice & Kenyon, 1962 |
| *D. immutabilis* | 2,450 | 279 | 64 | c. 165 | Frings, 1961; Rice & Kenyon, 1962 |
| *Phoebetria palpebrata* | 3,000 | 225 | c. 65 | 136 | Sorensen, 1950 |
| **PROCELLARIIDAE** | | | | | |
| *Macronectes giganteus* | 4,000 | 237 | 59 | 108 | Warham, 1962 and pers. comm. |
| *Daption capensis* | 450 | 67 | 44 | 49 | Prévost, 1953, 1958 |
| *Fulmarus glacialis* | 720 | 98 | 49 | 49 | Dunnet et al, 1963 and pers. comm. |
| *Priocella antarctica* | 800 | 103 | 44 | 50 | Prévost, 1953, 1958 |
| (= *Fulmarus glacialoides*) | | | | | |
| *Pachyptila desolata* | c. 200 | 33 | (45+) | 50 | Tickell, 1962 |
| *P. turtur* | 130 | 25 | — | 50 | Richdale, 1964 |
| *Puffinus griseus* | 790 | 95 | — | 97 | Richdale, 1963 |
| *P. tenuirostris* | 530 | 85 | 53 | 94 | Serventy, 1957, 1958, 1966 |
| *P. nativitatis* | 324 | 63 | 54+ | 70+ | Ashmole, pers. comm. |
| *P. puffinus* | 400 | 58 | 51 | 70 | Harris, 1966 |
| *Pterodroma macroptera* | 570 | 80 | 53 | 131 | Warham, 1956 |
| *P. alba* | 269 | 56 | c. 53 | (96+) | Ashmole, pers. comm. |
| *Pagodroma nivea* | 425 | 57 | — | 45 | Prévost, 1953, 1958 |
| **HYDROBATIDAE** | | | | | |
| *Oceanites oceanicus* | 34 | 9 | 43 | (52+) | Roberts, 1940 |
| *Pelagodroma marina* | 47 | 12 | (46) | 57 | Richdale, 1943–44 |
| *Nesofregetta albigularis* | 68 | 20 | — | — | Ashmole, pers. comm. |
| *Hydrobates pelagicus* | 28 | 7 | 41 | 63 | Davis, 1957 |
| *Oceanodroma castro* | 44 | 11 | 38 | 65 | Allan, 1962 |
| *O. leucorhoa* | 50 | 10 | 42 | 66 | Huntington in Palmer, 1962 and pers. comm. |

33

| Species | Adult weight (grams) | Weight of egg (grams) | Incubation period (days) | Fledging period (days) | Main references (egg-weights in Schönwetter, 1960–66, if not in authors cited) |
|---|---|---|---|---|---|
| PELECANOIDIDAE | | | | | |
| Pelecanoides urinatrix | 124 | 19 | — | 54 | Richdale, 1943, 1945 |
| PHAETHONTIDAE | | | | | |
| Phaethon aethereus | 750 | 67 | 43 | 94 | Stonehouse, 1962 |
| P. rubricauda | 665 | 72 | — | — | Ashmole, pers. comm. |
| P. lepturus | 300 | 40 | 41 | 70 | Stonehouse, 1962 |
| PELECANIDAE | | | | | |
| Pelecanus occidentalis | 3,500 | 91 | — | 63 | Palmer, 1962 |
| SULIDAE | | | | | |
| Morus (Sula) bassanus | 3,300 | 106 | 44 | 90 | Nelson, 1964 |
| Sula nebouxii | 1,800 | 65 | 41 | 100 | Nelson, pers. comm. |
| S. dactylatra | 1,900 | 68 | 44 | 118 | Dorward, 1962; Nelson, pers. comm. |
| S. sula | 1,070 | 54 | 45 | 130 | Nelson, pers. comm. |
| S. leucogaster | 1,300 | 53 | 45 | 120 | Dorward, 1962 |
| PHALACROCORACIDAE | | | | | |
| Phalacrocorax auritus | 1,870 | 48 | 28 | (c. 46) | Palmer, 1962 |
| P. carbo | 2,500 | 58 | 28 | (c. 49) | Palmer, 1962 |
| P. penicillatus | 2,430 | 51 | — | — | Palmer, 1962 |
| P. aristotelis | 1,760 | 49 | 30 | 53 | Snow, 1960, 1963; Potts, 1966 |
| P. pelagicus | 1,870 | 44 | 31 | (c. 53) | Palmer, 1962 |

| | | | | | |
|---|---|---|---|---|---|
| **FREGATIDAE** | | | | | |
| *Fregata magnificens* | 1,250 | 76 | 44 | 180 | Stonehouse, 1963b |
| *F. minor* | 1,425 | 85 | 55 | — | Nelson, in prep. |
| **ANATIDAE** | | | | | |
| *Branta bernicla* | 1,400 | 91 | — | — | |
| *Tadorna tadorna* | 1,000 | 78 | 28 | 56 | Witherby et al, 1938-41 |
| *Tachyeres brachyptera* | 3,000 | 147 | — | — | |
| *Somateria mollissima* | 2,000 | 110 | 28 | — | Witherby et al, 1938-41 |
| **HAEMATOPODIDAE** | | | | | |
| *Haematopus ostralegus* | 500 | 47 | 28 | 31 | Safriel, pers. comm. |
| **CHARADRIIDAE** | | | | | |
| *Charadrius hiaticula* | 60 | 11 | 24 | 25 | Witherby et al, 1938-41 |
| *C. alexandrinus* | 43 | 9 | 24 | — | Witherby et al, 1938-41 |
| **DROMADIDAE** | | | | | |
| *Dromas ardeola* | 275 | 70 | — | — | Heinroth, 1922 |
| **CHIONIDAE** | | | | | |
| *Chionis alba* | — | 46 | 30 | 55 | Jones, 1963 |
| *C. minor* | 430 | 43 | — | — | |
| **STERCORARIIDAE** | | | | | |
| *Catharacta skua* | — | 91 | 28 | 45 | Witherby et al, 1938-41 |
| *Stercorarius parasiticus* | 500 | 48 | 26 | (35) | Witherby et al, 1938-41 |

| Species | Adult weight (grams) | Weight of egg (grams) | Incubation period (days) | Fledging period (days) | Main references (egg-weights in Schönwetter, 1960-66, if not in authors cited) |
|---|---|---|---|---|---|
| LARIDAE | | | | | |
| Larus canus | 420 | 54 | 24 | 35 | Witherby et al, 1938-41 |
| L. argentatus | 895 | 82 | 27 | 45 | Harris, 1963, 1964; Heinroth, 1926-28 |
| L. (a.)glaucescens | — | 98 | 27 | 40 | Drent et al, 1964 |
| L. fuscus | 837 | 76 | 26 | — | Harris, 1963, 1964 |
| L. dominicanus | — | 80 | 27 | 49 | Fordham, 1964 |
| L. marinus | 1,600 | 105 | 29 | 56 | Harris, 1963, 1964; Heinroth, 1922 |
| L. hyperboreus | 1,400 | 118 | 28 | — | Witherby et al, 1938-41 |
| L. ridibundus | 250 | 38 | 23 | 30 | Ytreberg, 1956; Tinbergen's group, pers. comm. |
| Rissa tridactyla | 350 | 50 | 27 | 43 | Coulson, pers. comm. |
| Creagrus furcatus | — | 73 | 34 | 60 | Snow, 1967 and pers. comm. |
| STERNIDAE | | | | | |
| Sterna hirundo | 135 | 20 | 23 | 30 | Witherby et al, 1938-41 |
| S. paradisaea | 110 | 19 | 22 | — | Witherby et al, 1938-41 |
| S. dougallii | — | 20 | 24 | — | Witherby et al, 1938-41 |
| S. anaethetus | 100 | 25 | — | — | Ashmole, 1963a |
| S. fuscata | 175 | 34 | 30 | 60 | Witherby et al, 1938-41 |
| S. albifrons | 40 | 9 | 21 | 30 | Witherby et al, 1938-41 |
| Thalasseus sandvicensis | 250 | 35 | 23 | 35 | Ashmole, pers. comm. |
| Procelsterna cerulea | 45 | 12 | — | — | Ashmole, 1962; Stonehouse, 1963a |
| Anous tenuirostris | 120 | 26 | 35 | 45 | Dorward, 1963; Stonehouse, 1963a |
| Gygis alba | 138 | 25 | 36 | 83 | |

| ALCIDAE | | | | | |
|---|---|---|---|---|---|
| Plautus alle | 125 | 24 | 24 | — | Kartaschew, 1960 |
| Alca torda | 700 | 94 | 34 | — | Kartaschew, 1960 |
| Uria lomvia | 930 | 110 | 29 | — | Kartaschew, 1960 |
| U. aalge | 1,000 | 113 | 33 | — | Kartaschew, 1960 |
| Cepphus grylle | 425 | 52 | 29 | 36 | Kartaschew, 1960 |
| C. columba | 450 | 55 | 30 | 35 | Drent et al, 1964 |
| Ptychoramphus aleutica | — | 28 | 37+ | 45 | Thoresen, 1964 |
| Fratercula arctica | 500 | 65 | 38 | 42 | Kartaschew, 1960 |

# David Lack

## TIMING OF THE MOULT

The moult is strictly outside the theme of this address, but is relevant in that its timing may affect the breeding cycle. In many marine birds, as in most others, the adults moult their flight-feathers once a year shortly after they finish breeding. As this may impair flight, and hence feeding efficiency, the moult must take place when food is reasonably easy to obtain, and it is therefore possible that in some species the breeding season is curtailed by the need to moult before the winter, though this possibility has not been studied in marine birds. The moult is particularly drastic in penguins (Spheniscidae), which come on land and take no food, but depend on big stores of subcutaneous fat laid down shortly beforehand (Richdale, 1957).

Long-distance migrants like the shearwaters *Puffinus tenuirostris* and *P. gravis* (Marshall & Serventy, 1956b) defer moult of the flight-feathers until they have completed their long journey and have reached an area of abundant food; then the moult is rapid and heavy, which is possible for them as they do not catch their food in flight. A few gulls, such as *Larus f. fuscus* and *Xema sabini*, also moult their flight-feathers after the autumn migration (Stresemann, 1963). More remarkably, at least four marine species in different families moult their flight-feathers while breeding, the Snow Petrel *Pagodroma nivea* (Maher, 1962), the gull *Larus hyperboreus* (Johnston, 1961), the Gannet *Sula bassana* (Nelson, 1964) and the auk *Ptychoramphus aleutica* (Payne, 1965). Presumably their food is so much more plentiful during than outside the breeding season that it is advantageous for them to moult while raising young, and in the short summer at high latitudes they might not otherwise have time to complete both breeding and the moult before leaving their summer quarters. In a similar ecological situation the Ivory Gull *Pagophila eburnea* moults just prior to breeding (Stresemann, 1963).

Another unusual pattern of moult occurs in the tern *Sterna fuscata* in the Line archipelago, where those individuals which raise a chick moult after breeding in the normal way, and breed again a year later, but those which fail in breeding start their moult earlier and then suspend it temporarily in order to breed again after 6 months (Ashmole 1963c). Similarly the booby *Sula leucogaster*, which breeds at less than annual intervals on Ascension Island, temporarily suspends its wing-moult while breeding (Dorward, 1962). In this species the primaries are, as usual, moulted in sequence from the innermost outwards, but a full cycle of replacement takes 3 years instead of 1. However, when the first cycle has reached about the seventh primary, a new cycle is initiated from the first, and both continue concurrently. By this means each primary is replaced once a year, as in other species, but two adjacent features are not in moult simultaneously, which might seriously impair the efficiency of flight in a species which especially depends on its wings for obtaining food.

Such a gradual moult is in marked contrast to the rapid and heavy moult of the transequatorial migrant species of *Puffinus* already mentioned. The moult is heavier still in the larger species of Alcidae (Storer, 1960), and the Pelecanoididae (Murphy, 1936), which are temporarily unable to fly though they can still use their wings under the water to catch their food. The marine ducks (Anatidae), like other members of this family, are also flightless in moult. This brief survey shows that in marine birds there are as divergent patterns in the moult as in breeding biology and in both cases they are closely adapted to the ecological requirements of the species concerned.

# Presidential Address

## REFERENCES

ALEXANDER W.B. (1928) *Birds of the Ocean*. London.

ALLAN R.G. (1962) The Madeiran Storm Petrel *Oceanodroma castro*. Ibis **103b**, 274–295.

ASHMOLE N.P. (1962) The Black Noddy *Anous tenuirostris* on Ascension Island. Part 1. General biology. *Ibis* **103b**, 235–273.

ASHMOLE N.P. (1963a) The biology of the Wideawake or Sooty Tern *Sterna fuscata* on Ascension Island. *Ibis* **103b**, 297–364.

ASHMOLE N.P. (1963b) The regulation of numbers of tropical oceanic birds. *Ibis* **103b**, 458–473.

ASHMOLE N.P. (1963c) Molt and breeding in populations of the Sooty Tern *Sterna fuscata*. *Postilla* **76**, 1–18.

ASHMOLE N.P. (1965) Adaptive variation in the breeding regime of a tropical seabird. *Proc. Nat. Acad. Sci.* **52**, 311–318.

AUSTIN O.L. & AUSTIN O.L. (Jr.) (1956) Some demographic aspects of the Cape Cod population of Common Terns (*Sterna hirundo*). *Bird Banding* **27**, 55–66.

CARRICK R., KEITH K. & GWYNN A.M. (1960) Fact and fiction on the breeding of the Wandering Albatross. *Nature* **188**, 112–114.

CHAPIN J.P. (1954) The calendar of Wideawake Fair. *Auk*, **71**, 1–15.

COULSON J.C. (1966) The influence of the pair-bond and age on the breeding biology of the Kittiwake Gull *Rissa tridactyla*. *J. Anim. Ecol.* **35**, 269–279.

CROOK J.H. (1965) The adaptive significance of avian social organizations. *Symp. zool. Soc. Lond.* **14**, 181–218.

CULLEN J.M. (1960) Some adaptations in the nesting behaviour of terns. *Proc. XII Internat. Orn. Congr.*, 153–157.

DAVIS P. (1957) The breeding of the Storm Petrel. *Brit. Birds* **50**, 85–101, 371–384.

DORWARD D.F. (1962) Comparative biology of the White Booby and the Brown Booby *Sula* spp. at Ascension. *Ibis* **103b**, 174–220.

DORWARD D.F. (1963) The Fairy Tern *Gygis alba* on Ascension Island. *Ibis* **103b**, 365–378.

DRENT R. *et al* (1964) The breeding birds of Mandarte Island, British Columbia. *Canad. Field-Nat.* **78**, 208–263.

DUNNET G.M., ANDERSON A. & CORMACK R.M. (1963) A study of survival of adult Fulmars with observations on the pre-laying exodus. *Brit. Birds* **56**, 2–18.

FORDHAM R.A. (1964) Breeding biology of the Southern Black-backed Gull. *Notornis* **11**, 3–34, 110–126.

FRINGS C. (1961) Egg-sizes of Laysan and Black-footed Albatrosses. *Condor* **63**, 263.

GALLAGHER M.D. (1960) Bird notes from Christmas Island, Pacific Ocean. *Ibis* **102**, 489–502.

GROSS A.O. (1947) Recoveries of banded Leach's Petrels. *Bird Banding* **18**, 117–126.

GWYNN A.M. (1953) The egg-laying and incubation periods of Rockhopper, Macaroni and Gentoo Penguins. *Australian National Antarctic Research Exped. Rep.* (B) *Zool.* **1**, 1–29.

HARRIS M.P. (1963) Some aspects of the biology of *Larus* gulls. Ph.D. thesis, Swansea.

HARRIS M.P. (1964) Aspects of the breeding biology of the gulls *Larus argentatus*, *L. fuscus* and *L. marinus*. *Ibis* **106**, 432–456.

HARRIS M.P. (1966) Breeding biology of the Manx Shearwater *Puffinus puffinus*. *Ibis* **108**, 17–33.

E

# David Lack

HEINROTH O. (1922) Die Beziehungen zwischen Vogelgewicht, Eigewicht, Gelegegewicht und Brutdauer. *J. Orn.* **70**, 172–285.

HEINROTH O & HEINROTH M. (1926–28) *Die Vögel Mitteleuropas.* Berlin.

JOHNSTON D.W. (1961) Timing of annual molt in the Glaucous Gulls of northern Alaska. *Condor* **63**, 474–478.

JONES N.V. (1963) The Sheathbill *Chionis alba* (Gmelin) at Signy Island, South Orkney Islands. *British Antarctic Survey Bull.* **2**, 53–71.

KARTASCHEW N.N. (1960) *Die Alkenvögel des Nordatlantiks.* Neue Brehm-Bücherei No. 257. Wittenberg.

LACK D. (1947–48) The significance of clutch-size. *Ibis* **89**, 302–352; **90**, 25–45.

LACK D. (1954) *The Natural Regulation of Animal Numbers.* Oxford.

LACK D. (1956) *Swifts in a Tower.* London.

LACK D. (1965) *The Life of the Robin* 4th ed. London.

LACK D. (1966) *Population Studies of Birds.* Oxford.

LÉVÊQUE R. (1964) Notes sur la réproduction des oiseaux aux Iles Galapagos. *Alauda* **32**, 5–44, 81–96.

MACKWORTH-PRAED C.W. & GRANT C.H.B. (1952) *Birds of Eastern and Northeastern Africa* vol. 1. London.

MAHER W.J. (1962) Breeding biology of the Snow Petrel near Cape Hallett, Antarctica. *Condor* **64**, 488–499.

MARSHALL A.J. & SERVENTY D.L. (1956a) The breeding cycle of the Short-tailed Shearwater, *Puffinus tenuirostris* (Temminck), in relation to transequatorial migration and its environment. *Proc. Zool. Soc. Lond.* **127**, 489–510.

MARSHALL A.J. & SERVENTY D.L. (1956b) Moult adaptation in relation to long-distance migration in petrels. *Nature* **177**, 943.

MILNE H. (1965) Seasonal distribution and breeding biology of the Eider *Somateria mollissima mollissima* L. in the northeast of Scotland. Ph.D. thesis, Aberdeen.

MOREAU R.E. (1944) Clutch size: a comparative study, with special reference to African birds. *Ibis* **86**, 286–347.

MURPHY R.C. (1936) *Oceanic Birds of South America* vols. 1 and 2. New York.

MYRBERGET S. (1962) (Contribution to the breeding biology of the Puffin *Fratercula arctica* (L.). Eggs, incubation and young.) *Pap. Norwegian State Game Research Inst.* 2nd Series, No. 11, 49 pp.

MYRBERGET S. (1963) Systematic position of *Fratercula arctica* from a north Norwegian colony. *Nytt Mag. Zool.* **11**, 74–84.

NELSON J.B. (1964) Factors influencing clutch-size and chick growth in the North Atlantic Gannet *Sula bassana. Ibis* **106**, 63–77.

NELSON J.B. (1966) Clutch-size in the Sulidae. *Nature* **210**, 435–436.

PALMER R.S. (1962) *Handbook of North American Birds* vol. 1. New Haven.

PAYNE R.B. (1965) The moult of breeding Cassin Auklets. *Condor* **67**, 220–228.

PERRINS C.M. (1965) Population fluctuations and clutch-size in the Great Tit, *Parus major* L. *J. Anim. Ecol.* **34**, 601–647.

PERRINS C.M. (1966) Survival of young Manx Shearwaters *Puffinus puffinus* in relation to their presumed date of hatching. *Ibis* **108**, 132–135.

# Presidential Address

POTTS G.R. (1966) Studies on a marked population of the Shag (*Phalacrocorax aristotelis*), with special reference to the breeding biology of birds of known age. Ph.D. thesis, Durham.

PRÉVOST J. (1953) Notes sur la réproduction du Fulmar Antarctique *Fulmarus glacialoides* (A.Smith). *Alauda* 21, 157–164.

PRÉVOST J. (1958) Note complémentaire sur l'écologie des Pétrels de Terre Adélie. *Alauda* 26, 125–130.

PRÉVOST J. (1961) Ecologie du Manchot Empereur. Paris.

RAND R.W. (1960) The distribution, abundance and feeding habits of the Cape Penguin, *Spheniscus demersus* . . . (The biology of guano-producing seabirds.) *Investigational Report 41. Commerce & Industry (South Africa)*.

RICE D.W. & KENYON K.W. (1962) Breeding cycles and behavior of Laysan and Black-footed Albatrosses. *Auk* 79, 517–567.

RICHDALE L.E. (1940) Random notes on the genus *Eudyptula* on the Otago Peninsula, New Zealand. *Emu* 40, 180–217.

RICHDALE L.E. (1943) The Kuaka or Diving Petrel, *Pelecanoides urinatrix* (Gmelin). *Emu* 43, 24–48.

RICHDALE L.E. (1943–44) The White-faced Storm Petrel or Takahi-kare-moana. *Trans. Roy. Soc. New Zealand* 73, 97–115, 217–232, 335–350.

RICHDALE L.E. (1944) The Titi Wainui or Fairy Prion *Pachyptila turtur* (Kuhl.). *Trans. Roy. Soc. New Zealand* 74, 32–48, 165–181.

RICHDALE L.E. (1945) Supplementary notes on the Diving Petrel. *Trans. Roy. Soc. New Zealand* 75, 42–53.

RICHDALE L.E. (1952) *Post-egg Period in Albatrosses*. Biol. Monogr. No. 4, Nuffield Publ. No. 1. Dunedin.

RICHDALE L.E. (1954) The starvation theory in albatrosses. *Auk* 71, 239–252.

RICHDALE L.E. (1957) *A Population Study of Penguins*. Oxford.

RICHDALE L.E. (1963) Biology of the Sooty Shearwater *Puffinus griseus*. *Proc. zool. Soc. Lond.* 141, 1–117.

RICHDALE L.E. (1965) Biology of the birds of Whero Island, New Zealand. *Trans. zool. Soc. Lond.* 31, 1–155.

ROBERTS B. (1940) The life cycle of Wilson's Petrel *Oceanites oceanicus* (Kuhl). *British Graham Land Expedition 1934–37. Sci. Reps.* 1, 141–194.

ROBERTSON W.B. (1964) The terns of the Dry Tortugas. *Bull. Florida State Mus.* 8 (1), 1–94.

SAPIN-JALOUSTRE J. (1960–4) *Ecologie du Manchot Adélie*. Paris.

SCHÖNWETTER M. (1960–66) *Handbuch der Oologie*, ed. W.Meise. Berlin.

SERVENTY D.L. (1957) Duration of immaturity in the Short-tailed Shearwater *Puffinus tenuirostris* (Temminck). *C.S.I.R.O. Wild Res.* 2, 60–62.

SERVENTY D.L. (1958) Recent studies on the Tasmanian Mutton-bird. *Aust. Mus. Mag.* 12, 327–332.

SERVENTY D.L. (1963) Egg-laying timetable of the Slender-billed Shearwater, *Puffinus tenuirostris*. *Proc. XIII Internat. Orn. Congr.*, 338–343.

SERVENTY D.L. (1967) Population ecology of the Short-tailed Shearwater *Puffinus tenuirostris*. *Proc. XIV Internat. Orn. Congr.*, 165–190.

SNOW B. (1960) The breeding biology of the Shag *Phalacrocorax aristotelis* on the Island of Lundy, Bristol Channel. *Ibis* 102, 554–575.

# David Lack

SNOW B.K. (1963) The behaviour of the Shag. *Brit. Birds* **56**, 77–103, 164–186.

SNOW D.W. (1965) The breeding of Audubon's Shearwater (*Puffinus lherminieri*) in the Galapagos. *Auk* **82**, 591–597.

SNOW D.W. & SNOW B.K. (1966) The breeding season of the Madeiran Storm Petrel *Oceanodroma castro* in the Galapagos. *Ibis* **108**, 283–284.

SNOW D.W. & SNOW B.K. (1967) The breeding cycle of the Swallow-tailed Gull *Creagrus fureatus*. *Ibis* **109**, 14–24.

SORENSEN J.H. (1950) The Light-Mantled Sooty Albatross at Campbell Island. *D.S.I.R. New Zealand. Cape Expedition Series, Bull.* 8, pp. 5–30.

STONEHOUSE B. (1960) The King Penguin *Aptenodytes patagonica* of south Georgia. 1. Breeding behaviour and development. *Falkl. Is. Depend. Surv. Sci. Rep.* 23.

STONEHOUSE B. (1962) The tropic birds (genus *Phaethon*) of Ascension Island. *Ibis* **103b**, 124–161.

STONEHOUSE B. (1963a) Egg dimensions of some Ascension Island sea-birds. *Ibis* **103b**, 474–479.

STONEHOUSE B. & STONEHOUSE S. (1963b) The Frigate Bird *Fregata aquila* of Ascension Island. *Ibis* **103b**, 409–422.

STORER R.W. (1960) Evolution in the diving birds. *Proc. XII Internat. Orn. Congr.*, 694–707.

STRESEMANN E. (1963) Zeitraum und Verlauf der Handschwingen-Mauser palaearktischer Möwen, Seeschwalben und Limicolen. *J. Orn.* **104**, 424–435.

TAYLOR R.H. (1962) The Adelie Penguin *Pygoscelis adeliae* at Cape Royds. *Ibis* **104**, 176–204.

THORESEN A.C. (1964) The breeding behavior of the Cassin Auklet. *Condor* **66**, 456–476.

TICKELL W.L.N. (1960) Chick feeding in the Wandering Albatross *Diomedea exulans* Linnaeus. *Nature*, **185**, 116–117.

TICKELL W.L.N. (1962) The Dove Prion, *Pachyptila desolata* Gmelin. *Falkl. Is. Depend. Surv. Sci. Rep.* 33.

TINBERGEN N. (1963) On adaptive radiation in gulls (tribe Larini). *Zool. Med. (Leiden)* **39**, 209–223.

TINBERGEN N. (1967) Adaptive features of the Black-headed Gull *Larus ridibundus* L. *Proc. XIV Internat. Orn. Congr.*, 43–59.

WARHAM J. (1956) The breeding of the Great-winged Petrel *Pterodroma macroptera*. *Ibis* **98**, 171–185.

WARHAM J. (1958) The nesting of the Little Penguin *Eudyptula minor*. *Ibis* **100**, 605–616.

WARHAM J. (1962) The biology of the Giant Petrel *Macronectes giganteus*. *Auk* **79**, 139–160.

WARHAM J. (1963) The Rockhopper Penguin, *Eudyptes chrysocome*, at Macquarie Island. *Auk* **80**, 229–256.

WARHAM J. (1964) Breeding behaviour in Procellariiformes. *Biologie Antarctique Symp.* 1, pp. 389–394. Ed. R.Carrick, M.Holdgate, J.Prévost.

WITHERBY H.F. *et al* (1938–41) *The Handbook of British Birds.* London.

WYNNE-EDWARDS V.C. (1955) Low reproductive rates in birds, especially in sea-birds. *Proc. XI Internat. Orn. Congr.*, 540–547.

WYNNE-EDWARDS V.C. (1962) *Animal Dispersion in Relation to Social Behaviour.* Edinburgh.

YTREBERG N.U. (1966) Contribution to the breeding biology of the Black-headed Gull (*Larus ridibundus* L.) in Norway. *Nytt Mag. Zool.* **4**, 5–106.

# Adaptive features of the Black-headed Gull
## *Larus ridibundus* L.

N. TINBERGEN

Dr Lack's wide-ranging review (this volume, pp. 3–42) has no doubt impressed upon all of us the rich and varied spectrum of features to be found among the many species of seabirds, and his evidence (which he rightly calls 'circumstantial') will in many cases have convinced us that these characteristics are indeed adaptive. It is now my task to discuss what contributions the experimental method can make in this field. I will do this with special reference to one particular species, the Black-headed Gull *Larus ridibundus*, which my co-workers and I have been studying for several years. However, before reviewing the data, I shall try to put the two methods in perspective.

Lack's procedure is in essence based on accurate descriptions and measurements of certain properties of species or groups, particularly those in which these taxa are either divergent or convergent in comparison with other taxa. These properties of the animals are set against other aspects of their ecology, with a view to comparing the two sets of data and of finding correlations between them. These correlations are then interpreted in terms of function, or survival value. For instance, nesting on cliffs or islands is correlated with the relative inaccessibility of such places to mammalian predators, and therefore interpreted as a defence against such predators. Characteristics such as colonial breeding, small clutch size, long incubation period and breeding for the first time when more than one year old are, as he has shown, correlated with offshore as distinct from inshore feeding, and are therefore considered adaptations related to feeding the brood.

The net result of this procedure is a set of hypotheses of the following type: 'If this species did not possess this particular feature, it would be less successful than it is.'

This formulation leads naturally to that of the experiment required. Such an experiment, wherever necessary, and possible, amounts to no more (and no less) than finding out whether a deviation from the norm is penalized. The ideal experiment (which, however, for reasons I shall not now discuss, is hardly ever possible) would therefore consist of measurements of success of two groups of

43

animals: one consisting of more or less normal individuals, and one of animals which differ from this roughly normal group in the particular feature which one wants to test, and in this feature only. Since we are of course concerned with success in the animals' natural habitat, such experiments have to be done in a setting which is as close as possible to the natural environment. If they are done well, and if they are considered in their proper context, they will yield more than mere figures about differential survival—they will provide information about the agency which does the penalizing, that is, about the relevant environmental pressure which at least prevents the species from degeneration and so to speak 'keeps it on its toes'; and, in addition, about the way this pressure exerts its influence.

Although, as we shall see, the practice very often falls short of this ideal, I hope to show that even limited experiments can both broaden and deepen our knowledge of the effects of natural selection.

However, while I shall try to demonstrate the usefulness of experiments as well as I can, I also want to point out that their value must not be overrated. First, it is the descriptive, interpretative method which provides the ideas, and the experimenter does not really do much more than check the validity of these ideas. Experiments can either confirm our hypothesis, or make us reject it. If it is rejected (and even if it is confirmed), we have to return to the interpretative method for new inspiration. The interpretative method requires, as we have seen, a great deal of sound intuition and imaginativeness.

Secondly, we must not forget that there are many interpretations that do not really demand experimental verification, simply because they are so plausible that they can assume the status of conclusions. For instance, to demand an experiment simply to show that a moulting wing is less effective than an intact wing would border upon the pedantic, and it would be over-critical to question the correctness of the functional interpretations of the timing of the moult quoted by Lack. Nor will anybody who has seen a Gannet throw an intruder off its nest site have any doubt about the effects of such an attack.

Thirdly, experimental evidence, however straightforward and convincing it may be in itself, is usually not sufficient to determine the part played by any given feature in an animal's relations with its natural environment. This is because we have to put the results of each experiment into the wider contexts of (1) the animal as a whole, and (2) the environment as a whole, and this, at the present stage, involves a considerable amount of guesswork.

To illustrate this latter point I shall consider the coloration of the eggs of the Black-headed Gull. The commonplace statement that these eggs are camouflaged requires experimental verification; we have to demonstrate that their particular colour patterns actually contribute to success by making the eggs, in their natural environment, less vulnerable to predation than differently coloured eggs. This was tested (Tinbergen *et al*, 1962) by laying out, in a habitat similar to that of the gulleries, equal numbers of normally and differently coloured eggs and observing the natural predation for the two types laid out in each test. So far, uniformly white and uniformly khaki eggs have been compared with natural eggs. This was done outside the gulleries in order to eliminate at least two possible variables: the nests themselves, and the attacks by which the parent gulls can drive off certain bird predators. This simplification of the situation as compared with the full natural situation is of course an essential aspect of the experimental method, but it has disadvantages as well as advantages. Our tests showed that in these circumstances white eggs, and to a lesser extent uniformly coloured khaki eggs, suffered more predation by Carrion Crows *Corvus corone* and Herring Gulls *Larus argentatus* than naturally coloured eggs.

This result is not of course surprising, even though it was interesting to see how much more effective the crows, and to a lesser extent the Herring Gulls, were than we are ourselves. But to what extent and with what degree of confidence can we extrapolate these results and apply them to the natural situation? Kruuk (1964) has shown that the mass attacks by the parent gulls are actually very effective in driving off crows and Herring Gulls; if these attacks were 100 per cent effective, the actual coloration of the eggs might be totally irrelevant. Nor did we test the effect of the eggs' colour on other predators, some of which, like the Fox and the Hedgehog, hunt mainly by night. Now fortunately we know that the attacks are *not* 100 per cent effective even against crows and Herring Gulls. And although Foxes are hardly deterred by the attacks of the adult gulls and take quite a number of eggs, we have indications that camouflage is effective against them too—contrary to an often expressed belief, camouflage is undoubtedly more, rather than less effective by night than by day. So even though we know something about the effect of other parts of the defences of the species, and of the effect of camouflage itself on other predators, quantitative assessments of these other effects would require additional experiments. And even the combined results of all these tests would not necessarily give us the full information about their joint effect, because the separate effects might well interact rather than just be additive. All this shows how much has to be left to 'inspired guessing' to evaluate the relevance of such experiments even for this limited problem: to what extent would success be impaired by certain deviations from the normal coloration, and by these deviations alone?

One could of course ask: but why not lay out differently coloured eggs in the nests themselves, so that one could measure the combined effects of camouflage, attack, and the nest, and extend the tests over day and night, so that one could directly measure the total effect of all predation in the complete natural situation? An experiment done by Kruijt with the eggs of Herring Gulls provides the answer. He reports (1958) that in these circumstances another factor intervenes: the incubating gulls themselves respond to differences in egg colour by sitting better on spotted than on uniformly coloured eggs. And while he found that the latter suffered heavier predation, he had to point out that this effect was, at least in part, and possibly entirely, due to the gulls leaving the abnormally coloured eggs more often exposed. It so happens that Kruijt discovered this disturbing variable, but with this type of experiment one can never be sure that one knows, or even suspects, all possible variables, and this is of course the reason why one simply has to work in an impoverished, more constant situation—this is the essence of the experimental method.

Similar considerations apply to all the experimental evidence obtained so far— in fact to experiments of any kind—and it is therefore clear that our conclusions simply have to involve a certain amount of, one could say, 'playful' speculation: first in the formulation of the hypotheses and the design of the experiment, second in the evaluation of its results. It is partly for these reasons that my review will not be strictly confined to experimental evidence.

After this brief discussion of the limitations as well as the potentialities of the experimental method, I shall now summarize, very sketchily, the main results obtained so far with the Black-headed Gull; this review will repeat much of what I reported in a previous paper (Tinbergen, 1964b) but a few new facts will be included.

*Colonial nesting*. The clumped nesting of Black-headed Gulls is not entirely determined by limited availability of nest sites; the gulls are truly colonial. Patterson (1965) has shown that 'house hunting' pairs attempt to settle first in the densest parts of an existing colony; it is likely that this preference is at least in part determined by true sociality. As these preferred areas become saturated, house hunters are repelled by already established pairs, and they then select sites in less densely occupied areas near by. Patterson further showed that the success of broods, as expressed in numbers of fledglings produced, is much higher in the colony proper than in the more scattered nests outside the colony. The high mortality of such outlying nests is mainly due to predation. Kruuk (loc. cit) collected data on the part played by various predators (Fox, Hedgehog, Herring

# Adaptive features of the Black-headed Gull

Gull, other Black-headed Gulls and Carrion Crows). The main factor accounting for the differential success of nests inside and outside the colony is the mass attack by parent gulls. This was demonstrated by the following experiment: Kruuk placed hens' eggs outside the gulls' nests; half of these eggs were inside the colony area, half outside. The success rate of observed predation attempts was counted and was shown to be higher for outside than for inside eggs; and this resulted in a higher mortality of outside eggs. The feature that deterred predators such as Herring Gulls and Carrion Crows from entering the colony was, as already mentioned, the mass attacks. Because each parent gull attacks these predators over an area round its nest which is much larger than its territory, a predator which enters the colony is attacked by more than one, often by dozens of pairs. And since, in addition, mass attacks deter the predators much more effectively than attacks by single pairs, we must conclude that colonial nesting in this species is part of its defence against predators. Whether this is the whole story depends of course on the effect of other defences of the species (of which it has several) and on the effects of colonial nesting on other relationships with the environment, including colony members. In view of the work of Darling (1938) and Coulson & White (1960) it is likely that colonial nesting does in fact have other effects.

*Coloration.* I have already briefly reviewed the evidence which we have on the effectiveness of the camouflage of the eggs. I think we can safely assume that the colour of the young likewise acts as camouflage. I believe (and we know now that it will be possible to test this) that the full camouflage effect of the eggs is not a matter of overall coloration and dotting alone, but that the special character-istics of the blotching, viz. the irregularity in size, shape, placing and hue of the dots is adaptive in this respect as well. This was suggested by the outcome of some pilot experiments. A little thought will make it clear that, if this idea is correct, the functioning of the pigment glands in the oviduct deserves a close study.

Another interesting aspect of camouflage is found in its behavioural correlates, of which I may mention the habit of the incubating bird to leave the nest at the slightest disturbance (Heinroth & Heinroth, 1928), the crouching and use of cover by the chicks, and the removal of the empty egg shell shortly after the chick has hatched (Tinbergen *et al*, 1962). As I will argue in a moment, the territorial spacing-out of broods may also contribute to the full effectiveness of camouflage.

It has only recently become clear that some aspects of the coloration of the adults are adaptive as well. Phillips (1962), following up the suggestion made by Craik (1944), has shown that the white colour of the head, front, and underside found in so many gulls, and in our species in the winter plumage, acts as 'aggressive camouflage'—because it contrasts less with the sky than a darker plumage, it allows gulls that plunge-dive for fish to approach their prey from the air a little more closely before eliciting flight than if they were dark. This was demonstrated in experiments in which the responses of fish were observed to white and black models moved overhead. The conclusion was strengthened by comparative evidence found in the literature on the feeding habits of different species, which showed some striking correlations between coloration and the degree of plunge diving; thus the Black-headed Gull and its relatives feed mainly on earthworms and insect larvae, at least in summer; the Black Tern *Chlidonias niger* feeds less on fish than our other terns, etc. Incidentally, the evidence available in the literature falls far short of what is required for this particular purpose. Phillips finally studied an apparent exception at first hand, viz. the yearlings of the Herring Gull, and found, in accordance with the two other lines of evidence, that the immature birds feed much less often over the open sea than adults, and hug the coast more closely.

In view of this we understand why the Black-headed Gull can afford a dark face, and why immature Herring Gulls can afford not to be white. But this is of course only part of the answer; we will also have to find positive advantages of the colour patterns as they are in these species. The plumage of immature Herring Gulls seems camouflaged; this is particularly striking when they feed on rocky coasts. Pressure by skuas and White-tailed Eagles *Haliaetus albicilla* may well have to do with this.

The function of the dark facial mask of the Black-headed Gull has been studied by Mash (see Tinbergen, 1964b) who recorded the responses of territory-owning breeding birds to brown-faced and white-faced dummies. His results show that the brown mask assists in the intimidation of territorial rivals, and so plays a part in the territorial spacing-out in the colony; a phenomenon to which I will return presently.

Some aspects of the coloration of the bill seem also to be adaptive. This has been demonstrated with respect to the red spot on the lower mandible of the Herring Gull (Tinbergen & Perdeck, 1950), which acts as a signal to the chicks and seems to have no other function. The tricky question of to what extent the bill coloration is adapted to its signal function (not only with respect to the chick, but also with respect to other adults), and to what extent, conversely, the chick's selective responsiveness is adapted to the parent's bill colour, has been discussed by Quine & Cullen (1964); the comparative studies required for this kind of problem are still in progress.

## Adaptive features of the Black-headed Gull

In view of these encouraging beginnings, it becomes fruitful to inquire into the possible adaptive significance of other aspects of colour. About the possible significance of the widespread pearl-grey colour of the mantle (and the dark mantles found in several species) I have not as yet any suggestion to make. The significance of the dark wing-tip patterns seems to be twofold. First, it is well known that dark pigment strengthens the feathers, and increases the resistance of the hard-worked wing tips against wear (see e.g. Plate 23a in Tinbergen, 1953). But it seems as if the need for whiteness imposes a limit on the size of these black parts. In addition, however, the black tips are in many species patterned with white. There are indications that the resulting patterns as seen in flight differ markedly between species living in the same region but repeat themselves in different regions, often in unrelated species. This, together with the fact that experienced field observers use the wing-tip pattern for species recognition, and the fact that parallel conditions in the wing specula of ducks have to do with species recognition, suggests that the wing-tip patterns of gulls may well act as species-recognition signals, a suggestion which may conceivably be open to experimental verification (see Addendum.)

*Territorialism.* When I discussed the advantages of colonial nesting, I mentioned only one aspect of the spatial distribution of broods. Within the colony, the nests are spaced out, i.e. compared with random scatter within the colony area, very short inter-nest distances are disproportionally rare (Patterson, loc. cit.). Although it is usually assumed that territorial fighting and threat result in the prevention of high densities (a problem that of course arises with regard to territoriality in any species) the very absence of unequivocal experimental evidence gives room for difference of opinion. Pursuing further the lines already initiated by Stewart & Aldrich (1951) and Hensley & Cope (1951) who showed that the presence of territory owners deters newcomers from settling, Patterson investigated the effect of agonistic behaviour (as distinct from mere 'presence') by comparing the behaviour of intruders in territories in which the owners were present but immobilized by a stupefying drug which prevented them from displaying, with that of intruders in territories whose owners were displaying normally. He found that the normal agonistic displays had a strong deterring effect. We have seen that the brown facial mask assists in this task, but the relative contributions made by postures and by calls have yet to be analysed, although there are indications that both play a part. The analysis can and should certainly be pursued further; there is for instance circumstantial evidence that slight variations in both calls and postures (such as the degree of pointing the head up or down) are responded to, and thus

49

are part of the signalling system that effects spacing-out. As I shall argue later, this is important for our understanding of pair formation behaviour.

The next step in the functional analysis of territorialism is to ask what advantage this degree of spacing-out may have. In a previous paper (Tinbergen, 1956) I suggested several functions. Two of these have now been studied in some more detail. One is intraspecific. We have found that the breeding Black-headed Gulls themselves prey on each others' broods to an astonishing extent. Certain individual 'robber' gulls feed predominantly on pipped eggs and newly hatched chicks (Tinbergen *et al*, 1962). Our observations indicate that such gulls are hampered, perhaps considerably so, by their inhibition against entering strange territories—inhibitions which they can be seen to acquire in the course of the weeks of territorial fighting prior to egg laying. I believe that in these weeks they acquire an increasingly accurate knowledge of the actual boundaries.

Another function of territorial spacing-out seems to be an interspecific one. We have numerous indications, other than the experiments quoted above, showing that the camouflage of eggs and chicks is relatively effective; thus years of regular tracking of Foxes, which visit the gulleries by night, revealed that a Fox has actually to stumble upon eggs or chicks in order to find them at all—even during the concentrated 'surplus-kill' raids many eggs and chicks are not found that are less than a metre away from the path followed by the Fox. Our suspicion that spacing-out may well be a corollary of camouflage in many other animals made us test the mortality of groups of well-camouflaged eggs laid out in different densities. We found that the risk which such a camouflaged prey runs, as a consequence of a predator having discovered another, similar prey, increases sharply with increasing density (Tinbergen, Impekoven & Franck, 1967).

Intra- and interspecific consequences of territoriality thus are different in kind: robber gulls are deterred by *boundaries*, irrespective of the distance between nests; other predators are hampered by *low density* but boundaries are irrelevant to them.

The studies summarized so far reveal the close functional interrelations between a number of features: the spatial distribution of broods is subject to pressure in favour of colonialism, and a counter-pressure towards spacing-out, which is achieved by territorialism. The advantages of both components of spatial distribution have been demonstrated with a fair degree of plausibility; and the mechanism which achieves spacing-out has been in part analysed. Here again it will be clear that, in spite of several series of straightforward experimental results, a great deal of conjecture enters into the full functional interpretation of these results. In view of these data it becomes, of course, of great interest to investigate the density patterns of other colonial birds, and to ask whether interspecific differences are likewise adaptive.

*Courtship.* As our insight into the functional significance of territorial behaviour grew, we also began to acquire a better understanding of courtship. Briefly, the picture emerging from the studies of Moynihan (1955) and Manley (1960) is as follows: the postures adopted during the 'meeting ceremony' (which is the opening stage of pair formation) are very similar though not identical to the threat postures. We explain this by submitting that, when the female joins the male, she unwittingly presents some of the stimuli typical of a territorial intruder, and so cannot help but elicit, in the male, agonistic responses as well as such sexual responses as approach, and inhibition of attack and fear. The courtship postures differ from the threat postures in showing, in the rigid 'typical intensity'-manner (Morris, 1957), the less 'offensive', less intimidating forms of these postures: in the meeting ceremony the birds stand parallel to each other, point their bills up, and perform highly ritualized 'Facing Away'. These are all forms of the agonistic postures which, in hostile encounters, reveal (and signal) that actual attack is unlikely. For a detailed discussion of this interpretation see Tinbergen (1964a).

This interpretation of courtship is relevant to my general topic in two respects: (1) it shows indirect effects exerted by one vital system (spacing-out) on another (mating); and (2) it points the way to urgently needed experimental checks, such as testing, with dummy experiments, whether a parallel posture and pointing up of the head really reduce the hostile response of another bird in one way or an-other—for it is on this assumption that our interpretation of the detailed adapted-ness of the threat postures and of the courtship postures rests. A beginning has been made by Mash (loc. cit.) who showed that Facing Away reduces both aggression and fear, and thus allows prospective partners to stay together long enough at each meeting to prevent agonistic tendencies from breaking up the process of pair formation.

*Synchronization of the breeding cycle.* Beer (1960) and Patterson (loc. cit.) have collected data on the temporal distribution of egg laying. It is clear that in comparison with numerous other birds the cycle is synchronized within relatively narrow limits. Knowing ever since Heinroth & Heinroth (1928) that breeding seasons are geared at least to the season of greatest abundance of food suitable for the young, we naturally think first of the possibility that there is perhaps a sharp peak of such food in the month or so following the peak of hatching. There

51

is convincing evidence that the present food supplies for the young Black-headed Gulls at Ravenglass do not demand this degree of synchronization: the gulls feed their young on a great variety of food; some of the staple foods are undoubtedly available during a much longer time than the peak period, and no signs have been observed of starvation of repeat broods, although there are some signs of reduced viability of late eggs. However, Patterson (loc. cit.) has conclusive evidence of predation affecting both early and (particularly) late broods more severely than peak broods. We have indications that the strong pressure on late broods is due to the predators becoming conditioned in the course of the season, and perhaps also to the increasing demands of their own growing families as the season progresses. At any rate there seems to be little doubt that predation rather than food is the critical ultimate factor for this degree of synchronization in this species.

Admittedly the evidence on which this conclusion is based is not itself experimental, yet it is the increased awareness of the importance of predator pressure which we acquired in our experiments on camouflage and its corollaries that led us to inquire about the value of synchronization at all.

*The daily rhythm of habitat selection.* Years ago (1953) I suggested that the well-known 'panics' or 'dreads' which many observers have reported of seabirds when they first arrive on their breeding grounds might be due to genuine fear of predators in the breeding habitat. Systematic observations of Fox killings of adult Black-headed Gulls (Kruuk loc. cit.) gave evidence in favour of the supposition that the breeding habitat is more dangerous to the adults than the winter and roosting habitats.

Until the first egg is laid, adults are in the colony by day only. They invariably roost on wide open spaces, such as beaches, mud flats, or water. In the gulleries which we studied Foxes killed in the course of 3 years over 1,300 adult gulls. Most of these killings took place in the colony during the actual breeding season, but some were also observed on the night roosts. However, here the Foxes were only rarely successful; they succeeded only on very dark nights, particularly those during the new moon, when the sky was overcast and it was raining hard. While such nights produced peak killings in the colony too, the gulls were by no means safe on other nights. My interpretation is that the breeding habitat, with its cover, is more dangerous to the gulls than are wide-open spaces, and that the reluctance to visit the breeding grounds, of which the 'dreads' are an expression, is a true adaptation to reduce predation. This interpretation is strengthened by Ashmole's observations (1963) on the diurnal rhythm of habitat selection by the Sooty Terns *Sterna fuscata* of Ascension Island. Until domestic cats were introduced, these birds were not subjected to night predation. Their rhythm is just the opposite of that of the Black-headed Gulls: during the pre-egg season many spend the nights at the breeding site; but they avoid it by day. That this habit is deep rooted and not easily broken by adverse experiences is shown by the fact that heavy nocturnal predation by cats during the last 150 years has not made the birds change their rhythm.

*Conclusions and outlook.* When, after this very condensed review, we make up the balance of what has been achieved so far with this one species, it must be admitted that the results are still meagre. In part they can be said to do no more than confirm 'what we knew all along'. It comes for instance as no surprise to hear that territoriality really promotes spacing-out and that it reduces intra-specific predation, nor that colonial nesting, through social attack, helps in defence against predators. But the degree of confidence of some conclusions has been considerably upgraded by experiments; thus the notions that white coloration is effective as aggressive camouflage in plunge-diving forms, that spacing-out reduces the chance of mass predation and that the brown facial mask assists in territorial spacing-out have definitely been strengthened. In some cases, our experiments have produced results which to almost all of us are really new; thus the survival value of egg-shell removal and the effectiveness of Facing Away in reducing hostility between prospective sex partners could hardly have been established without experiment.

Quite apart from these concrete, straightforward results, however, our findings can serve as a basis for some general remarks.

1. It will be clear, even from the limited evidence which Dr Lack and I have been able to marshall, that a picture is gradually emerging of astonishing *finesse* of the ways in which the different types of seabirds are adapted to their environments. Similar studies of other groups are beginning to lead to the same general insight, and I feel that this field of research may well become one of the real 'growing points' of ornithology in which our science will once more make a contribution to Biology in general.

2. Perhaps the main gain of such studies is the increased awareness, already stressed by Lack, of the fact that the adaptedness of features cannot be understood in isolation, but that they all form parts of larger systems, characterized not only by the individual features, but by the way these are functionally interrelated. Three types of such interrelations deserve special mention.

Firstly, we find evidence of many indirect selection effects—secondary adjustments in one functional sphere to pressures primarily important in another.

Thus the relaxation of the pressure favouring white heads as part of aggressive camouflage has allowed the Black-headed Gull to evolve the dark facial mask, which is of distinct advantage in the spacing-out of broods. This again has led to the highly ritualized Facing Away in pair formation. As Fogden (1964) has shown, this has even been evolved independently in at least one species of the Herring Gull group. Thus a sexual feature is affected by the requirements of spacing-out, and this in turn is influenced by a pressure in connection with feeding.

Secondly, there are numerous examples of conflicting pressures, which have been met by compromise of one kind or another. Thus one kind of predator pressure favours immediate removal of the egg shell, while another (exerted in part by the same predators) tends to penalize even momentary exposure of the brood just at the time of hatching. The Black-headed Gull compromises by showing a reluctance to remove the egg shell as long as the chick is wet and hence vulnerable. Another example has been worked out by Kruuk (loc. cit) who has shown convincingly that the responses of the adult gulls to predators are each the outcome of a nicely adjusted balance between attack (which protects the brood) and escape (which protects the adult); this balance varies adaptively with the threat which each predator represents to the adults.

Thirdly, there is evidence of direct selection for distinctness. The best example of intraspecific distinctness is that of Facing Away, which is effective in pair formation, in comparison with the various threat postures; in its essential feature Facing Away can be said to be the opposite of threat in that it conceals rather than shows off the facial mask—a good example of Darwin's principle of anti-thesis (Darwin, 1872). Interspecific distinctness is most obvious in the feeding habits of the different sympatric species; in mating ceremonies, where one might expect it, little evidence can be presented in gulls (but see Addendum).

3. Another important consequence of our increasing awareness of the nature and the true relevance of the evidence is that one develops a healthy caution with respect to conclusions based on absence of evidence rather than on positive data—conclusions denying the operation of pressures without proper investigation. I will briefly mention two examples.

When one considers one single character of a species, one's first conclusion is often: 'But this could be done much better'—in other words: 'The character is not optimally effective'. Apart from recognizing that one has to keep the historic-ally determined limitations of a species or group in mind, and that one must not assume that the animal could do what we can do, one has to realize that for any character there may be counterpressures, perhaps as yet unknown or even un-suspected, that have prevented perfection of this character for a particular func-tion. To mention a commonplace example, Guillemots, if they are to stay out of reach of predatory mammals, cannot afford to lose their ability to fly, and this has of course prevented them from going as far as penguins of the same size in adapt-ing the wings to swimming. It is clear that this consideration will apply to very many characters, behavioural as well as structural. While one could argue that it might be better for the broods of the Black-headed Gull if the parents would attack Foxes outright, this might not make the species more successful, for the adults' fear of the Fox, which prevents it from driving home the attack, is un-doubtedly of vital importance, and as we have seen the species has developed nice-ly adjusted compromises for each predator. Therefore, the rash statement that a more aggressive gull would be 'better' is based on lack of knowledge, or appreci-ation, of the survival value of caution, or fear. Thus a gap in our knowledge, or even in our imaginativeness, is, by false reasoning, in effect turned into an argument in favour of a positive conclusion.

It is a regrettable circumstance that a similar, unsatisfactory type of reasoning is often applied when problems of survival value are discussed. For instance, I feel that Wynne-Edwards (1962) makes this fundamental methodological mistake when in his recent book (which has rendered a great service by calling attention to many unsolved problems) he argues that many features of seabirds and other animals are 'altruistic' in the sense of being short of optimal, perhaps even harmful to the individual, though of obvious advantage to whole populations. Of the vast range of such features which he discusses that of dispersion is relevant in my context because, as we have seen, Black-headed Gulls space out by means of a territorial system, and probably derive advantage from this. As long as territoria-lism was considered to be a matter of aggressiveness only, it was difficult to see why a bird which was more aggressive than the norm should not be more success-ful than normal birds. It is now, however, abundantly clear that such a bird would not necessarily be more successful; on the contrary, it is clearly advanta-geous to a bird not only to attack when he is on his territory, but also to avoid an opponent on the latter's territory. Again, therefore, it is the balanced attack-cum-escape system that ensures success. Failure to recognize that an animal may profit from avoiding others as well as from driving off others—in other words, a gap in knowledge—has led to the notion that individuals living at low densities are somehow altruistic, that they exert restraint to the benefit of the population rather than the individual or pair.

# N.Tinbergen

This issue is of great importance when it comes to assessing the value of the data used by Wynne-Edwards as evidence for the importance of group selection as a force in evolution. Most if not all examples amassed by Wynne-Edwards in support of group selection seem to me similar in one respect: no attempt is made to propose, let alone to test, possible 'egotistic' functions, and—whether spacing-out, small clutch-size, late maturity, epideictic displays or other characters are considered—the nature of the argument (implicit or explicit) is throughout: 'This cannot *conceivably* be of advantage to the individual or pair.' Admittedly, negative evidence can be useful, viz. when it is based on a thorough process of elimination; but where obvious hypotheses are rejected without proper check, or are not even considered, the argument rests merely on the limitations of our imagination. And if our field studies have convinced me of one thing, it is of the fact that the imagination of even the best field biologist falls far short of the reality; what has been found so far about the nature of selection pressures ought to make us realize how little we know of their true nature and of their variety. And with this admission of our ignorance the basis of Wynne-Edwards' case for group selection must be considered very fragile indeed.

4. It is interesting to notice that the experiments quoted, while constituting real evidence, have in no single case completely settled the question at issue, viz.: 'In *which* way do *which* environmental agents affect *which* properties of the animal?' In all my examples the evidence is incomplete. For instance, with respect to colonial breeding, the reduced success of individuals that nest farther from other birds has actually been measured, but the penalizing agents are known only in part. With egg-shell removal we have measured the potentialities of one or two predators, but the total effect of all predators in the natural situation has to be estimated. For other characters, such as synchronization of the breeding cycle, or night roosting outside the colony, the evidence, while quantitative, is not even really experimental, although the systematic observations do at least point the way to relevant experiments. It will be clear that we have still a long way to go, and that further progress will depend on the joint application of accurate observation, comparison and interpretation, and experimentation. In such a concerted attack it is not only observation that takes the lead and provides ideas for experiments; the latter, in their turn, lead in a variety of ways to new dis-coveries, to new problems, and to renewed comparative study. For instance, Phillips's observation that immature Herring Gulls are much more coastal than adults (which was prompted by the outcome of his experiments), makes us suspect that even in this non-specialized species the adult way of life involves sur-

prisingly long practice, which may well be required to develop even the moderate skill it has in plunge diving. This in turn makes it even more evident why, for instance, terns require a long period of dependence during which to acquire their even more demanding skill. And this again, incidentally, makes it imperative to know why our Gannet, with its extremely difficult method of plunge diving, yet with its considerable first-winter mortality (Nelson, 1964), does *not* extend parental care beyond the moment of fledging. The need for long practice may also have to be considered in relation to the issue of later maturity.

5. Even without further elaboration of this theme, the general conclusion we have to draw from our first steps of functional research is surely that we have as yet no more than an inkling of the extent and the details of adaptedness. This is not really astonishing, for, in spite of Ernst Mayr's remark that 'the environment is one of the most important evolutionary factors' (1963, p. 7) modern biologists have so far made insufficient attempts to study the environment in terms of the pressures which it exerts on each species. This is particularly true of biotic factors. To the experienced field worker it is obvious that 'field craft', atrophied alarmingly even among biologists, is in urgent need of re-development.

After this 'cri de cœur' let me, in conclusion, try to assess in what way the joint attack on problems of adaptedness promotes our understanding. What has been found so far allows us to make, with increasing confidence and in increasing detail, statements about the ways in which pressures act on animals, and the ways in which the animals meet these pressures. It does *not* allow us to ascribe to these pressures actual selection effects—it reveals *potential* selection pressures, but whether or not they can really be influential in evolution depends, of course, on the extent to which the deviants are genetically different from the normals. While it is, of course, extremely likely that many of the features I have described are subject at least in part to genetically determined variation, the need for at least some probes into the extent and the nature of genetic control is obvious if we are really to link this work with the genetics of evolution. In addition it is good to realize that, given genetical variation underlying the variation in the characters discussed, evidence on the penalties incurred by deviant individuals actually *proves* stabilizing selection, but no more than *suggests* that the same selection pressures have been instrumental in moulding the species in the past, even though it is true that the latter conclusion can be made highly probable in many cases.

One could ask; with all these qualifications, what then is the value of this work? My personal value judgement is that it is not completely satisfying to establish merely the principle of natural selection, but that it is fascinating to understand, in concrete detail, to what extent the present properties of the multitude of different animal species reflect this principle—to what extent evolutionary radiation has to be considered adaptive.

It is more than merely fascinating, and I submit that a biological science which gives all its energies to the analysis of causal mechanisms underlying life processes and neglects to study, with equal thoroughness, how these mechanisms allow the animals to maintain themselves, is a deplorably lop-sided Biology. I should like to end, therefore, with a plea for the application of the available and proved methods, including experiments, to the study of effects as well as of causes. This study is in its infancy, but it has revealed just enough to make us see, on the one hand, how poor our understanding still is, but on the other hand, how exciting further exploration could be.

## REFERENCES

ASHMOLE N.P. (1963) The biology of the Wideawake or Sooty Tern *Sterna fuscata* on Ascension Island. *Ibis* **103b**, 297–364.

BEER C.G. (1960) Incubation and nest building in the Black-headed Gull. Doctor's thesis, Oxford.

COULSON J.C. & WHITE E. (1960) The effect of age and density of breeding birds on the time of breeding of the Kittiwake *Rissa tridactyla*. *Ibis* **102**, 71–93.

CRAIK K.J.W. (1944) White plumage of sea-birds. *Nature* **153**, 288.

DARWIN CH. (1872) *The Expression of the Emotions in Man and Animals*. London.

DARLING J.F. (1938) *Bird Flocks and the Breeding Cycle*. Cambridge.

FOGDEN M.P.L. (1964) The reproductive behaviour and taxonomy of Hemprich's Gull *Larus hemprichi*. *Ibis* **106**, 299–321.

HEINROTH O. & M. (1928) *Die Vögel Mitteleuropas*. Berlin.

HENSLEY M.M. & COPE J.B. (1951) Further data on removal and repopulation of the breeding birds of a spruce-fir forest community. *Auk* **68**, 483–493.

KRUIJT J.P. (1958) Speckling of the Herring Gull egg in relation to brooding behaviour. *Arch. néerl. Zool.* **12**, 565–567.

KRUUK H. (1964) Predators and anti-predator behaviour of the Black-headed Gull (*Larus ridibundus* L.). *Behaviour* Suppl. **11**, 1–130.

LACK D. (1967) Interrelationships in breeding adaptations as shown by marine birds. *Proc. XIV Internat. Orn. Congr.*, 3–42.

MANLEY G.H. (1960) Agonistic and pair formation behaviour of the Black-headed Gull. Doctor's thesis, Oxford.

MASH R. Unpublished work.

MAYR E. (1963) *Animal Species and Evolution*. Cambridge (Mass.).

MORRIS D. (1957) 'Typical intensity' and its relationship to the problem of ritualization. *Behaviour* **11**, 1–12.

# Adaptive features of the Black-headed Gull

MOYNIHAN M. (1955) Some aspects of reproductive behaviour in the Black-headed Gull and related species. *Behaviour* Suppl. **4**, 1–201.

NELSON J.B. (1964) Some aspects of breeding biology and behaviour of the North Atlantic Gannet on the Bass Rock. *Scott. Birds* **3**, 99–137.

PATTERSON I.J. (1965) Timing and spacing of broods in the Black-headed Gull, *Larus ridibundus*. *Ibis* **107**, 433–460.

PHILLIPS G.C. (1962) Survival value of the white colouration of gulls and other sea birds. Doctor's thesis, Oxford.

QUINE D.A. & CULLEN J.M. (1964) The pecking response of young Arctic Terns and the adaptiveness of the 'Releasing Mechanism'. *Ibis* **106**, 145–173.

STEWART R.E. & ALDRICH J.W. (1951) Removal and repopulation of breeding birds in a spruce-fir forest community. *Auk* **68**, 471–482.

TINBERGEN N. (1953) *The Herring Gull's World*. London.

TINBERGEN N. (1956) On the functions of territory in gulls. *Ibis* **98**, 401–411.

TINBERGEN N. (1964a) Aggression and fear in the normal sexual behaviour of some animals. In *The Pathology and Treatment of Sexual Deviation*, pp. 3–23. Ed. I.Rose. Oxford.

TINBERGEN N. (1964b) On adaptive radiation in gulls (Tribe *Larini*). *Zool. Mededel.* **39**, 209–223.

TINBERGEN N., BROEKHUYSEN G.J., FEEKES F., HOUGHTON J.C.W., KRUUK H. & SZULC E. (1962) Egg shell removal by the Black-headed Gull, *Larus ridibundus* L.; a behaviour component of camouflage. *Behaviour* **19**, 74–118.

TINBERGEN N., IMPEKOVEN M. & FRANCK D. (1967) An experiment on spacing-out as a defence against predation. *Behaviour* (in the press).

TINBERGEN N. & PERDECK A.C. (1950) On the stimulus situation releasing the begging response in the newly hatched Herring Gull chick (*Larus a. argentatus* Pontopp.). *Behaviour* **3**, 1–39.

WYNNE-EDWARDS V.C. (1962) *Animal Dispersion in Relation to Social Behaviour*. Edinburgh and London.

## ADDENDUM

After the present paper had gone to the press, the long-awaited study by Smith of isolating mechanisms in gulls appeared (N.G.Smith, 1966. Evolution of some arctic gulls (*Larus*); an experimental study of isolating mechanisms. *Ornithol. Monogr.* 4). Smith showed that the colour of the eye and eye-ring, and to a lesser extent the wing-tip pattern are surprisingly effective in sexual isolation between *Larus hyperboreus*, *L. glaucoides kumlieni*, *L. argentatus* and *L. thayeri* in N.E. Canada.

# The use of adaptive characters in avian classification

WALTER J.BOCK

Department of Biological Sciences,
Columbia University, New York, N.Y.
U.S.A.

and

Department of Ornithology,
American Museum of Natural History

## INTRODUCTION

The classification of birds originated with the first comparative studies of their morphology. And over the years, comparative morphological investigations were the mainstay, if not the only support, for systematic studies of the higher categories of birds. It is not surprising when doubts developed about the correctness of long-established systems of relationships within the class Aves, that ornithologists also doubted the value of the anatomical characters upon which these relationships were founded. A great decline occurred in morphological studies, as avian systematists turned more and more to other newly discovered systems of characters as foundations for their classifications. This trend in morphology has been reversed during the past two decades, and today a vigorous group of avian anatomists are working on morphological and systematic problems. In this renewed effort, new anatomical features are being studied and traditional characters reanalyzed, new methods and approaches are being tested, and a range of old and new taxonomic problems are being reopened, with an optimistic confidence in the usefulness of morphological features for avian classification replacing the earlier pessimism. In this contribution to the symposium on avian systematics and evolution, I would like to examine some of the results of the recent work in avian anatomy and classification. Rather than concentrating on a detailed discussion of the many excellent recent investigations of anatomical systems that have added much to the clarification of avian relationships, I would like to present a theoretical problem which should provide a better basis upon which to judge the overall contribution by morphologists to avian classification and to general theory of systematics. Accordingly, I have chosen to discuss the long-existing central problem of adaptive characters and their use in classification, and to show how the theoretical and methodological approaches of 'evolutionary morphology' serve to provide clues to the solution of this problem.

## EVOLUTIONARY MORPHOLOGY

With the realization that new sets of goals had to be formalized in the classical field of comparative anatomy (see Davis, 1958, for an excellent statement on this matter) morphologists have begun to develop new approaches and concepts for the study of animal structure. The introduction of these new ideas into morphology is quite similar to the development leading to 'the new systematics' in the early 1940s. The rise of the new systematics never, for a number of good reasons, included comparative anatomy and the systematics of higher categories of animals. In the growth of the 'new morphology' as this area is sometimes called, a number of ideas were introduced that were not original to morphology, but were adopted from other fields of biology. Priority for the origin of these ideas is far less important than the interaction between morphologists and other biologists that has permitted the essential interchange of information and concepts. Nevertheless, the incorporation of new ideas into morphology and their integration into unified theory has progressed so far that morphology of today, while it is still a comparative study, has changed radically from the traditional concept of the field of comparative anatomy.

The outgrowth of these recent changes is a broadly based morphology—one which I would like to call 'evolutionary morphology'—built upon the foundations of traditional comparative anatomy, upon functional and biological morphology and upon evolutionary principles. Evolutionary morphology is based upon a comparative study of the forms, functions and biological roles of anatomical structures and of the interaction of these structures with environmental factors. It includes observations of animals living normally in their natural environment, the exact interrelationships between the organisms and their environment, and all other pertinent ecological factors. All parts of the study of evolutionary morphology must be based upon the general principles of evolutionary change. Thus, evolutionary morphology is a comparative study of the biology of morphological features in accordance with the principles of evolutionary biology.

The foundations of evolutionary morphology are very broad, as they well need be, because the general goal of this endeavor is the elucidation of the evolutionary history of morphological structures, and of animal groups.

It should be noted that it is not always possible to study each feature as thoroughly as would be desired in evolutionary morphology; indeed, it is only rarely possible to investigate a structure fully. Live animals may not be available for observations either in the field or in captivity, structures may not be suitable for the experimental testing required in functional studies, and many other difficulties hinder the morphologist. These difficulties should not discourage the worker from doing as much as possible, rather they should serve as reminders of the gaps still remaining in the analysis and of the dangers existing in his conclusions because of the gaps.

## THE DILEMMA OF ADAPTIVE FEATURES

Systematics of the higher categories differs in at least one basic aspect from that of the specific and subspecific level. The emphasis is placed on characters indicating relationships in the higher categories, while the importance of characters showing divergence is stressed in the lower levels. It is the simple distinction between the use of similarities in the former and of differences in the latter areas of systematics. Even before the emergence of evolutionary theory, systematists were troubled with the problem of distinguishing between similar features that indicate affinities, and similar features that did not indicate affinities. Before the end of the last century, avian systematists began to realize that similarity in many of their traditional taxonomic characters, such as the arrangement of the toes, the hooked raptorial bill, and the decurved finch bill, in different groups of birds did not necessarily indicate phylogenetic relationship between these groups. Similarity of these taxonomic characters in apparently unrelated groups could be attributed to similarity in habits: the same selection force acting upon members of several groups could result in similarly adapted structures through the process of convergent evolution. Avian systematists quickly realized that a correlation existed between these taxonomically misleading similar characters and their adaptiveness. From this conclusion followed the general statement in the literature that adaptive features are useless in classification and its obvious converse that valuable taxonomic characters are nonadaptive. The statements are often not clearly expressed, or the converse statement may be tacitly assumed, but the implication is always that adaptiveness and taxonomic usefulness are conflicting properties of characters.

On theoretical grounds, all existing features of animals are adaptive. If they were not adaptive, then they would be eliminated by selection and would disappear. All well-studied characters used in avian classification have been shown to be adaptive; some of these include bill shape, foot structure and arrangement of the toes. Many other traditional anatomical characters have been assumed to be adaptive, but this has not been shown definitely. Hence a dilemma exists between the belief that adaptive features are useless as taxonomic characters and the demonstration that all well-studied taxonomic characters are adaptive (plus the theoretical conclusion that all existing features must be adaptive). This dilemma only allows the conclusion that no useful taxonomic characters exist. Further, on the basis of this dilemma, one can only conclude that attempts to establish classifications are senseless because no useful taxonomic characters exist. This conclusion can and must be rejected at once as foolish and defeatist; it serves only to indicate the existence of flaws in the arguments upon which it is based.

A further conclusion from this dilemma may be mentioned at this point as an aside. Some workers have argued that because adaptive features are useless taxonomic characters, systematists should employ as taxonomic characters features whose functional significance is unknown. The reasoning behind this conclusion would be that if the functional significance of a character is unknown, perhaps it does not possess any functional significance in which case it could not be adaptive and hence would possess taxonomic value. This approach and conclusion should be rejected. The usual pattern in the history of taxonomic characters is that they were considered to be very useful when their functional significance was still unknown. But as their functional significance was uncovered their adaptive nature also became clear and their taxonomic value became more doubtful. There is no reason to expect a different historical pattern for features whose functional significance is unknown at present.

The dilemma cited above that all adaptive features are useless as taxonomic characters and that all features are adaptive is an artificial problem. It has resulted from an incomplete analysis of the evolutionary mechanisms by which features originate and change, with an artificial and overwhelming emphasis placed upon natural selection. I would reject this dilemma, and in its place would like to present the following dual hypothesis: that all features used in avian classification are adaptive and that adaptive features may be extremely useful taxonomic characters. That is to say, adaptiveness does not, in itself, negate the taxonomic value of a character; this property depends upon considerations quite apart from simply whether or not the feature is adaptive.

Support for this dual hypothesis is available from an analysis of all evolutionary mechanisms by which features originate and change. A clear distinction must be made between: (1) all evolutionary mechanisms associated with the appearance of new features and with the origin of modifications in their later evolution, e.g. with the formation of all types of genetical variation that gives rise to the phenotypical variation involved in the origin of new features and of their later modifications; and (2) natural selection which is that phase of the interaction between the environment and the organism resulting in differential survival and reproduction of genetical material. Features favored by selection are adaptive by definition. The consequences of both sets of evolutionary mechanisms upon the observed aspects of taxonomic features must be distinguished clearly and analyzed separately. Only after this is done will it be possible to evaluate the taxonomic value of avian features.

In the following discussion, I will discuss selection and adaptation first and then those evolutionary mechanisms associated with the origin of features and with the changes in their phylogeny.

## ADAPTATION

Adaptation is associated only with the evolutionary mechanism of natural selection. Features that are favored and maintained by selection are adaptive. Features that are not favored and are rejected by selection are nonadaptive. Judgement of adaptive features is always relative to the relationship between the organism and a particular stated environment, not only to the environment. Hence, whenever an adaptation is discussed, both the environment and the type of organism-environment relationship must be stated. Adaptations are not judged upon an either perfectly adaptive or nonadaptive basis, but always upon a relative scale as to the degree of adaptation. This degree of adaptation may be expressed in a variety of ways. One possible way is in some terms of relative efficiency, such as the amount of energy required by the animal to carry out the particular biological role associated with the selection force acting upon it. The reader is referred to Bock and von Wahlert (1965), Bock (1965), and von Wahlert (1965), for a detailed discussion of adaptation and related concepts.

The term nonadaptive has been used for at least two separate concepts. It has been used to describe (1) features that have been rejected by natural selection and (2) features that are selectively neutral or have not yet been favored or rejected by selection. For clarity of discussion, the term 'nonadaptive' should be restricted to one of these concepts, and I would recommend that nonadaptive be used for those features that have been rejected by selection. Unadaptive, disadaptive, and other similar terms are synonyms of nonadaptive. I shall not be concerned with 'selectively neutral' features in this presentation because these are doubtless rarities among taxonomic characters.

Therefore, features that are favored and maintained by selection are adaptive.

And those aspects or properties of the features that are responsible for the features being favored by selection would be the *adaptive aspects* of the features.

Natural selection is not the sole evolutionary mechanism controlling the evolution of features. Selection can only accept or reject features of organisms which are exposed to it. Selection can establish certain limits on the range of features that are acceptable. All features within this range will be retained by selection, those outside of these limits will be rejected. We shall see later that the range of acceptable features—the 'limits of selection'—is quite important to this discussion. Usually selection will accept a number of possible features ('answers') offered to it, in which case the selection is considered to have broad limits. When selection will accept only one answer (or a very restricted number of answers), it is considered to have very narrow limits; this case is of prime importance and will be covered in detail later (p. 72).

Although selection can establish limits on the range of the features that are acceptable, selection cannot predetermine the exact properties of the acceptable features that are exposed to it. This control lies outside the mechanism of natural selection and within the control of other evolutionary mechanisms. As long as a feature lies within the limits accepted by selection, it will be accepted and maintained. Selection cannot pick and choose between features within these limits or reject a feature within these limits because it is not the theoretically best possible one. Selection can only choose features according to rather fixed interactions between the organism and its environment. Selection and hence adaptation are, therefore, the 'design' aspect of evolution in the sense of Mayr (1962), who presents a lucid analysis of the 'design' and 'accidental' factors of evolution and clarifies the apparent dilemma.

## PARADAPTATION

The appearance of all new features, be they adaptive or nonadaptive and the origin of all modifications in these features in their evolutionary history, lies outside the control of natural selection. Selection can accept or reject features, but it cannot determine the exact properties of these features. The origin of these features, e.g. the basis for the phenotypical variation to be acted upon by selection, lies under the control of a different series of evolutionary mechanisms and phenomena such as: (1) mutations, recombinations, gene flow and other chance-based genetical processes that generate the genotypical variation that underlies the phenotypical variation; (2) the nature of the pre-existing features of the ancestral group (which features happened to exist); (3) the geographic and ecological location of the ancestral group (where this group happened to live); and (4) the timing of events, such as which group had acquired the necessary genetical changes first (see Mayr, 1960, for a discussion of these factors). Only the first of these could be regarded as a real mechanism. The others could be grouped together under the heading of 'the evolutionary situation'. The significant property of all these factors, be they a mechanism or part of the evolutionary situation, is that they are all chance-based and that they constitute the 'accidental' aspect of evolutionary change in the sense of Mayr (1962). These factors are accidental because the aspects or the properties of the features which they control are chance-based (possibly even random in some cases) with respect to the demand of the selection forces that will either accept or reject the feature. These factors are also chance-based with respect to the future evolution of the feature and the future selection forces that will act upon the feature.

Those aspects of a feature that are dependent upon, resulting from, or under the control of chance-based evolutionary mechanisms may be termed *paradaptive* (from 'para' and 'adaptive'), meaning 'besides adaptive' in the sense that these aspects are not dependent upon selection and hence cannot be judged in the range of adaptive to nonadaptive. *Paradaptive aspects* of a feature are dependent only upon the accidental evolutionary mechanisms and hence may be either adaptive or nonadaptive according to whether they are accepted or rejected by selection.

The most essential property of paradaptive aspects of features is that their occurrence is chance-based (or accidental) and thus whether a particular paradaptation will appear (and thus be exposed to selection) depends upon the probability of its occurrence. This probability is based upon a series of complex factors and cannot be easily ascertained if at all. In most cases, an approximate guess of the probability can be reached.

The probability of the appearance of a certain paradaptive aspect of a feature is central for ascertaining the taxonomic value of that feature and will be discussed in detail below (p. 70).

Adaptive and paradaptive aspects of a feature are not necessarily different ones. An aspect of a feature, as for example the heterodactyl toe arrangement of the trogons, may be adaptive and paradaptive simultaneously. The heterodactyl foot is paradaptive because the second toe happened to reverse in the ancestors of the trogons and is adaptive because it was accepted by the selection forces for a perching foot. Adaptiveness and paradaptiveness do not exclude one another. Indeed, each feature or aspect of a feature would be paradaptive and adaptive.

67

# Walter J. Bock

This must be, at least theoretically, because of the dual and simultaneous interaction of the chance-based mechanisms of origin and of natural selection upon the evolution of every feature. Because each existing feature has originated (and has generally been modified during its later evolution) and has been accepted by selection, it is both paradaptive and adaptive. This conclusion is not new, but has been emphasized by Mayr (1962) under the heading of accident versus design in evolution.

## HORIZONTAL AND VERTICAL COMPARISONS

Not all comparisons between biological organisms are of the same sort, and the same set of conclusions cannot be drawn from each comparison. A clear distinction must be made between horizontal and vertical comparisons (Figure 1).

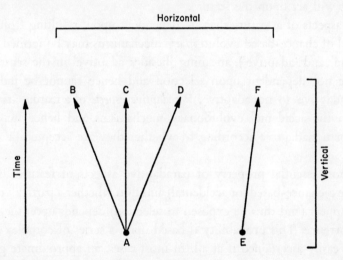

FIGURE 1. Schematic diagram to show the difference between horizontal comparisons and vertical comparisons. Vertical comparisons are those between members of the same phyletic lineage, e.g., between A and B, or A and C, or A and D, or E and F, along the time axis. Horizontal comparisons are those between members of different phyletic lines, e.g. between B, C, D and F, or A and E, or B, C, D and E, or A and F, no matter if the forms being compared are or are not at the same time level.

Vertical comparisons are ones between members of the same phyletic lineage, between ancestral and descendant groups. The differences noted in vertical comparisons are dependent upon the action of natural selection and hence are adaptive differences. To be sure the origin of the changes during phyletic evolution is dependent upon accidental evolutionary mechanisms and are hence paradaptive,

68

but the essential thing is whether these paradaptive aspects were accepted by selection and hence are adaptive.

Horizontal comparisons are ones between members of different phyletic lines, no matter whether or not the organisms exist at the same time level. In horizontal comparisons, one attempts to compare not only homologous features, but also different adaptive answers to the same selection force. A clear statement of the pertinent selection forces is essential in horizontal comparisons, and usually it is best to treat one selection force at a time. The differences observed in horizontal comparisons are paradaptive as they are based upon the accidental mechanisms of origin. These differences are outside of the realm of adaptation with respect to the selection force that has controlled the evolution of these features. To be sure, each of the features being compared horizontally is adaptive because it has been accepted by the selection force, for if these features were rejected by selection, they would disappear and would not be available for comparisons; but the important factor is the differences between the paradaptive aspects. It must be emphasized that these paradaptive differences may well be adaptive with respect to another set of selection forces, but this is outside the scope of this discussion.

The distinction between vertical and horizontal comparisons is shown clearly by the concept of multiple pathways of adaptation (Figure 2) (Bock, 1959; Bock & de W. Miller, 1959). Each of the several multiple pathways of adaptation depends upon a different paradaptation. Each of these several paradaptive features are adaptive because it has been favored by the same selection force. The several types of perching feet in birds—anisodactyl, syndactyl, zygodactyl and heterodactyl —represent a different paradaptation dependent upon the accidental evolutionary mechanisms associated with their origin. And each represent a different adaptation to the selection force for a more efficient perching foot because each is an adaptive advance for perching as compared to the ancestral foot.

## CLASSIFICATION

Classification is essentially the distinction between monophyletic (vertically based) groups of animals. As such, classification is the distinction between groups of animals possessing different paradaptive aspects of taxonomic characters. Paradaptive aspects of features, being associated with the origin of the taxonomic features, will also be associated with the origin of the taxonomic groups. Thus, the paradaptive aspects of taxonomic characters would provide a good guide to the existence and the limits of groups of animals. The sequential appearance of paradaptations would provide clues to the hierarchies of taxonomic groups.

In addition, the adaptive aspects of these features would be quite useful in the arrangement along phyletic lineages—that is, in making the correct vertical comparisons. Thus, it is the paradaptive aspects of adaptive taxonomic features which are of importance in classification, and it is basically the nature of these paradaptive aspects that determines the value of a taxonomic feature.

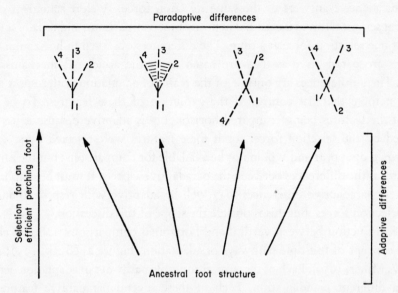

FIGURE 2. Schematic diagram to show the pattern of multiple pathways of evolution of perching feet. The evolution of the four different arrangements of the toes from the ancestral arrangement was under the control of the same selection force for a more efficient perching foot. Differences observed in vertical comparisons are adaptive, while horizontal differences are paradaptive.

## TAXONOMIC VALUE OF CHARACTERS

If paradaptive aspects of taxonomic features are the most important for determining the taxonomic value of these features, the question immediately arises of whether all paradaptive aspects have equal taxonomic value, and if not, what factors influence the taxonomic value of paradaptations. It is quite obvious that paradaptive aspects vary in their taxonomic usefulness because, as pointed out above, all features possess paradaptive aspects and all features are certainly not of equal taxonomic value. Paradaptive aspects of features are under the control of generally complex series of accidental, chance-based evolutionary mechanisms which are generally different for each paradaptive aspect. Hence, one of the major differences between various paradaptations is the probability of their occurrence. And the important property of paradaptive aspects of features is the probability of their unique origin in the history of the taxonomic group. This probability of unique origin can vary from very low to very high.

When the limits of the selection forces acting upon the paradaptations are broad (as appears to be the usual case), then whenever the probability for the unique occurrence of a paradaptation is high, the feature possessing that para-daptive aspect would be useful taxonomically. Or we would say that the feature would possess much taxonomic value. When the probability for the unique occurrence of a paradaptation is low, then that feature would have little taxonomic value (see Bock, 1963, for a discussion of features possessing paradaptations with very low probabilities for unique origin). I should emphasize that this probability does not depend upon how many times a particular paradaptation has appeared, but only upon the chances of its unique origin. The various arrangements of the toes for perching feet in birds appear to be restricted to the anisodactyl, syndactyl, heterodactyl and zygodactyl arrangements. If one considers the ancestral bird with its particular toe arrangement of three anterior toes and a short posterior hallux, then the probability of any of these four paradaptive aspects of toe arrangement arising is about 0.25. Hence the probability for the unique occurrence of any of the toe arrangements would be rather low. For this reason, the arrangement of the toes would possess little taxonomic value (the reasons I gave earlier, Bock and de W. Miller, 1959:42, are not valid). Each of these types possesses little taxonomic value no matter if it is the zygodactyl foot that apparently arose independently in nine groups of birds or the heterodactyl foot that seems to have occurred only in the trogons. Although the arrangement of the toes has little taxonomic value, other anatomical features associated with the toe arrangements may have great taxonomic value. Whenever a toe is reversed, certain modifications must occur in the distal condyles of the tarsus to reverse the direction of the tendons to this toe (see Steinbacher, 1935, for details). The detailed paradaptive aspects of the modifications in these condyles may be such that the probability for their unique occurrence is very high, and hence these structures would have much taxonomic value. Therefore, the zygodactyl foot of the Pici, Psittaci and Cuculidae would have little taxonomic value, but the detailed structure of the distal condyles of the tarsus may have great taxonomic value. Similarly, the heterodactyl foot of the Trogones would have little taxonomic value, but the details of the distal condyles of the tarsus may have great taxonomical value.

I would suspect that as a general rule, the more complex structures would have paradaptive aspects with a higher probability for unique occurrence and hence have a greater taxonomic value than simpler structures. This relationship should not come as a surprise to any systematist working with the higher categories of animals.

Another problem exists when the selection acting on the features has very narrow limits, i.e. when selection will accept only a single feature or a very restricted range of structures. In this case, most of the paradaptive aspects that appear would be selected against and would be eliminated. Only those paradaptive aspects that conform to the rigid limits of selection would be accepted and retained. In this case, the paradaptive aspects would possess little taxonomic value because one could not judge the probability of the unique occurrence of a particular paradaptation. I would also suspect that in most examples of this type, the paradaptations would be ones with a very low probability for unique occurrence because they would probably be morphologically simple paradaptations. Moreover, if these paradaptations had a high probability for unique occurrence, then the combination of this high probability and the rigid limits of selection would make the appearance and evolution of this feature most unlikely and systematists would not have the opportunity to study it.

The decurved bill of finches that crack seeds between their jaws is a good example of this case. Because of the arrangement of external forces upon the bill, the only possible shape of the bill in a seed-cracking bird is a decurved bill (see Bock, 1966, for a detailed analysis). Hence the limits of selection are very narrow for the acceptable bill shape. A decurved bill is a simple structure so that the probability for the unique occurrence of this paradaptation is very low indeed. Thus, as avian systematists have concluded long ago, the shape of the decurved finch bill possesses very little taxonomic value. On the other hand, the details of the bony structure and of the jaw muscles probably have considerable taxonomic value. The heavy-billed cardueline finch, *Coccothraustes*, and ploceid grosbeak-weaver, *Amblyospiza*, are quite similar in bill-shape and also in general development and shape of the jaw muscles. However, upon closer inspection, the jaw muscles of *Coccothraustes* are enlarged from the typical cardueline pattern while the jaw muscles of *Amblyospiza* have been modified from the typical ploceid pattern. In this case, the accidental component of the paradaptive aspects of the jaw muscles in these two genera depends upon the different morphology of the jaw muscles in the ancestral group of each genus. Hence the probability for the unique occurrence of the different paradaptive pattern of the jaw muscles in each genus is very high and hence these paradaptations possess much taxonomic value.

Thus, the most valuable taxonomic features will be those possessing paradaptive aspects in which the probability for unique occurrence is very high and which are acted upon by selection forces with wide limits. Whether these paradaptive aspects are adaptive is of no real importance for their taxonomic value; presumably, all existing taxonomic characters possess paradaptive aspects that are also adaptive.

I would submit that the taxonomic characters which systematists have considered to be valuable for constructing classifications are those possessing paradaptive aspects whose probability for unique occurrence is very high. Features possessing these properties were often described as nonadaptive. Moreover, I would submit that systematists have intuitively realized this important property of taxonomic characters, when they assigned much taxonomic weight to a particular character. Thus a taxonomic character possessing a paradaptive aspect whose probability for unique occurrence is very high would have great taxonomic weight, and those characters having paradaptations whose probability for unique origin is low, would have little taxonomic weight. After all, taxonomic weight is just another way of expressing the value or usefulness of the character in constructing classifications.

Similarly, ornithologists have rejected as useful taxonomic characters features possessing paradaptive aspects whose probability for unique origin is very low (or whose probability for multiple origins is very high). And they have rejected characters which are acted upon by selection forces with very narrow limits. These characters have generally been called adaptive, and quite rightly so, and were regarded as useless taxonomic characters because of their adaptiveness. But the taxonomic uselessness of these characters is not the result of their adaptiveness, but because of the particular nature of the paradaptive aspects or perhaps because of the very restrictive limits of the selection forces.

### RECOGNITION OF PARADAPTIVE ASPECTS AND CONCLUSION

Having considered the theoretical basis for paradaptations, the practical methods by which adaptive and paradaptive aspects of features are recognized and separated becomes an important question. I do not know at this time how this distinction can be made in all cases (or even in many cases on which I have worked), nor do I know how to treat all of the methodological principles for recognizing and separating adaptive and paradaptive aspects. The elucidation of these practical methods must wait until many more examples have been analyzed fully.

It can be suggested at this time that the recognition of paradaptive aspects is possible only after the adaptive aspects of the feature have been clarified. Thus the first step in studying paradaptations must be the analysis of the adaptive aspects of

# Walter J.Bock

the features. The methods of evolutionary morphology provide a sound approach to the recognition, separation and elucidation of the adaptive and paradaptive aspects of biological features.

For these reasons, I would submit that the methodology already developed and currently being developed in evolutionary morphology provides a sound foundation upon which to construct avian classification, and I would predict that with the concepts and approaches of evolutionary morphology, the study of avian anatomy, in spite of its being the oldest contributor to the classification of birds, will provide a major share of the insights and exciting new results for avian classification in years to come.

### ACKNOWLEDGEMENTS

I would like to thank Mr H. Morioka for his useful comments and suggestions, and Frances Richter for her usual skill in drawing the figures. Most of my background work upon which this analysis was based was done during the tenure of pre- and postdoctoral fellowships from the National Science Foundation and later under grants NSF-B5-1103 and NSF-GB-1235 from the N.S.F. My travel to the 14th International Ornithological Congress was supported by grant GB-5070 from the N.S.F.

### REFERENCES

Bock W.J. (1959) Preadaptation and multiple evolutionary pathways. *Evolution* 13, 194–211.

Bock W.J. (1963) Evolution and phylogeny in morphologically uniform groups. *Amer. Nat.* 97, 265–285.

Bock W.J. (1965) The role of adaptive mechanisms in the origin of higher levels of organization. *Syst. Zool.* 14, 272–287.

Bock W.J. (1966) An approach to the functional analysis of bill shape. *Auk* 83, 10–51.

Bock W.J. & von Wahlert G. (1965) Adaptation and the form-function complex. *Evolution* 19, 269–299.

Bock W.J. & Miller W. de W. (1959). The scansorial foot of the woodpeckers, with comments on the evolution of perching and climbing feet in birds. *Amer. Mus. Novitates* #1931, 45 pp.

Davis D.D. (1958) The proper goal of comparative anatomy. *Proc. Cent. and Bicent. Cong. Biology, Singapore*, pp. 44–50.

Mayr E. (1960) The emergence of evolutionary novelties. In *The Evolution of Life*, pp. 349–380. Ed. S.Tax. The University of Chicago Press, Chicago.

Mayr E. (1962) Accident or design, the paradox of evolution. In *The Evolution of Living Organisms*, pp. 1–14. Ed. G.W.Leeper. Melbourne Univ. Press, Victoria.

Steinbacher G. (1935) Funktionell-anatomische Untersuchungen an Vogelfüssen mit Wendezehen und Rückzehen. *Journ. f. Ornith.* 83, 214–282.

Wahlert G. von (1965) The role of ecological factors in the origin of higher levels of organization. *Syst. Zool.* 14, 288–300.

# Inheritance and adaptation in moult

ERWIN STRESEMANN

Near the end of the last century, Alfred Newton complained in his *Dictionary of Birds*, in the article on 'moult': 'Important as is all that relates to the subject, yet it is one that has been sadly neglected by ornithologists'. Nowadays, this remark is only partially true. In recent years the number of important contributions to this field of research has markedly increased. Yet, in general, lack of interest in these matters still prevails, and misleading statements are perpetuated in our current handbooks without being criticized.

This is the more surprising, as the study of the physiological process of moult and its interlacement with other biological processes, such as growth, migration and the cycle of reproduction, should be of considerable importance to those who aim to record and to understand the biology of a given species in all phases of its life.

Species monographs which give the moult due consideration are still infrequent, and even if they do, conclusions drawn from the study of only one particular species are often conjectural, unless confirmed by parallel cases.

For this reason we endeavoured to lay the foundations for a comparative study of bird moult, based on the examination of a fair number of species which include representatives of almost all orders of the system. In this monograph, which has now appeared as a special number of *Journal für Ornithologie*, facts are combined with what we took to be their most probable interpretation from the point of view of the taxonomist or biologist.

If one tries to interpret moult patterns, especially those in which the flight-feathers are renewed in an unusual sequence, two questions have to be considered. (1) Is this particular pattern shared by several related species, or is it a specific peculiarity? (2) Does it seem possible to interpret the facts as due to adaptation? Are they connected with the ecology of the bird, or with a special shape of wing or tail?

In the majority of birds, the remiges and rectrices are replaced annually in regular sequence which maintains a certain degree of flying ability during the period of moult. Strict regulation of the process has probably been enforced by selection in the ancestry of birds. At present the most widespread regulation consists of the following moult pattern: primaries are replaced in sequence according to the so-called descending mode, starting with the innermost one. Rectrices are moulted from within to without, i.e. centrifugally. This type of regulation is likely to represent the original one since it occurs in a number of orders which are but distantly related to each other and differ in habitat requirements as well as in manner of flight. This deep-rooted pattern may be modified: the rate of moult may be accelerated to an almost synchronous or even wholly synchronous loss of flight-feathers, or slowed down to such a degree that it takes the distal primaries far more than 1 year to be replaced by the next feather generation. In the latter case, another descending moult cycle will start with the innermost primary, while the preceding one is still on the move in the outer primaries.

These regulations are upheld by selective factors. Loss of flying capacity leads inevitably to deviations from the descending mode, resulting in an arbitrary sequence of primary replacement. In a number of cases, however, disorder is the result of a different evolutionary trend: after having accelerated the rate of wing moult to synchrony the need for constantly being able to fly may have become urgent once more in the course of phylogeny, as a consequence of changed ecological requirements. In such cases the primaries are shed in sequence anew, but apparently never in the descending mode, which has, so to say, been forgotten during evolution. The newly 'invented' sequence may either start with the outermost primary, from there proceeding more or less consecutively to the innermost, or it may follow a quite irregular course.

All deviations from the descending mode so far mentioned are adaptive and can be used for taxonomic purposes on the genus level only. Criteria suitable for phylogenetic conclusions of greater importance may, however, be gained from some other deviations, for instance the following.

In certain groups of birds, such as the falcons, parrots, some hornbills and kingfishers, the replacement of primaries does not start with the innermost, but with a definite feather situated within the series of primaries. Beginning at this point, called the focus of wing moult, the process diverges in both directions, to end with the innermost and outermost primaries. Such a shift of the focus from the proximal end of the series to a central feather seems to have been caused by some accident in the genome, for the new pattern is apparently not coupled with functional advantage, as far as flight is concerned. Here we have to do with features that furnish infallible proof of monophylety of a family or a group of genera within a family. Chance-based genetical mishaps affecting the moult sequence of flight-feathers may not have been rare in the course of time but may, with a few exceptions, have been quickly eliminated by selection. Of rather recent origin is the radical change of flight-feather replacement in the Spotted Flycatcher *Muscicapa striata*, consisting in ascending moult of primaries and centripetal moult of rectrices. This mode is unique among song-birds. One of the expressions of the underlying genetic change seems to have been favoured by selection, since all specimens of this wide-ranging species so far examined replace the flight-feathers in the same 'perverse' order.

In certain cases taxonomic conclusions can be drawn from the sequence of secondaries or rectrices. For instance, among the Gallinaceous birds only one natural group replaces the tail-feathers centrifugally, by beginning with the inner-most pair and ending with the outermost. This sequence is confined to the Perdicinae. On the other hand all Tetraoninae and Phasianinae replace these feathers in the opposite direction. This reliable character has already been used by William Beebe, some 60 years ago, for dividing the Galliformes into several affinity groups. A special way of moulting the first generation of secondaries and rectrices, not shared by any other group of Galliformes, is a joint feature of all species of the family Cracidae.

However, in exceptional cases inherited sequences have been replaced by another sequence which is obviously an adaptive one. For example, the Snow Cocks of Asia, *Tetraogallus*, a group of giant species clearly belonging to the Perdicinae, have a tail composed of twenty fairly long rectrices. They are expanded to the utmost during soaring flight which carries the heavy bird from one slope of a ravine to the opposite one. To have an almost complete tail even during moult is therefore a biological necessity to *Tetraogallus*. The problem is solved by an adaptive mode: the tail moult does not proceed centrifugally, as in all other Perdicinae, but starts in the middle of each half of the tail, from which focus it rather slowly diverges, to end on the right and the left with the innermost and outermost rectrix.

Just as in the Perdicinae, the moult of the rectrices is a centrifugal one in almost all Passeriformes; in some species the process is speeded to almost synchronous replacement of the tail-feathers. In the treecreeper *Certhia*, however, a bird which uses its tail as a climbing support, just as the stiff-tailed woodpeckers do, the some-what elongated central pair of rectrices is not replaced first, but last, for it has to support the body while the other tail-feathers are growing. The central pair is not dropped until the other pairs are renewed and fit for supporting the body provisionally. This mode has its counterpart in the woodpeckers.

## Erwin Stresemann

Alteration of moult sequence has been induced by unequal length of the tail-feathers in the case of *Enicurus*. This south Asiatic genus, perhaps related to the redstarts, consists of several species with a deep-forked tail, in which the fourth and fifth rectrices are much longer than the three inner ones. Unlike other Passeriformes, *Enicurus* begins the tail moult with rectrices 4 and 5.

Primaries have been transformed to ornamental plumes in the male sex of two genera of African nightjars, *Macrodipteryx* and *Cosmetornis*. In both, primary 2 projects far beyond the outline of the wing, its biological design being to render the courtship flight very showy, after which period this pair of wing-feathers is no longer significant. The problem of its renewal has been solved in an extraordinary way, most so in *Cosmetornis*. In this nightjar, primary 2 has been compared with a long whitish pennant waving behind the flying bird. Soon after the period of courtship, this pennant is removed, not through moult, but in a way unique among birds. It is bitten off by the bird at the level of the wing's outline, the stump remaining in its follicle. Some months later, *Cosmetornis* migrates from southern Africa across the equator to the adjoining savannah countries, and it is there that the wing is moulted. While all other Caprimulgidae adhere to the descending mode of renewal, in the male of *Cosmetornis* primaries 5 and 6 are moulted first, and from this focus the process diverges, to end with primary 10 and the stump of primary 2. One of the advantages of this sequence is obvious. It consists in the fact that the courtship feather, primary 2, is brand-new at the time the bird returns to its breeding territory and starts attracting the other sex. The wing of the female does not differ from that of *Caprimulgus*, and is accordingly moulted in the ordinary descending way. Here we have one of the few sexual differences in moult pattern.

The question may be asked: Are adaptive alterations of moult sequences likely to persist even if in the further course of evolution the selective factors cease to work by which these alterations have once been enforced? We regret that we are not aware of any case which would prove such tenacity.

Let us now turn to another subject, the adaptive timing of moult. Investigation of the co-operative action of the various time-regulating factors belongs to the domain of the ecologist, not of the physiologist. While the latter is concerned with the proximate factors producing the effect, the ecologist has to trace the ultimate factors responsible for the activity of physiological processes at a given time.

The metabolic demands of moult are considerable, if the whole plumage has to be replaced in a short time. Therefore complete moult may be intercalated between other energy-consuming biological phases. In most resident birds of the temperate and arctic regions, moult follows the cycle of reproduction provided the food-supply still remains sufficient for the extra energy required. Most migratory birds moult either between reproduction and migration or in winter-quarters between the two periods of migration.

In a number of cases, however, a sharp separation of plumage renewal from the breeding cycle or period of migration is not compatible with certain properties of the species.

Some holarctic song-birds of large size, for instance, *Nucifraga* and *Corvus corax*, start moulting the primaries in the egg-laying period or during incubation and replace the greater part of the plumage before their young become independent. Such a very early start of moult seems to be connected in song-birds with large body-size and long primaries. If such species had to delay the start of moult until the end of the breeding period, food shortage would be likely to occur during the moult.

Even a small palaearctic song-bird, the Crag Martin *Ptyonoprogne rupestris*, replaces the wing-feathers while rearing the young. The causality is obvious. Contrary to all other European swallows, which moult in tropical or subtropical winter-quarters, this species spends the winter in Mediterranean countries where food is too scarce during that season and the temperature too low for supporting moult, even a slow one.

Because of the shortness of the antarctic summer all non-migratory petrels of that region are forced to renew the whole plumage during the breeding cycle.

Another fascinating theme is the relation of moult to migration. Distant migration is practically never performed as long as a primary or secondary is growing, but nearly always with a complete wing, either composed of fresh feathers only, or of worn feathers only, depending on properties of the species in question. There is, however, still a third group of species, which migrate with a mixture of worn and fresh, full-grown flight-feathers. In these species the moult begins during the cycle of reproduction, but is suspended as soon as the individual is overcome by migratory impulses. When all its growing primaries have reached full length, the bird starts its migration, resuming the moult of flight-feathers after reaching winter-quarters or while resting on the way for a long period. In this category belong those species of falcons which migrate from the Holarctic to or beyond the equatorial belt, and also *Pernis apivorus*, *Otus scops*, *Streptopelia turtur*, some waders and the young of *Coturnix coturnix*. All these are early migrants. The standstill of the moult may last some weeks. It has been been noticed in captive specimens of *Falco subbuteo* and young quail, contemporaneous with the suspension of moult in wild birds of their kind.

In some species whose range in the breeding season extends from the temperate to the arctic region, population differences have developed in the timing and extent of migration. Such differences may lead to a difference in moult. The Peregrine Falcon *Falco peregrinus* is such a bird. In all its populations the replacement of primaries starts at the same stage of the breeding cycle, to wit in the female during incubation and in the male somewhat later. The southern populations are more or less sedentary; in western Europe they have eggs mostly in April, and their moult ends in September or October in the breeding area. On the other hand, the arctic populations are strong migrants; they have eggs in June and start migrating to the tropics in August or early September. The intervening time is far too short for all primaries to be renewed. Accordingly these arctic Peregrines interrupt the process before migration and take it up again in winter-quarters, where it may last until March or April.

Even more marked are the population differences in the Ringed Plover *Charadrius hiaticula*. The southern populations, for instance the British, renew the whole plumage rapidly from late July to September, immediately after the period of reproduction, and migrate in fresh plumage not farther than south-western Europe. Adults of the arctic population, however, migrate to southern Africa by early August, without having moulted a single feather, and it is in winter-quarters that the moult of the whole plumage takes place, beginning in November and lasting about 4 months.

The young Ringed Plovers of the southern populations retain the first generation of flight-feathers for about 1 year; they undergo a complete moult from July to September, after reproducing for the first time. The young of the arctic populations, on the other hand, already undergo a complete moult in their first African winter, before spring migration, and during the first breeding cycle carry the second set of wing-feathers.

I have mentioned some remarkable examples of adaptation in the domain of moult. How are we to explain such cases from the evolutionary point of view? Some of them suggest that a radical morphological transformation may automatically entail a physiological one that gives the former survival value. For instance, exaggerated lengthening of one of the wing-feathers or tail-feathers goes together with an adaptive change in the sequence of moult. How this congruity is achieved I cannot say; but I have an impression that the current explanations may need a supplement.

We owe many of our results to the untiring assistance of ornithologists of various countries, some of whom we have already had the pleasure of meeting at this Congress. We wish to thank all our helpers again!

# Circadian rhythms in birds

JÜRGEN ASCHOFF

Max-Planck-Institut für Verhaltensphysiologie,
Seewiesen und Erling-Andechs, Germany

Like most other animals, birds show in their behaviour a distinct temporal organization. In diurnal as well as in nocturnal species, this pattern often includes a major peak at the beginning of the bird's activity and a minor one towards its end (Figure 1). Since the two peaks are related to dawn and dusk, it has been assumed that they may be caused by environmental conditions, especially by light intensity. This conclusion seems to be supported by observations of many field workers who have watched the awakening and roosting or the first and last calls of birds at different times of the year. As shown in Figure 2, onset and end of the daily activity of Jackdaws *Corvus monedula* are more or less bound to civil twilight (although there are trends in the relationship between activity rhythm and day length which need attention—see p. 99). Furthermore, there is evidence that on clear days activity starts earlier and on cloudy days later (Scheer, 1952). Therefore, light intensity without doubt influences the bird's activity (as many other environmental factors do). But this does not mean that either the rhythmic changes from wakefulness to sleep or the basic patterns during the time of activity are exclusively caused by the periodically changing environmental conditions. On the contrary, it has been demonstrated during the last 15 years by several workers that the diurnal rhythms are primarily endogenous, i.e. that they are built-in characteristics of each living system. The experimental evidence for this conclusion, and some generalizations derived from those experiments, are discussed in the following sections.

## CIRCADIAN OSCILLATIONS

### The Free-running Circadian Rhythm

If a diurnal rhythm is considered to be endogenous, i.e. not caused by environmental factors, one has to assume that, under constant conditions in the laboratory, the rhythm continues (a) undamped and (b) with a period which deviates to some extent from 24 hours. The latter prediction is based on the notion that a biological rhythm—a biological 'clock'—is very unlikely to have the same high precision as has the rotation of the earth. After some time of confinement, a biological rhythm therefore should deviate from local time. It is this deviation of the bio-

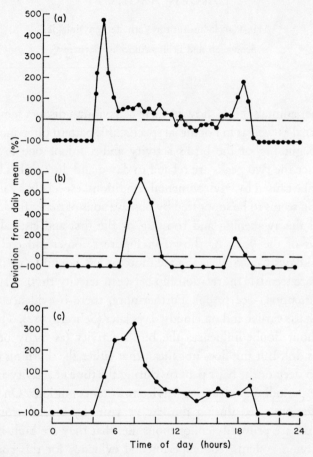

FIGURE I. The common two-peak pattern of activity in three species of birds. Field observations of (a) *Parus major* song by Hinde (1952); (b) *Phylloscopus trochilus* nest building by Kuusisto (1941); and (c) cage records of *Zonotrichia leucophrys* activity by Farner *et al* (1954).

logical period from 24 hours which excludes environmental factors as possible clues and gives proof of an internal origin of the rhythm (Aschoff, 1951, 1960, 1963a). In order to emphasize the significance of this phenomenon, Halberg (1959) called such a rhythm 'circadian' (from the Latin *circa* = about, and *dies* = a day).

# Circadian rhythms in birds

Examples of circadian rhythms are given in Figure 3. The locomotor activity of Chaffinches *Fringilla coelebs*, kept in isolation under constant conditions, has been recorded by microswitches mounted below the perches. It is measured by print-out counters as the number of contacts elicited per hour. Three parameters of the rhythm seem to depend on light intensity: (1) The period $\tau$ is shorter in brighter light than in dimmer light; (2) the ratio between activity-time

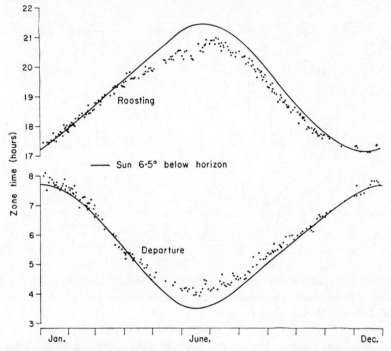

FIGURE 2. Departure and roosting (closed circles) of Jackdaws *Corvus monedula* at 49° N, as compared with the beginning of civil twilight in the morning and end of civil twilight in the evening (continuous line). (After Aschoff & v. Holst, 1960.)

and rest-time (the $\alpha : \rho$ ratio) is greater and (3) the amount of activity, given by the integrals of the curves above $\alpha$, is larger.

The dependency of the circadian period $\tau$ on light intensity becomes more evident in Figure 4. The graph shows the original records of the activity of a Chaffinch, made by an event recorder. Each time when the bird elicits a contact by hopping on the perch, a black mark appears on a slow-moving paper. With heavy activity, these marks fuse to a black horizontal bar. The strips of paper, each representing 1 day, are pasted beneath each other on a chart. For better

# Jürgen Aschoff

reading, this chart is then duplicated. Therefore, in Figure 4 the right half of the diagram is exactly the same as the left half. As is easily seen, the bird when kept in 4.8 lux starts its main activity each day about 2 hours earlier than on the preceding day; the circadian period is roughly 22 hours. It is also possible to differentiate between heavy activity (black bars, representing α) and scattered activity during the rest of the period (representing ρ). When on the seventeenth day of confinement the light intensity is lowered to only 0.16 lux, the bird immediately starts

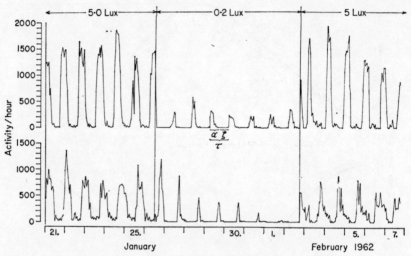

FIGURE 3. Locomotor activity of two Chaffinches in constant conditions with two intensities of illumination. The period $\tau$ is divided into activity-time $\alpha$ and rest-time $\rho$. (From Aschoff & Wever, 1962a.)

to be active a little later each day; the period $\tau$ is now longer than 24 hours. In addition, a clear rest-time of zero activity is established. With the reintroduction of the original light intensity, the bird reassumes the short period and again becomes more active and for longer. In 1.3 lux, the values for the period $\tau$ and for the $\alpha:\rho$ ratio fall between the two values measured before.

Results like those presented in Figure 3 and Figure 4 suggest that circadian rhythms may be considered as self-sustained oscillators in a technical sense (Pittendrigh & Bruce, 1957; Pittendrigh, 1960; Aschoff, 1964a). Under constant conditions, the oscillation will probably continue as long as the animal is in a healthy state. So far, measurements have been made for several weeks with birds, and for months with mammals. The frequency of the free-running oscillation is determined by the characteristics of the organism (species, sex, age, breeding

84

condition and so on) and by environmental conditions, among which the intensity of illumination seems to play a major role.

*The Circadian Rule*
The positive correlation between the three main parameters of the circadian

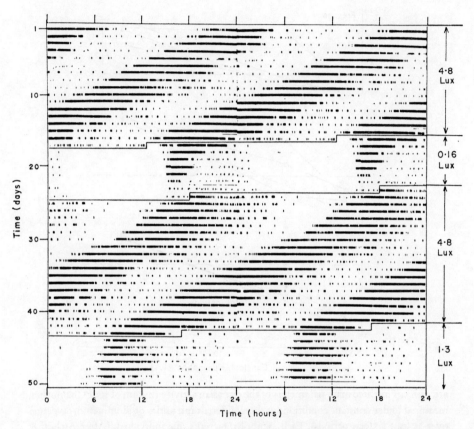

FIGURE 4. Original records of the activity rhythm of a Chaffinch in constant conditions. The daily strips of the event recorder are pasted beneath each other on a chart, and the whole chart is then duplicated. Intensities of illumination for the four sections of the experiment are given on the right margin. (From Aschoff, 1966b.)

oscillation and light intensity is shown in Figure 5. It contains the average values for four Chaffinches measured at three different light intensities. Between 0.4 lux and 120 lux, amount of activity, $\alpha:\rho$ ratio and frequency (reciprocal of period) increase linearly with the logarithm of light intensity. Similar findings have been obtained with other species of birds as well as with mammals. All these species behave alike in that they are active in the day and rest at night. In contrast to this group, nocturnal animals, when tested in constant conditions, show a decrease in frequency as well as in the $\alpha:\rho$ ratio when light intensity is increased. The

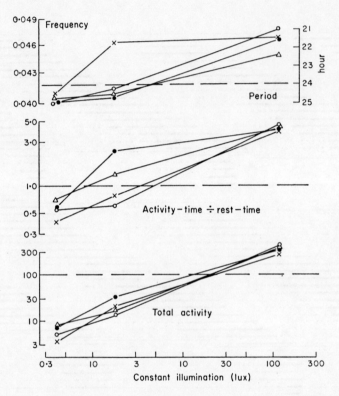

FIGURE 5. The three main parameters of the circadian activity rhythm of four Chaffinches, measured under constant conditions at three different intensities of illumination (averages over at least sixteen periods). Each symbol represents one individual. (After Aschoff & Wever, 1962a.)

results from experiments with four nocturnal and three diurnal species are compared in Figure 6.

The generalization indicated in Figure 6 has been called the 'circadian' rule (Aschoff, 1960, 1963b). Recently, Hoffmann (1965a) has discussed its validity. In all but one species studied so far, the period $\tau$ follows the rule. With regard to amount of activity and $\alpha:\rho$ ratio, more exceptions have been claimed, especially in nocturnal insects. Measurements on birds were in agreement with the circadian rule in all three parameters. It seems justified to take the circadian rule as a fair generalization, at least for birds, and to use it as the basis for a circadian model.

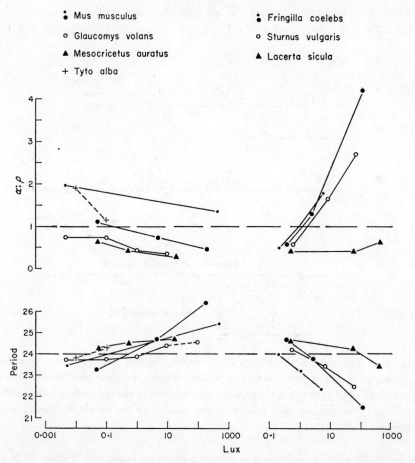

FIGURE 6. Circadian period and ratio of activity-time to rest-time ($\alpha:\rho$) as a function of light intensity under constant conditions. Average values for four night-active (left) and three day-active species (right). (From Aschoff, 1963b.)

## The One-oscillator Model

The regular alternation between a state of activity ($\alpha$) and a state of rest ($\rho$) can be considered as being based on an underlying (unknown) physiological oscillation which passes through a threshold twice during each period (Aschoff &

# Jürgen Aschoff

Wever, 1962c). The bird is active as long as the oscillation is above the threshold; the bird comes to rest when the oscillation passes downwards through the threshold. We call the assumed basic oscillation the circadian oscillator (Figure 7 A and B). Like any oscillator, the circadian oscillator has a 'level'. The level is defined as the arithmetic mean of all instantaneous values of the oscillating variable. We now assume that the level can change its position relative to the

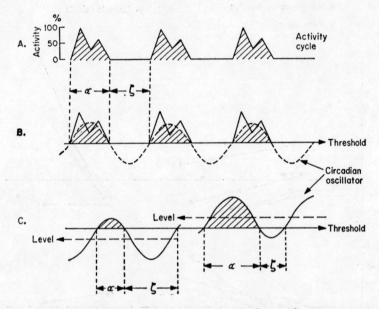

FIGURE 7. Schematic representation of an activity rhythm with activity-time $\alpha$ and rest-time $\rho$ (A), and its description by an oscillator which passes through a threshold twice per cycle (B). In C, changes in the $\alpha$:$\rho$ ratio are described by changes in the position of the oscillator's level (dashed line) relative to the position of the threshold. Shaded area, activity.

position of the threshold (which is considered to be constant) (Figure 7C). If the level (dashed line in Figure 7) is below the threshold, the activity-time $\alpha$ is short, the rest-time $\rho$ is long, and the amount of activity (shaded area above $\alpha$) is small. If, on the other hand, the level is above the threshold, the activity-time is long, the rest-time short, and the amount of activity is large. Obviously, this model, involving level and threshold, describes the positive correlation between amount of activity and $\alpha$:$\rho$ ratio which is contained in the second part of the circadian rule.

In order to explain the full circadian rule by the one-oscillator model we have

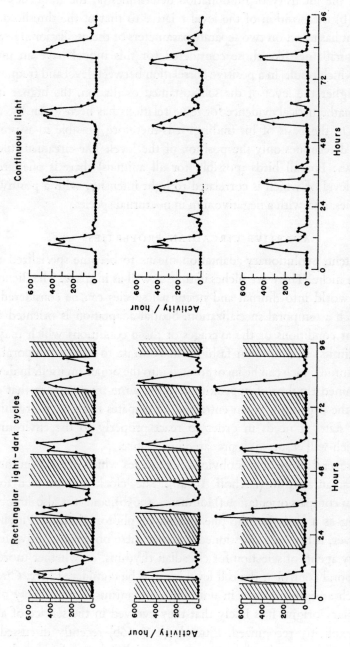

FIGURE 8. Activity pattern of three Greenfinches *Chloris chloris* kept first in artificial light-dark cycles and then in continuous illumination. (From Aschoff, 1966a.)

to assume that the intensity of illumination determines (a) the frequency of the oscillator and (b) the position of the level relative to that of the threshold. That means that light has to act on two separate parameters of the oscillation. However, self-sustained oscillators like those considered for this model have an intrinsic characteristic which results in a positive correlation between level and frequency—namely, the higher the level of the self-sustained oscillation, the higher its frequency. The mathematical evidence for these relations has been given by Wever (1964, 1965). On the basis of his findings it is therefore possible to assume that light intensity determines only the position of the level. The circadian rule then reads as follows: For all birds (possibly for all animals) there is one circadian oscillator, the level of which is correlated to light intensity, with a positive sign in diurnal species, and with a negative sign in nocturnal species.

## ADAPTIVE CIRCADIAN PROPERTIES

To a large extent, evolutionary adaptation means to become specialized to the conditions of a niche. There are niches in time as well as in space. The dichotomy of the living world into diurnal and nocturnal species can be considered as an example of such a temporal specialization. Spatial adaptation is oriented to the niche's constant conditions or the averages of those conditions which may vary (within their limits) in a random fashion. In contrast to this, a temporal niche offers a programme which can be incorporated into the organism itself. In developing a self-sustained rhythm of approximately the same frequency as that of the environment, the organism, when entrained, anticipates in its own organization the respective states it needs in order to react properly to the environmental conditions which will ensue—it is prepared in advance.

There are several more or less obvious advantages which depend on the presence of a circadian rhythm (Aschoff, 1964b). The 'clock' can be used for true chronometry in compass orientation (Hoffmann, 1965b), and it is also involved in seasonal timing as a basis for the phenomena of photoperiodism (Pittendrigh, 1966a). However, it has been questioned whether these obvious adaptive features are the primary agents of selection for circadian rhythms, or whether more basic needs for temporal control at the cell level have to be considered here. Circadian rhythms, which are present even in unicellular organisms, are probably of very early evolutionary origin. It is likely that they evolved in the service of a function not yet explicitly recognized. Pittendrigh (1966b) recently discussed these aspects with regard to molecular processes, especially those of photochemistry and gene induction.

# Circadian rhythms in birds

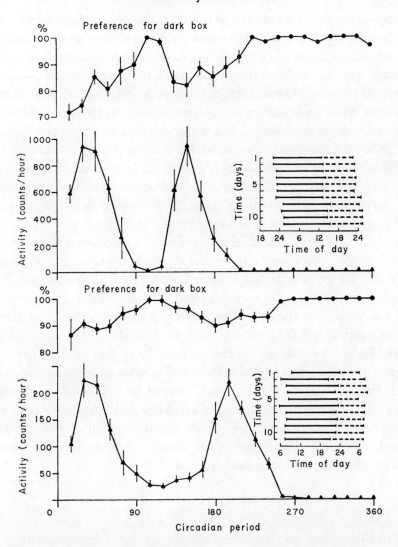

FIGURE 9. Circadian activity rhythm and change in preferred light intensity of two Starlings, each isolated in constant conditions. ▲ activity per hour, averaged for eleven periods (full period = 360°). ● preference for the darker of two boxes between which the birds can choose (dark box, 0.5 lux; bright box, 1.7 lux). Inset diagrams: sequence of activity-time (———) and rest-time (– – –) for the eleven periods. (From Gwinner, 1966a.)

Whatever the final answer may be here, it is also of interest to see to what an extent circadian rhythms match the environmental conditions. In the introduction, the common occurrence of two peaks per day has been mentioned. They could be a passive response to the environment, even if the basic rhythm is endogenous. However, as shown experimentally, the two peaks often appear in their typical fashion even when birds are kept in constant conditions (Figure 8). This means that natural selection has resulted in a rhythmicity which is adaptive in features which go beyond the appropriate period. It includes a pattern, fitted to the ecological requirements of the species (Aschoff, 1966a). Another example is given by the fact that birds have a preference for either brighter or dimmer light depending on the phase of their circadian rhythm. This has been shown in experiments with Starlings *Sturnus vulgaris* which were kept in an apparatus in which they were able to choose between two chambers with different constant light intensities (Gwinner, 1966a). Locomotor activity was measured in each chamber. Examples of the results are given in Figure 9. Both Starlings have a circadian period close to 24 hours (as shown in the inset diagrams). The patterns of activity show the typical two peaks, and the curves representing a preference for the darker box change in a mirror-like fashion.

These findings emphasize that caution must be applied in the interpretation of correlations between animal behaviour and concurrent environmental conditions. Before it is accepted that certain features of behaviour or physiology, such as a peak of activity or the hiding of a bird in a dark place towards the end of its activity-time, are exclusively or mainly the direct result of external stimuli, experiments should be performed to test whether these features also appear in conditions where the suspected stimuli are absent.

### ENTRAINMENT OF CIRCADIAN RHYTHMS

*The Zeitgeber*

Under natural conditions, circadian rhythms are never free-running, or only under very special circumstances. They are synchronized to exactly 24 hours by means of periodic factors in the environment. These factors have been called Zeitgebers (Aschoff, 1951, 1954, 1958). The daily changes in light intensity and in

---

FIGURE 10. Original records of the activity rhythms of two Chaffinches kept in either a light–dark cycle (LD) with 200 lux in L and 0.5 lux in D, or in constant conditions with a dim illumination of 0.5 lux (DD). Shaded area, 0.5 lux; white area, 200 lux. (From Aschoff & Wever, 1966.)

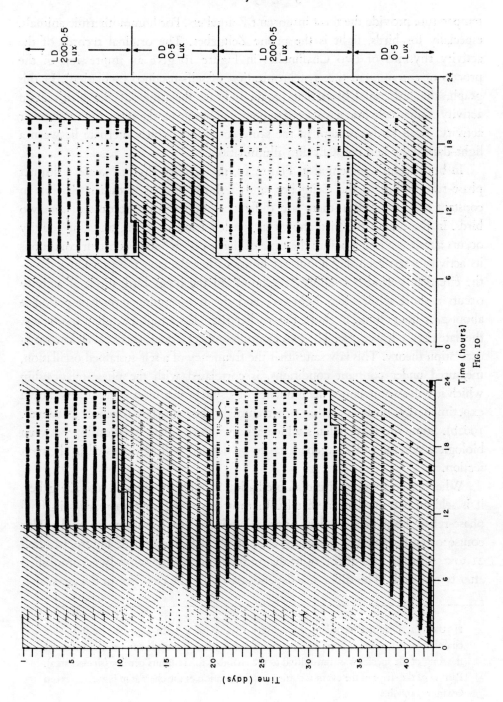

LD
200:0·5
Lux

DD
0·5
Lux

LD
200:0·5
Lux

DD
0·5
Lux

Time (hours)

Fig. 10

Time (days)

93

# Jürgen Aschoff

temperature provide the most important Zeitgebers. For homoiothermic animals, especially for birds, light is the prime Zeitgeber. The original records of the activity rhythms of two Chaffinches in Figure 10 give an impression of the process of entrainment (i.e. synchronization of self-sustained oscillation). In this graph, the horizontal black bars again indicate the times of the bird's main activity; they shade into a scattered sequence of single marks at the time of weaker activity. Both birds are kept in the same conditions which alternate between a light–dark cycle and constant dim illumination.

In both records presented in Figure 10, the activity rhythm keeps a distinct phase-relationship to the Zeitgeber, and it shows a clear circadian rhythm in constant conditions. But there are differences between the records of the two birds. In the case of the bird shown in the left-hand diagram, onset of activity occurs about 1–2 hours before the time of 'light-on', while in constant conditions its activity starts each day about 1.5 hours earlier than on the preceding day—the circadian period is roughly 22.5 hours. In the other bird, onset of activity occurs a short while after 'light-on', and the free-running circadian period is about 24.5 hours long. In short, the 'earlier riser' has a high circadian frequency, the 'late riser' a lower one. The two examples reflect a general law, well known in oscillation theory. This law states that the frequency of a self-sustained oscillation, measured under constant conditions, is correlated with the phase-relationship which it will assume under the influence of a synchronizing oscillation. As shown experimentally, birds as well as other animals obey this law (Aschoff & Wever, 1962b). Some special problems which arise when the phase-relationship between biological systems and Zeitgebers has to be defined will be discussed in the next section.

When a free-running circadian oscillation is suddenly exposed to a Zeitgeber, it is seldom entrained immediately. In most cases, the rhythm reaches its final phase-relationship in a gradual approach which lasts for several periods. This course of entrainment is especially clear in the left diagram of Figure 10 (days 21 to 25). In the case of the right diagram, entrainment is already accomplished after two periods. This difference depends partly on the fact that, in the two cases,

FIGURE 11. Original record of the activity rhythm of a Serin kept in a sound-proof chamber and at constant dim illumination of about 3 lux. From the 22nd to the 85th day, the song of the species was transmitted to the chamber for 12 hours per day (shaded area). Pasting of the strips of the event recorder and duplication of the chart as in Figure 4. (From Gwinner, 1966b.)

94

# Circadian rhythms in birds

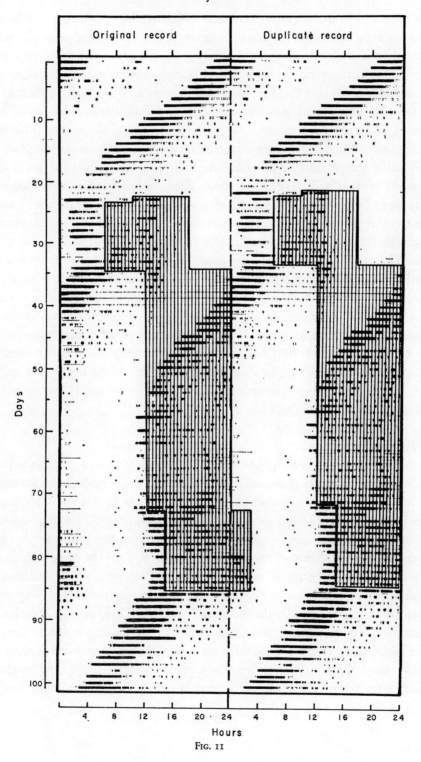

FIG. 11

the Zeitgeber hits the circadian system at different phases, which differ in their sensitivity to light. It is out of the scope of this paper to discuss the principles which are involved here (for details, see Aschoff, 1965a). For practical purposes it suffices to remember that several days may elapse before a steady-state of entrainment is reached. This holds true also for other experiments such as a sudden shift of the Zeitgeber by which an organism is entrained, or the transfer of an organism in an eastward or westward direction over several degrees of longitude. Both these examples are of interest for experiments in the field of compass orientation.

Whether temperature or other abiotic environmental factors can act as Zeitgebers for birds is still an open question. There is, however, now evidence for entrainment by social stimuli (Gwinner, 1966b). The record in Figure 11 shows the activity rhythm of a Serin *Serinus canarius*, kept in constant dim illumination. For the first 22 days, the rhythm is free-running with a period of about 23.0 hours. Then the song of this species is transmitted to the chamber from a tape recorder via a loudspeaker for 12 hours per day. As can be seen in the graph, the activity rhythm immediately locks on to the song cycle. When, after 12 days, the song cycle is shifted by 6 hours, the activity rhythm drifts away and scans through the Zeitgeber. However, after a long series of advancing transients (as they are called), the rhythm becomes again entrained, and remains entrained after another 3-hour shift of the Zeitgeber. For the rest of the time of the experiment, the bird is again in constant conditions and shows nearly the same free-running period as before (23.4 hours).

*The Phase-angle Difference*
Entrainment of a circadian rhythm by a Zeitgeber fulfils a biological function in providing a very distinct phase-relationship between the periodicity of the organism and that of the environment. The whole process can be described in technical terms as phase control of one oscillator by another oscillator. The phase-relationship between two coupled oscillators is measured as the difference between two corresponding phases or, more exactly, phase-angles. (The phase-angle is the value of the abscissa corresponding to a point of the curve which describes the oscillation; it is given either in degrees or in other fractions of the whole period.) The situation is schematically illustrated in Figure 12. Three cases of entrainment are graphed. If corresponding phases (i.e. points on the curve, such as the maxima or the minima) are reached at the same time, the two oscillations are in phase and the phase-angle difference is zero (middle graph). In the left example, the controlled oscillation reaches its maximum earlier than the Zeitgeber; the resulting 'leading'

phase is measured as a positive phase-angle difference. If the phase of the controlled oscillation lags behind that of the controlling oscillation (the Zeitgeber), the phase-angle difference has a negative sign (right example in Figure 12). (For comparison, in Figure 10, the left diagram shows a positive phase-angle difference, the right diagram a negative one.)

It is easy to compute the phase-angle difference between two oscillations which are described by curves of exactly the same kind, for there is no doubt about corresponding phases. With the two synchronized sinusoidal oscillations, presented in Figure 13A, the controlled (entrained) oscillation leads the controlling one by

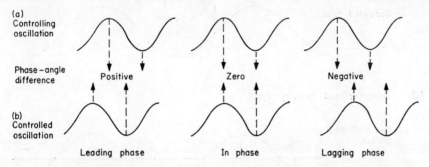

FIGURE 12. Schematic drawing of three sets of coupled oscillators to illustrate different possibilities of phase-relationships between a controlled and a controlling oscillator. (From Aschoff, 1965b.)

$+ 30°$. In such a simple system it makes no difference which phase is used to measure the phase-angle difference; the maxima as well as the turning points or the minima yield the same value of $+ 30°$. In both oscillations, the phases correspond to each other in the mathematical sense.

However, in case of an activity rhythm which is synchronized with a Zeitgeber, it may be difficult to define true corresponding phases. The uppermost of the three curves in Figure 13B schematically represents the sun's movement, showing sunrise and sunset where the curve crosses the horizon. Each of the two lower curves represents a circadian oscillator. The oscillator $b_1$ has a high level and therefore a long activity-time. The oscillator $b_2$ has a low level and a short activity-time. Both oscillations have the same actual phase-angle difference of $+ 30°$ to the Zeitgeber. Which 'corresponding' phases of the Zeitgeber and of the biological oscillation lead to this value? If onset of activity and sunrise are used for reference (as is often done), a phase-angle difference of $+ 60°$ is obtained for curve $b_1$ and one of $0°$ for curve $b_2$. Another possibility is provided by sunset and

end of activity; the phase-angle differences measured by these two phases are 0°
for curve $b_1$ and $+60°$ for curve $b_2$. Neither of the two sets gives the right

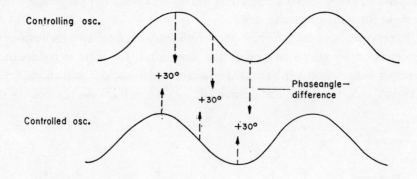

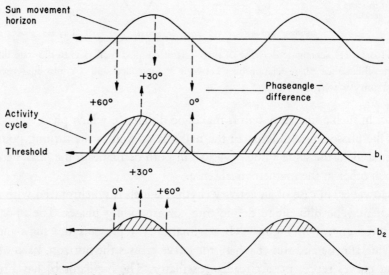

FIGURE 13. Synchronized oscillators, the controlled oscillation showing a phase-angle
difference of $+30°$ to the controlling one. A, sinusoidal oscillations; B, Zeitgeber, and circadian oscillator with either a high level ($b_1$) or a low level ($b_2$). (From Aschoff, 1964c.)

phase-angle difference of $+30°$. This value is obtained for both curves, however,
if the midpoint of activity-time (i.e. the midpoint between onset and end of
activity) is related to the midpoint between sunrise and sunset (i.e. to noon).

These two points are here the true corresponding phases of the circadian oscillator and the Zeitgeber. In contrast to this, onset and end of activity depend upon the position of the level relative to the threshold. Each change in the position of the level also changes the relation between onset of activity and sunrise, as well as between end of activity and sunset—though there may be no change in the true phase-angle difference. Since onset and end are shifted in opposite directions, the errors are cancelled out when the phase-angle difference is measured between the midpoints. The usefulness of this 'midpoint' approach will be discussed in the following section on the basis of field observations.

*The Rule for Season and Latitude*
As mentioned in the introduction and demonstrated in Figure 10, the phase-angle difference between organism and Zeitgeber depends on the natural frequency of the circadian oscillator. 'Natural' here means that specific frequency which the oscillator would assume if it were not entrained. The higher this frequency, the more positive (or the less negative) is the phase-angle difference. If the circadian rule, which is derived from experiments under *constant* conditions, is also valid for *entrained* organisms, one should expect that a change in the Zeitgeber's average light intensity results in a change of the phase-angle difference. In day-active animals, the phase-angle difference should become more positive when the average light intensity is increased.

Under natural conditions, the average light intensity per 24 hours is higher in a summer than in a winter day. One therefore should expect, because the level is higher when the light is brighter (a) a longer activity-time and (b) a more positive phase-angle difference in summer than in winter. The first, rather commonplace, statement is exemplified in Figure 2. The validity of the second statement can be tested with data from field observations where onset and end of activity have been recorded over the year. The left diagram of Figure 14 contains data for the Black Woodpecker *Dryocopus martius* and for the Great Spotted Woodpecker *Dendrocopos major* (Blume, 1965). The two species differ markedly in the way in which the distance between onset of activity and sunrise changes from winter to summer. However, with regard to the midpoints of their activity-times both species behave alike, showing a positive phase-angle difference in summer and one of zero degree in winter.

The influence of the season on the phase-angle difference should become more conspicuous with an increase in latitutde. Data for the Great Tit *Parus major* are available from observations at 48° N and at 67° N (Figure 14, right diagram).

99

In both areas, the changes in phase-angle difference, measured between midpoint and noon, follow the rule. As expected, the differences between summer and winter values are larger at the higher latitude.

In the literature, there are a few more reports which contain field data on onset and end of activity for a sufficient part of the year. From these data, the time intervals between onset of activity and sunrise as well as the intervals between

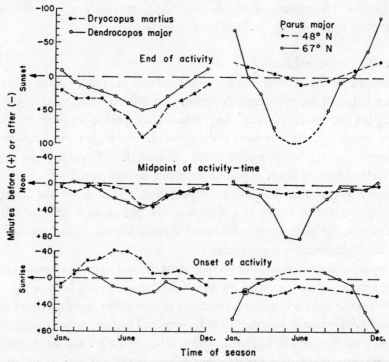

FIGURE 14. Phase-relationship of the activity rhythm of birds to sunrise, noon and sunset throughout the year. Field observations on two woodpeckers at 50° N (Blume, 1965) and on Great Tits at 48° N and at 67° N (Franz, 1949).

midpoint of activity-time and noon have been computed for mid-winter (November to January) and for midsummer (May to July). The results for ten species are summarized in Figure 15. The values for 'onset of activity to sunrise' change from winter to summer in an irregular fashion; no generalization seems possible. The true phase-angle differences, however, measured between midpoint of activity-time and noon, confirm the prediction in all ten species. The regularity of slopes of the 'midpoint' lines as compared to the irregular slopes of 'onset' lines suggests

# Circadian rhythms in birds

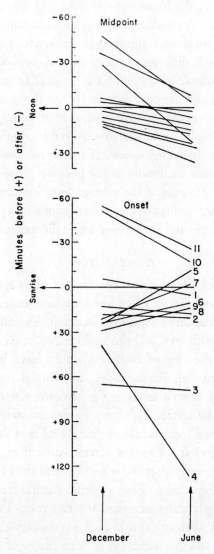

FIGURE 15. Onset of activity related to sunrise and midpoint of activity-time related to noon for 10 diurnal species of birds. Values computed from field data for midwinter (November to January) and midsummer (May to July) are connected by straight lines. 1, *Picus viridis* and 2, *Dendrocopos major* (Blume, 1963–64); 3, *Emberiza citrinella* (Wallgren, 1956); 4, *Erithacus rubecula* (Palmgren, 1949); 5, *Parus major* (Kluijver, 1950); 6, *P. major*, 7, *P. caeruleus* and 8, *Passer domesticus* (Franz, 1949); 9, *Corvus monedula* (Aschoff & v.Holst, 1960); 10, *Tympanuchus cupido* and 11, *T. pallidicinctus* (Jones, 1964).

(1) that there is reality in the hypothesis of level and threshold from which the use of midpoints has been derived, and (2) that the circadian rule, based on observations under constant conditions, can rightly be applied to entrained organisms.

In judging phase-angle differences under natural conditions, it is necessary to bear in mind those possible changes of the natural frequency which are not caused by changes in light intensity but might be the result of changes in the general physiological, especially the hormonal, state of the organism. Some observations suggest, for example, an increased sensitivity to light in many species of birds during their early breeding season. If this is reflected in a higher natural frequency of the circadian oscillator, larger positive phase-angle differences are to be expected at this time even if the average light intensity of the Zeitgeber is kept constant. For other limitations and restrictions in applying the circadian rule to entrained organisms and their phase-angle differences, see Aschoff (1965b).

## CONCLUSION

The attempt to treat circadian activity rhythms of birds as self-sustained oscillators is justified by a great variety of experimental evidence. The laws of oscillation theory apply to circadian systems even in detail (Aschoff, 1964a). The specific model of an oscillator with level and threshold is also based on a large amount of experimental data. In the case of birds, no results have been published so far which contradict the model. Furthermore, this model not only explains data from field observations as well as from the laboratory, but also makes definite predictions which can be tested. This may be demonstrated by a last example. It is an often-documented fact that the earlier a bird rises the later it roosts. This means that the early riser has a longer activity-time than the late riser. Or, in terms of the model: the early riser has a higher level than the late riser. If this is true, the early riser is expected to have a higher natural frequency and, hence, a more positive phase-angle difference than the late riser. Two sets of data from Mori (1945) and from Wright (1913), each for twenty-three species, confirm this prediction (Figure 16). Accidentally, at both places of observation (in Japan and in the U.S.A.), the local time differs by the same amount from standard zone time. Therefore, the same abscissa can be used for all data. In both diagrams, the phase-angle difference, measured between midpoint of activity-time and noon, becomes more positive with an increase in length of activity-time.

In spite of the pleasant agreement between theory, field observations and experimental results, the question remains whether the one-oscillator model discussed above reflects the true mechanism of the circadian system. It is possible to describe the same facts with models of two oscillators as well. Some findings in experiments with mammals seem to suggest the presence of at least two oscillators (Pittendrigh, 1960). And quite recently, Gwinner, after a long series of experiments with migrating birds, has concluded that the nocturnal

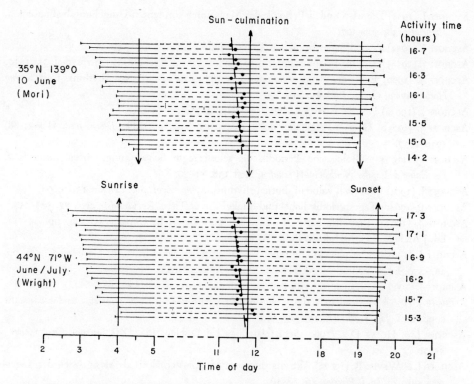

FIGURE 16. Activity-times from first to last calls for twenty-three bird species in Japan (Mori, 1945) and in U.S.A. (Wright, 1913) respectively. Both sets of data are arranged with respect to length of activity-time (numbers on the right margin). Abscissa, zone time. Midpoint of each activity-time indicated by a closed circle. (From Aschoff & Wever, 1962c.)

*Zugunruhe* (migratory restlessness) can be explained only with great difficulty on the basis of the one-oscillator model (unpublished data). He proposes a model with two coupled oscillators, both of which have level and threshold, but are correlated to light intensity with opposite signs. This model, therefore, differs fundamentally from the two-oscillator model which has been developed by Pittendrigh & Bruce (1957) and Pittendrigh (1960). At the present state, it is

# Jürgen Aschoff

impossible to decide whether one model suffices to describe all phenomena known so far (or whether different models apply to different groups of animals), and whether this will be a one- or a multi-oscillator model.

## REFERENCES

ASCHOFF J. (1951) Die 24-Stunden-Periodik der Maus unter konstanten Umgebungsbedingungen. *Naturwiss.* **38**, 506–507.

ASCHOFF J. (1954) Zeitgeber der tierischen Tagesperiodik. *Naturwiss.* **41**, 49–56.

ASCHOFF J. (1958) Tierische Periodik unter dem Einfluss von Zeitgebern. *Z. Tierpsychol.* **15**, 1–30.

ASCHOFF J. (1960) Exogenous and endogenous components in circadian rhythms. *Cold Spring Harbor Symp. Quant. Biol.* **25**, 11–28.

ASCHOFF J. (1963a) Diurnal rhythms. *Ann. Rev. Physiol.* **25**, 581–600.

ASCHOFF J. (1963b) Gesetzmässigkeiten der biologischen Tagesperiodik. *Dtsch. med. Wochr.* **88**, 1930–1937.

ASCHOFF J. (1964a) Biologische Periodik als selbsterregte Schwingung. *Arbeitsgemeinsch. f. Forschung d. Landes Nordrhein-Westfalen*, Heft **138**, 51–79.

ASCHOFF J. (1964b) Survival value of diurnal rhythms. *Symp. Zool. Soc. London* **13**, 79–98.

ASCHOFF J. (1964c) Tagesperiodik licht- und dunkelaktiver Tiere. *Revue suisse zool.* **71**, 528–558.

ASCHOFF J. (1965a) Response curves in circadian periodicity. In *Circadian Clocks*, pp. 95–111. Ed. J.Aschoff. North-Holland Publ., Amsterdam.

ASCHOFF J. (1965b) The phase-angle difference in circadian periodicity. In *Circadian Clocks*, pp. 262–276. Ed. J.Aschoff. North-Holland Publ., Amsterdam.

ASCHOFF J. (1966a) Circadian activity pattern with two peaks. *Ecology* **47**, 657–662.

ASCHOFF J. (1966b) Circadian activity rhythms in Chaffinches (*Fringilla coelebs*) under constant conditions. *Jap. J. Physiol.* **16**, 363–370.

ASCHOFF J. & HOLST D.v. (1960) Schlafplatzflüge bei Dohlen. *Proc. XII Internat. Orn. Congr.*, 55–70.

ASCHOFF J. & WEVER R. (1962a) Aktivitätsmenge und $\alpha:\rho$-Verhältnis als Messgrössen der Tagesperiodik. *Z. vergl. Physiol.* **46**, 88–101.

ASCHOFF J. & WEVER R. (1962b) Über Phasenbeziehungen zwischen biologischer Tagesperiodik und Zeitgeberperiodik. *Z. vergl. Physiol.* **46**, 115–128.

ASCHOFF J. & WEVER R. (1962c) Beginn und Ende der Aktivität freilebender Vögel. *J. f. Ornithol.* **103**, 1–27.

ASCHOFF J. & WEVER R. (1966) Circadian period and phase-angle difference in Chaffinches (*Fringilla coelebs* L.). *Comp. Biochem. Physiol.* **18**, 397–404.

BLUME D. (1963–64) Die Jahresperiodik von Aktivitätsbeginn und -ende bei einigen Spechtarten I. und II. Teil). *Vogelwelt* **84**, 161–184; **85**, 11–18.

BLUME D. (1965) Revierverhalten der Vögel als Unterrichtsthema. *Der Biologie-Unterricht* **3**, 29–48.

FARNER D.S., MEWALDT L.R. & KING J.R. (1954) The diurnal activity patterns of caged migratory White-crowned Sparrows in late winter and spring. *J. comp. physiol. psychol.* **47**, 148–153.

FRANZ J. (1949) Jahres- und Tagesrhythmus einiger Vögel in Nordfinnland. *Z. Tierpsychol.* **6**, 309–329.

# Circadian rhythms in birds

GWINNER E. (1966a) Tagesperiodische Schwankungen der Vorzugshelligkeit bei Vögeln. *Z. vgl. Physiol.* **52**, 370–379.

GWINNER E. (1966b) Entrainment of a circadian rhythm in birds by species-specific song cycles (Aves, Fringillidae: *Carduelis spinus, Serinus serinus*). *Experientia* **22**, 765–766.

HALBERG FR. (1959) Physiological 24-hour periodicity: General and procedural considerations with reference to the adrenal cycle. *Z. Vitamin-, Hormon- u. Fermentforschg.* **10**, 225–296.

HINDE R.A. (1952) The behaviour of the Great Tit (*Parus major*) and some other related species. *Behaviour Suppl.* **2**.

HOFFMANN KL. (1965a) Overt circadian frequencies and circadian rule. In *Circadian Clocks*, pp. 87–94. Ed. J.Aschoff. North-Holland Publ., Amsterdam.

HOFFMANN KL. (1965b) Clock mechanisms in celestial orientation of animals. In *Circadian Clocks*, pp. 426–441. Ed. J.Aschoff. North-Holland Publ., Amsterdam.

JONES R.E. (1964) The specific distinctness of the Greater and Lesser Prairie Chickens. *Auk* **81**, 65–73.

KLUIJVER H.N. (1950) Daily routines of the Great Tit, *Parus m. major* L. *Ardea* **38**, 99–135.

KUUSISTO P. (1941) Studien über die Ökologie und Tagesrhythmik von *Phylloscopus trochilus acredula* (L.) *Acta zool. fenn.* **31**, 1–120.

MORI S. (1945) (Diurnal rhythms of song in birds, in Japanese.) *Rep. ecol. physiol. morphol. Zool. Inst. Kyoto.* **20**.

PALMGREN P. (1949) Studien über die Tagesrhythmik gekäfigter Zugvögel. *Z. Tierpsychol.* **6**, 44–86.

PITTENDRIGH C.S. (1960) Circadian rhythms and the circadian organization of living systems. *Cold Spring Harbor Symp. Quant. Biol.* **25**, 159–184.

PITTENDRIGH C.S. (1966a) The circadian oscillation in *Drosophila pseudoobscura* pupae: A model for the photoperiodic clock. *Z. Pflanzenphysiol.* **54**, 275–307.

PITTENDRIGH C.S. (1966b) Biological clocks: The functions, ancient and modern, of circadian oscillations. In *Science and the Sixties*, pp. 96–111. U.S. Air Force Office of Scientific Research, Cloudcroft Symposium.

PITTENDRIGH C.S. & BRUCE V. (1957) An oscillator model for biological clocks. In *Rhythmic and Synthetic Processes in Growth*, pp. 75–109. Ed. D.Rudnick. Princeton University Press, Princeton.

SCHEER G. (1952) Beobachtungen und Untersuchungen über die Abhängigkeit des Frühgesanges der Vögel von inneren und äusseren Faktoren. *Biol. Abhandl.* **3/4**, 1–68.

WALLGREN H. (1956) Zur Biologie der Goldammer, *Emberiza citrinella* L. *Acta Soc. Faun. Flor. fenn.* **71**, No. 4.

WEVER R. (1964) Ein mathematisches Modell für biologische Schwingungen. *Z. Tierpsychol.* **21**, 359–372.

WEVER R. (1965) A mathematical model for circadian rhythms. In *Circadian Clocks*, pp. 47–63. Ed. J.Aschoff. North-Holland Publ., Amsterdam.

WRIGHT H.W. (1913) Morning awakening and evening-song. *Auk* **30**, 512–537.

# The control of avian reproductive cycles*

DONALD S.FARNER

Department of Zoology, University of Washington, Seattle,
Washington, 98105, U.S.A.

## INTRODUCTION

As in higher animals in general, reproduction in birds is intermittent. Some degree
of intermittency is imposed by the temporal requirements of the reproductive
processes. More significant, however, in the evolution of intermittent reproductive
function is the adaptive significance of control systems that so regulate reproduction that young are produced during the season in which the probability of survival
tends to be maximal and stress on the adults tends to be minimal (Aschoff, 1955;
Farner, 1961, 1964a, 1965; Immelmann, 1963; Marshall, 1960, 1961). Among
species that inhabit the distinctly annually periodic environments of the mid and
high latitudes reproductive activity is characteristically annual and the reproductive
seasons are clearly defined (Aschoff, 1955; Farner, 1959, 1961, 1964a; Lack, 1950b).
Even in the tropics and subtropics annual breeding cycles are widespread although
characteristically less precisely defined (e.g. Baker, 1938; Bouma, 1936; Chapin,
1932; Coomans de Ruiter, 1931; Frith & Davies, 1961; Heim de Balsac, 1952;
Lack, 1950a; Marshall, 1961; Miller, 1936; Moreau, 1950; Skutch, 1950; Voous,
1950; Wagner & Stresemann, 1950; see Immelmann, 1963, for review). There
are, of course, many cases of continuous breeding, when viewed from the aspect
of the population as a whole (e.g. Chapin, 1932; Meyer, 1930; Miller, 1963;
Moreau, 1950). Unfortunately little is known concerning the reproductive performance of individuals in such populations. Co-ordinated and detailed field and
laboratory studies of such populations could contribute much to our knowledge
of the control of reproduction in birds. Of special interest are those populations
with definite breeding seasons of less than annual periodicities (e.g. Ashmole,

* Previously unpublished data and observations on *Zonotrichia leucophrys gambelii*, *Taeniopygia
castanotis* and *Coturnix coturnix* are, in part, from investigations supported by grants from the
National Science Foundation (G-3416, GB-1380, and GB-4433) and the National Institutes of
Health (NB-01353 and NB-06187). I am grateful to Dr Robert D. Lisk, Princeton University,
for permission to use the unpublished results from his experiments on *Carpodacus mexicanus*.

1962; Dorward, 1962; Immelmann, 1962, 1963; Medway, 1962; Miller, 1962). Again, co-ordinated field and laboratory studies of these cases would certainly contribute extensively to our general understanding of the control of avian reproduction.

In desert and semi-arid regions with aperiodic rains many species have evolved mechanisms, still very inadequately understood, that cause the development of reproductive activity very rapidly after the beginning of a rainy period (e.g. Disney & Marshall, 1956; Frith & Tilt, 1959; Immelmann, 1963; Keast, 1959; Morel & Bourlière, 1956; Serventy & Marshall, 1957; Zedlitz, 1911). In *Taeniopygia castanotis* it appears that a substantial fraction of the birds, during non-breeding seasons, have partially developed gonads (Farner, unpublished observations; see also Immelmann, 1963) so that less time is required to develop completely functional gonads when the rainy period begins. There is some reason to believe that this is true of some other aperiodic breeders of the Australian desert (Immelmann, 1963).

Although the adaptive significances of the reproductive periodicities (and aperiodicities) described in the paragraphs above are generally apparent, the physiological mechanisms that bring individual birds into reproductive condition are by no means generally understood (Dolnik, 1963, 1964; Emme, 1960; Farner, 1959, 1961, 1964 a, b, 1965; Marshall, 1960, 1961; Wolfson, 1960 a, b). Nevertheless, there is now a significant, emerging body of experimental data and pertinent field observations that permit the construction of useful hypotheses concerning the basic temporal control of reproduction in birds.

The system of controls of reproduction in any species obviously employs a battery of mechanisms of diverse temporal relationships that derive information from external and internal sources. No single system of categorization of control mechanisms is entirely satisfactory. The following has some pragmatic value for periodically breeding species even though it is inapplicable to opportunistic desert breeders and some other species.

1. *Primary timing mechanisms.* These are the mechanisms that induce at least the essential initial phase of gonadal development. For information, these mechanisms may be solely dependent on *primary external information*, such as day length, or on the interaction of primary external information with an internal periodic function. *Primary external information*, as used here, is equivalent to the 'proximate factors' of Baker (1938) and the 'unmittelbare Faktoren' of Immelmann (1963). It seems clear that, for many species, rain or environmental changes associated therewith constitute *primary external information*. However, apart from the studies of Marshall

& Disney (1957) on *Quelea quelea* and my preliminary unpublished investigations on *Taeniopygia castanotis*, experimental evidence is lacking.

2. *Essential supplemental mechanisms.* These involve functions based on certain essential environmental requirements (e.g. suitable territory, nesting material, etc.), and on interactions among individuals in which reproductive development has been initiated by 1. They are involved, for example, in the final development of the oviduct and ovary in many species, and also in nest-building, incubation and parental behaviour. Many of these mechanisms have been explored in the ingenious and highly successful investigations of Professor Hinde (for review, see Hinde, 1965) and constitute the subject of his presentation in this volume.

3. *Modifying mechanisms.* These provide the precise, final adjustments in the schedule of reproduction to the season at hand. They operate on such environmental information as ambient temperature, phenologic succession of the season, availability of food and water, etc. Such modifying mechanisms may be sufficiently effective to completely suppress breeding (see, for example, MacGregor & Inlay, 1951). Mechanisms of categories 2 and 3 are by no means always separable.

4. *Terminal timing mechanisms.* The termination of the breeding period is of importance not only because it avoids the waste of producing young when the probability for survival is slight, or at least substantially reduced, but also because it permits diversion of energy to other functions such as moult and migration. These timing mechanisms are thus important in the mutual exclusion of physiologically important functions (Farner, 1964a).

This discussion is concerned almost exclusively with the *primary timing mechanisms* and the *terminal timing mechanisms*; these fix the general temporal pattern and seasons of reproductive activity.

Unfortunately much of this discussion must rest on investigations of species in which the primary timing mechanisms are photoperiodic simply because almost all experimental investigations have involved such species. Nevertheless, it is now clear that the mechanisms listed above must generally operate on and through a basic control core that is characteristic of all higher vertebrates (e.g. Benoit & Assenmacher, 1955; Davidson, 1966; Farner, Wilson & Oksche, 1967; Harris, 1955; Scharrer & Scharrer, 1963). This basic core includes the hypothalamus, the anterior pituitary gland and the gonads (Figure 1).

The great diversity in the timing of the initiation and termination of reproductive function has come through evolution with respect to the kinds of internal and external information used by the hypothalamus and the way in which such information is processed (Farner, 1964a, 1965).

# Donald S.Farner

## THE CORE OF THE CONTROL SCHEME IN AVIAN REPRODUCTION

The pioneer investigations of Benoit and his colleagues (Assenmacher, 1958; Benoit, 1936, 1937, 1961, 1964a; Benoit & Assenmacher, 1953 a, b, 1955) on the domestic mallard, and subsequent experiments on the domestic fowl (Ma & Nalbandov, 1963) and on *Zonotrichia leucophrys gambelii* (Wilson & Farner, 1965), permit the generalization that the gonadotropic function of the anterior pituitary,

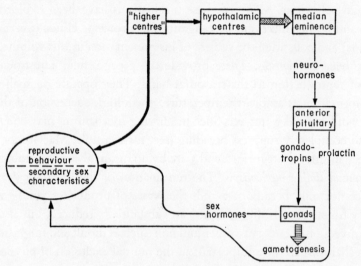

FIGURE I. The basic core of the control scheme of avian reproductive function.

and its regulation, are essentially totally dependent on neurohormone(s) transported from the median eminence of the hypothalamus via hypophysial portal vessels to the blood sinusoid system of the pars distalis. The anatomical basis of this control system has been worked out to a considerable extent at microscopic and ultrastructural levels (e.g. Assenmacher, 1952, 1958; Bern *et al*, 1966; Bern & Nishioka, 1965; Green, 1951; Kobayashi *et al*, 1961; Oksche, 1962 a, b, 1965; Oksche & Farner, unpublished; Vitums *et al*, 1964; Wingstrand, 1951). The median eminence is, in the truest sense, a *neurohemal organ*. In principle, this hypothalamo-hypophysial control scheme of birds is similar to that of mammals (Davidson, 1966; Flerkó, 1963, 1966; Harris, 1955, 1960; Szentagothai *et al*, 1962), although it appears that the gonadotropic function of the avian anterior pituitary, as revealed by ectopic pituitary grafts, is far more completely dependent on the hypothalamus than is the mammalian anterior pituitary (Assenmacher, 1958; Davidson, 1966).

## The control of avian reproductive cycles

Of substantial potential interest, with respect to the control system in birds, is the recent demonstration (Vitums *et al*, 1964) that the anatomically distinct anterior and posterior parts of the median eminence, at least in *Z. leucophrys gambelii*, are drained by separate rostral and caudal groups of hypophysial portal vessels into the

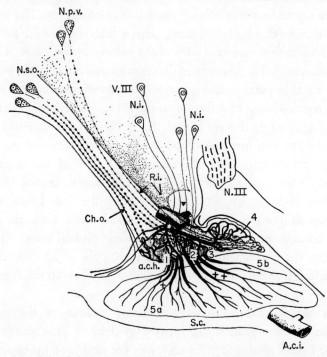

FIGURE 2. The hypothalamo-hypophysial system of *Zonotrichia leucophrys gambelii*. N.p.v., paraventricular nucleus; N.s.o., supraoptic nucleus; N.i., infundibular and ventro-medial nucleus; V. III, third ventricle; R.i. infundibular recess; Ch.o., optic chiasma; N. III, oculomotor nerve; ↗ neurosecretory tract; △ tuberohypophysial tract; a.c.n., anterior capillary network; + anterior bundle of portal vessels; ++ posterior bundle of portal vessels; S.c., cavernous sinus; A.c.i., infundibular artery. 1, anterior division of median eminence with predominance of neurosecretory fibres; 2, posterior median eminence with overwhelming predominance of non-neurosecretory fibres; 3, infundibular stem; 4, neural lobe; 5a, rostral lobe, and 5b, caudal lobe of anterior pituitary; 6, posterior pituitary. (From Oksche, 1965.)

separate sinusoid systems of the rostral and caudal lobes of the pars distalis respectively (Figure 2). Thus there exists the anatomical basis for two independent neurohemal control systems. The physiological reality of this inference is the subject of experiments now in progress.

# Donald S. Farner

The median eminence, as the neurohemal organ of the hypothalamo-hypo-physial control system, receives axons from two distinct groups of hypothalamic nuclei (e.g. Arai, 1963; Arai *et al*, 1963; Farner & Oksche, 1962; George & Naik, 1965; Grignon, 1956; Oksche, 1962 a, b, 1965; Oksche *et al*, 1959, 1963, 1964; Oksche & Farner, unpublished; Wingstrand, 1951). (1) The magnocellular *supra-optic* and *paraventricular nuclei* of the anterior hypothalamus. The cells of these nuclei, and the axons that lead therefrom, contain material that can be stained with classical neurosecretory stains (aldehyde fuschin, chromalum hematoxylin, pseudoisocyanin, etc.). The fibres from these nuclei pass through the hypothalamo-hypophysial tract, in part, to the pars nervosa (posterior pituitary) and, in part, to the median eminence. The former are involved in osmoregulation and the other functions through the release of the 'posteriorlobe' hormones, arginine vasotocin and oxytocin, into the blood stream in the pars nervosa. The latter pass directly, or indirectly, into the neurohemal zone of the anterior median eminence; only a few terminate in the posterior median eminence. (2) The *tubero-nuclear complex*. These groups of nerve cells lie in the dorsolateral walls of the infundibular recess (posterior hypothalamus) and send fibres into the neurohemal zone of the median eminence via the tuberohypophysial tract. Although this tract constitutes the overwhelmingly dominant supply of fibres to the posterior median eminence, it also sends significant numbers of fibres to the anterior median eminence.

Although the mechanism of hypothalamic control of the gonadotropic activity of the anterior pituitary in birds is evident in principle (see Farner & Follett, 1966; Farner *et al*, 1967, for reviews), the details of the neural pathways remain to be resolved. The extensive pioneer investigations of Benoit and his colleagues (for summaries, see Assenmacher, 1958; Benoit, 1964 a, b; Benoit & Assenmacher, 1953 a, b) and also subsequent investigations (Gogan *et al*, 1963; Novikov & Rudneva, 1964) on Mallards *Anas platyrhynchos* have yielded extensive, convincing evidence that the supraoptic nucleus and the hypothalamo-hypo-physial tract constitute the terminal hypothalamic elements in the control of the gonadotropic function of the anterior pituitary. Our initial investigations with *Zonotrichia leucophrys gambelii* (Farner, 1962; Farner *et al*, 1962; Oksche *et al*, 1959), and also investigations on *Z. albicollis* (Wolfson, 1963; Wolfson & Kobayashi 1962), *Zosterops palpebrosa japonica* (Hirano *et al*, 1962; Uemura & Kobayashi, 1963), and the domestic fowl (Legait, 1959; Mikami, 1960) yielded evidence that ap-peared to be consistent with this conclusion. However, subsequent investigations on *Zonotrichia leucophrys gambelii* with hypothalamic lesions (Farner *et al*, 1967;

# The control of avian reproductive cycles

Wilson & Farner, 1965) have definitely demonstrated that the fibres of the tubero-hypophysial tract are of primary importance as the terminal hypothalamic elements in the control of the gonadotropic function of the anterior pituitary in this species. Moreover, experiments on the hypothalamic neurosecretory system (supraoptic and paraventricular nuclei and their axons) of the domestic fowl (Graber & Nalbandov, 1965), *Coturnix coturnix* (Follett & Farner, 1966 a, b; Oksche *et al*, 1964), *Junco hyemalis* (Wolfson, 1963) and *Zonotrichia leucophrys gambelii* (Bern *et al*, 1966), have failed to support, but do not necessarily deny, a significant rôle for the hypothalamic neurosecretory system in the control of pituitary gonadotropic activity. Dolnik (1965), on the basis of experiments with *Fringilla coelebs*, has deduced indirectly that neurosecretory material is not involved in the seasonal changes in sensitivity of the photoperiodic testicular response mechanism.

The apparent differences between the control systems of the Mallard and *Zonotrichia leucophrys gambelii* are difficult to rationalize. Either they represent truly specific differences or there is a more complex, as yet unrecognized, common type of control system. I am inclined to believe the latter, although in mammals it appears that the tuberohypophysial tract is primarily, or exclusively, involved (for discussions, see Davidson, 1966; Flerkó, 1966; Sawyer, 1964; Spatz, 1954; Szentagothai *et al*, 1962).

Although the anterior pituitary glands (pars distalis) of birds generally contain both follicle-stimulating and luteinizing activities, it is by no means proved definitively that these activities are represented by two separate hormones (see Farner & Follett, 1966, and van Tienhoven, 1961, for reviews). Tixier-Vidal (1963, 1965), on the basis of tinctorial and electron-microscope studies, has identified seven types of cells in the pars distalis of the duck. She has concluded that the beta cell of the rostral lobe produces FSH and that the gamma cell of the caudal lobe produces LH. She has described similar cell types in several additional species. As in other vertebrates, there appear to be no sex differences in the kinds of anterior pituitary gonadotropins. Rather, the differences between the sexes reside in differences in control of their output and in differences in the target organs (gonads) and their responses. Although the identity and nature of avian gonadotropins remain to be resolved, it is clear that their functions in the control of the gametogenic and endocrine functions do not differ significantly from those of the general vertebrate pattern (van Tienhoven, 1961).

A further pituitary hormone, prolactin, although it has no known gonadotropic function in birds, is of importance in this discussion because of its rôle in the development of the incubation patch, incubation behaviour and parental care (for reviews, see Hinde, 1965; Lehrman, 1959 a, b, 1961, 1964); its possible anti-gonadal function (Bailey, 1950; Laws & Farner, 1960; Lofts & Marshall, 1956; Riddle, 1963); and its possible rôle in migratory behaviour and physiology (King & Farner, 1965; Meier *et al*, 1965; Meier & Farner, 1964). Tixier-Vidal (1963, 1966; also Tixier-Vidal & Assenmacher, 1966) has concluded that prolactin is produced by the eta cells of the caudal lobe of the pars distalis. In birds it seems clear that the hypothalamus has a positive stimulatory role in the release of prolactin by the anterior pituitary, in contrast to its inhibitory role in mammals (Assenmacher & Baylé, 1964; Baylé & Assenmacher, 1965; Kragt & Meites, 1965).

Therefore, although much remains to be learned, it seems clear that the basic core control, as described above and depicted in Figure 1, is probably common to all avian species. The basis for the great diversity of temporal patterns of reproduction lies in adaptive evolution with respect to the information used by the hypothalamus in its control of the gonadotropic function of the anterior pituitary.

## INFORMATION USED BY THE HYPOTHALAMUS IN THE CONTROL OF THE GONADOTROPIC FUNCTION OF THE ANTERIOR PITUITARY

The hypothalamus, because of its unique dual rôle as a part of both the endocrine and nervous systems, occupies a central position in the basic control scheme. Its efferent neuroendocrine component must operate, at least in part, on transduced information from the external environment either directly by afferent neural pathways, or indirectly as the result of environmental modification of some internal component. It may be assumed that processed information is relayed to the terminal hypothalamic nuclei which, in turn, control the release of neuro-hormone(s) into the hypophysial portal system. Little is known about the receptors, afferent pathways and the processing of information in the 'higher centres' and in the subterminal hypothalamic centres. Even among the photoperiodic species, which have been studied to the greatest extent, it now seems clear that the control mechanisms must be of multiple evolutionary origin. Therefore, a consideration of the entire spectrum of control mechanisms, and the history of the species in which they occur, can only lead to a picture of multiple solutions and convergent evolution that imposes stringent caution with respect to generalization. This must be borne in mind constantly in the following categorization of the sources and routes of transmission of information used by the hypothalamus in the control of the gonadotropic function of the anterior pituitary.

1. *Information of external origin.* Such information may reach hypothalamic

centres (a) via exteroceptors and neural transmission or, (b) possibly also via environmental modification of blood composition sensed, in turn, by hypothalamic receptors.

The afferent informational systems that have received the most extensive experimental attention are those involved in photoperiodic controls. Even for these, however, our knowledge is surprisingly sparse (see Benoit, 1964 a, b; Farner, 1961, 1964a; Farner & Follett, 1966, for reviews). In the domestic mallard there is evidence for the existence of both ocular and encephalic photoreceptors (for summaries, see Benoit, 1964b; Benoit & Assenmacher, 1953b) although neither has been definitely identified. Lisk (personal communication) has recently obtained evidence that suggests that encephalic receptors may also occur in the hypothalamus of *Carpodacus mexicanus*. Testicular growth was obtained by 'piping' long-days to the hypothalamus. However, since the eyes were intact, there is the slight possibility that light could have passed from the hypothalamus to photoreceptors in the eyes. In experiments with male *Coturnix coturnix* held under continuous light from hatching until sexually mature, Oishi *et al* (1966) have reported that on continuous light birds with both eyes removed and with eye sockets covered continued to maintain large testes whereas there was marked testicular regression in similarly treated controls transferred to 8-hour daily photoperiods after attaining near-maximal testicular growth on continuous light. A possible explanation of these results is the photostimulation of encephalic receptors by light penetration through a route other than orbital, the route apparently involved in the stimulation of the encephalic receptors of the Mallard (Benoit 1938 a, b, 1964b). The rôle of encephalic receptors in birds is now of further interest because of the demonstration that light can penetrate the brain and skull of mammals (van Brunt *et al*, 1964) and further that the impingement of light on the arcuate or mammillary nuclei of female rats causes constant oestrus (Lisk & Kannwischer, 1964). A direct retinohypothalamic tract has been described in the domestic fowl but it is not clear that it extends to the infundibular nucleus, as has been reported for some mammals (Jacobs & Morgane, 1964; Knoche, 1956, 1960), or that it is involved in photoperiodic control of gonadal function. A discussion of several parameters of light and daily photoperiod, other than its duration, is beyond the scope of this discussion (see Benoit 1964 a, b; Farner, 1959; Schildmacher, 1963).

There is much evidence that behavioural stimuli profoundly affect the development of the avian gonad (for reviews, see Immelmann, 1963; Lehrman, 1961, 1964; van Tienhoven, 1961). Unfortunately little is known concerning the neural pathways and centres involved in these mechanisms. Since such mechanisms fall primarily in the categories of *essential supplemental mechanisms* and *modifying mechanisms*, they will not be considered in detail. Of considerable general pertinence, however, is the demonstration by Phillips & van Tienhoven (1960) of low pituitary-gonadotropin levels in captive females of *Anas platyrhynchos* and *A. acuta* and the demonstration by Phillips (1964) that electrolytic lesions in the archistriatum or occipitomesencephalic tract, which eliminated escape reactions, were followed by normal ovarian development. Clearly higher brain centres must be involved in such inhibition of gonadotropic function.

Although an environmentally modified composition of the blood certainly represents information that could be used by the hypothalamus in its control of gonadotropin, there are as yet no completely proven cases of such in birds. In *Taeniopygia castanotis* there is good evidence (Farner & Serventy, unpublished experiments) that increased water intake induces gonadal development and ultimately, with the necessary supplemental mechanisms, reproductive function. Although we have no direct evidence, this could involve osmotic effects of reduced pressure of the blood on hypothalamic receptors. It is possible also that the experimentally established inhibitory effects (modifying mechanisms) of low environmental temperature (Burger, 1948; Engels & Jenner, 1956; Farner & Mewaldt, 1952; Farner & Wilson, 1957) could operate through the effect of reduced blood temperature on hypothalamic thermoreceptors. Assenmacher *et al* (1965) have recently demonstrated that reduced caloric intake causes gonadal regression at a rate far greater than the rate of reduction of body weight. This suggests a modifying mechanism that is possibly dependent on the alteration of some component of the blood. There have been a number of demonstrations in mammals of the antigonadal effect of low caloric intake.

2. *Endocrine information.* Although the well-vascularized hypothalamus is subjected to fluctuations in the blood concentration of numerous hormones, lack of information restricts discussion of the negative feedback effects of gonadal hormones, gonadotropic hormones and prolactin on the hypothalamus. The available evidence indicates that gonadal steroid hormones do exert a negative feedback effect on gonadotropin-promoting functions of the hypothalamus in varying degrees of sensitivity (Figures 3, 4) and that it is a reasonable hypothesis that negative feedback by gonadal hormones may be involved in gonadal regression in some species (see Farner & Follett, 1966; Kobayashi & Farner, 1966; Schildmacher, 1956, for discussion). Although it is probable that prolactin exerts an 'inside-loop' negative feedback on the gonadotropin-promoting function of

the hypothalamus in some species, it is clear that there must be extensive specific differences (Bailey, 1950; Laws & Farner, 1960; Meier & Farner, unpublished observations; Riddle, 1963). For mammals there is a growing body of information that indicates the existence of an 'internal' negative feedback loop involving

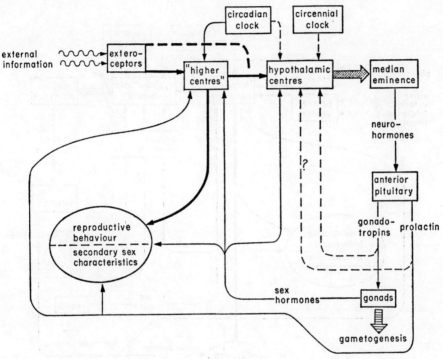

FIGURE 3. Neuroendocrine functions and external and internal information in the control of reproductive periods. A generalized scheme.

pituitary gonadotropins (see Flerkó, 1966, for review). Although firm evidence is lacking for birds, experiments with *Zonotrichia leucophrys gambelii* (castrated males) suggest the existence of such a mechanism (Kobayashi & Farner, 1966).

3. *Endogenous periodicities.* This category is not completely separable from category 2 since the effects of such periodicities may be transmitted through changes in hormones and also since endocrine glands may be components of oscillating systems. However, since oscillating systems provide a special and important type of internal information a separate category is useful. The role of endogenous periodicities in the control of reproductive cycles in birds has been the subject of relatively little experimentation but of a relatively vast amount of

discussion much of which, at least in retrospect, is semantically distressful. Indeed the term 'internal rhythm', because of a variety of ill-defined usages, has become relatively useless. This discussion will be restricted to *circadian* and *circennial periodicities*.

From a general aspect it must be emphasized that circadian periodicities are

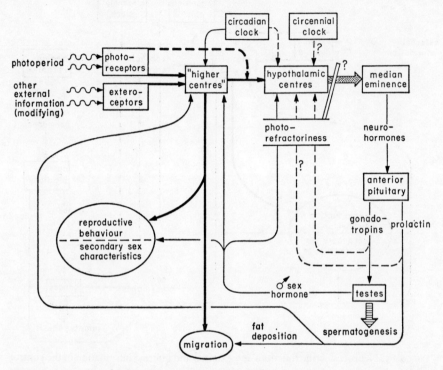

FIGURE 4. Sources of information and neuroendocrine relationships in photoperiodically controlled annual reproductive cycles. A generalized scheme for *Zonotrichia leucophrys gambelii*.

widespread and primitive among organisms (Aschoff, 1961, 1963; Bünning, 1963; Pittendrigh, 1961; Pittendrigh & Minis, 1964); they reside, at least in a large part, at the cellular level, and doubtless originated as primitive adaptations to the 24-hour light-dark cycle of the planet. Circadian periodicities in motor activity (e.g. Aschoff, 1963, 1961, 1963; Aschoff & Wever, 1963) and in food intake (J.R. King, personal communication; Morton, 1966) are well known in birds; these are clearly entrained, under natural conditions by the natural light-dark periodicity. Thanks to the pioneer investigations of Hamner (1963, 1964, 1965 a, b) with

*Carpodacus mexicanus* and confirmatory investigations on *Zonotrichia leucophrys gambelii* (Farner, 1964b, 1965), *Passer domesticus* (Menaker, 1965), and *Junco hyemalis* (Wolfson, 1965), it is now clear (p. 122) that a circadian periodicity is involved in the 'measurement' of the duration of the daily photoperiod in at least some of the photoperiodic species (Figure 5) as has been demonstrated earlier in some plants and insects (see Bünning, 1963, for review).

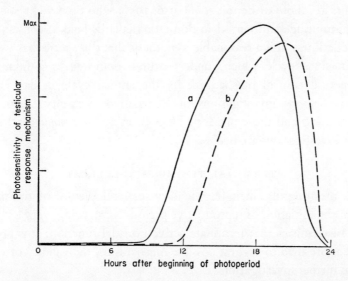

FIGURE 5. Phase-shifting in the circadian or daily photosensitivity function as a possible explanation for the differences in responses of spring and late-autumn birds to daily photoperiods of intermediate duration (e.g. 12 hours). (Based, in part, on Hamner, 1965b.)

Our knowledge of endogenous *circennial periodicities* in the control of avian gonadal cycles is scant and rather unconvincing. If such do exist they must not be as primitive as circadian periodicities since it seems improbable that they could have evolved until relatively long-lived animals evolved and invaded annually periodic environments. Intuitively, it seems probable that such periodicities would have evolved at supracellular (organ) levels rather than at cellular levels of organization. Within our knowledge of the control and feedback relationships among the hypothalamus, anterior pituitary and gonads, the basis for this sort of endogenous periodicity can be envisioned. However, the inevitable variability in these types of function and the problem of synchronization of birds hatched over a considerable span of time during the breeding season lead to the conclusion that such control systems are likely to be successful only if entrained by annual periodicities in the environment. Rather than suggestive field observations and speculative papers, we are sorely in need now of careful observations under constant conditions to ascertain whether gonadal cycles occur in an environment devoid of annually periodic variables. Two consecutive, accurately timed, cycles under such conditions would constitute the minimum evidence for such periodicities; more would be desirable. To date, the only experiments that conform with these requirements are those of Benoit *et al* (1956, 1959) who observed testicular cycles of varying amplitude and period in domestic mallards held in constant light and in constant darkness. It is a reasonable hypothesis that this species has a very crude, variable circennial cycle which, under natural conditions, is entrained, through the photoperiod control mechanism, by the annual cycle in day length. The field and laboratory investigations of Marshall & Serventy (1956, 1959) on *Puffinus tenuirostris* and those of Merkel (1963) on *Sylvia communis* are suggestive, but further investigations are necessary.

## TERMINAL TIMING MECHANISMS

Whereas a meaningful, albeit fragmentary, general picture of the mechanisms involved in the initiation of reproductive periods is emerging, very little is known about the mechanisms that terminate active gonadal function. It is possible now to do little more than to suggest possible mechanisms, the validity of which must be tested in further investigations.

1. *Termination because of cessation of primary external environmental information.* It has been demonstrated that the discontinuation of long daily photoperiods causes testicular regression, for example, in *Sturnus vulgaris* (Burger, 1947, 1949) and *Coturnix coturnix* (Follett & Farner, 1966 a, b). In the latter this may be involved in the natural testicular cycle whereas in *Sturnus vulgaris* the natural termination of testicular activity involves the development of photorefractoriness (Burger 1947, 1949, 1953). In *Taeniopygia castanotis* it appears that cessation of testicular activity may be induced by unavailability of water (Farner & Serventy, unpublished) and that this accounts, in part, for the summer interruption of breeding in south-western Australia (Farner & Serventy, 1960; Immelmann, 1963; see also Frith & Tilt, 1959).

2. *Termination through negative effects of essential supplemental mechanisms or modifying mechanisms* (p. 109). Although it seems probable that reproductive periods may be so terminated on emergency or catastrophic bases, there is no clear evidence that these constitute normal termination mechanisms at the popula-

tion level. However, the apparent rôle of low temperature in the suppression of re-productivity of *T. castanotis* in winter in south-western Australia (Farner & Serventy, 1960; Immelmann, 1963) may be a valid example. Possibly to be included in this category are cessations of breeding by some trophic opportunists, including some desert species.

3. *Termination through negative feedbacks on hypothalamus by gonadal and/or pituitary hormones* (see 2, p. 116). Although such feedbacks are attractive as possible mechanisms for termination of breeding periods, the involvement of a simple negative feedback above would produce an oscillating system. It seems unlikely that such would have a precisely annual periodicity although it is possible that the rate of response to negative feedback could be adaptive. In my opinion, it seems highly likely that negative feedback loops are involved in the termination of seasonal gonadal function but as components of more elaborate mechanisms (see Follett & Farner, 1966, for discussion).

4. *Termination by photorefractoriness in photoperiodic species.* In most truly photo-periodic species, each period of gonadal development, whether naturally or artificially induced, terminates abruptly with a rapid collapse of the gonads and is followed by a photorefractory period in which gonadal growth cannot be induced by long days. The available evidence, although fragmentary, suggests that the site of photorefractoriness is at the level of hypothalamic centres or higher, so that the hypothalamus discontinues its stimulatory effect on the gonadotropic function of the anterior pituitary (see Farner & Follett, 1966, for review and dis-cussion). Although the development of photorefractoriness doubtless involves negative feedbacks, it cannot be explained fully on this basis. In most, if not all, highly photoperiodic species a 'light-lock' is involved so that photosensitivity is not regained, at least within a physiologically reasonable time, without the effect of short daily photoperiods (Farner & Follett, 1966). There is, as yet, no convincing evidence that a similar refractoriness develops in primary timing mechanisms involving external sources of information other than day length.

### THE PHOTOPERIODIC SPECIES

Among the primary timing mechanisms, those of the photoperiodic species are by far the best known. To a great extent this is because of the ease with which the mechanisms can be manipulated experimentally and because of the relatively quantitative nature of the responses (Farner, 1964a, 1965). Photoperiodic mecha-nisms apparently vary considerably in detail reflecting both multiple origins and adaptive evolution. The degree of dependence on photoperiodic mechanisms

# Donald S.Farner

varies from obligately photoperiodic species, such as *Zonotrichia leucophrys gambelii*, in which annual gonadal development is completely dependent on day length, to the domestic mallard in which photoperiodic information may be critically important in the entrainment of a crude circennial cycle. Since photoperiodic controls in avian reproduction have been the subject of several reviews (Assenmacher, 1958; Benoit, 1964a, b; Burger, 1949; Dolnik, 1964; Emme, 1961; Farner, 1959, 1964a, 1965; Farner & Follett, 1966), attention will be directed here only to two or three aspects concerning which comment appears appropriate at this time.

As noted above, an important recent development in our knowledge of the photoperiod control of testicular development is the demonstration that a circadian periodicity in photosensitivity 'measures' the duration of the daily photoperiod and provides a rationalization for the quantitative relationship between day length and the rate of gonadal development demonstrated earlier by Dolnik (1963) and Farner & Wilson (1957). It now seems possible that the entrained periodicity in photosensitivity, by phase-shifting, may explain the puzzling observations that there is a range of photoperiods that are photostimulatory in spring but not in fall after the birds have become photosensitive (Farner, 1962; Wolfson, 1959, 1960a, 1965). The postulated nature of this relationship is shown in Figure 5. This raises the interesting possibility of a circennial periodicity in phase of the circadian periodicity in photosensitivity!

Although its adaptive significance is clear, the mechanism of photorefractoriness remains elusive. Photorefractory mechanisms are best developed in migratory species whose ranges are confined to mid and high latitudes of the northern hemispheres although it has been demonstrated also in non-migratory forms of these latitudes. Photorefractoriness in adults must be regarded as an adaptation that provides discontinuation of gonadal function and reproductive activity while the days are still long, thereby allowing favourable conditions for moult and preparation for fall migration. In young of the year it may be regarded as a device that prevents gonadal development in late summer. The evidence concerning the multiple origin of photorefractory mechanisms and the fragmentary information concerning their nature are summarized by Farner & Follett (1966). The photorefractory mechanisms constitute a most exciting challenge for the experimentalist. The resolution of the nature of these mechanisms would not only be a major contribution to our knowledge of the control of reproductive cycles but also an equally important contribution to our knowledge of the control of the anterior pituitary by the central nervous system. The possibility that the termination of

# The control of avian reproductive cycles

gonadal activity and the development of photorefractoriness are two separate processes must not be overlooked (Laws, 1961; Threadgold, 1960).

## OPPORTUNISTIC DESERT BREEDERS

Of very great interest to a comprehensive understanding of the control of avian reproduction are opportunistic breeders such as those of the parts of the great Australian desert in which rains are aperiodic.

Knowledge of the control mechanisms in these species is fragmentary in the

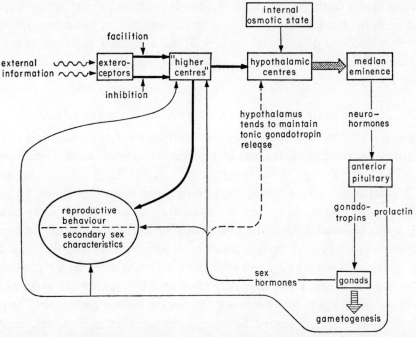

FIGURE 6. A hypothetical scheme for the control of the reproductive activity in an opportunistic breeder, *Taeniopygia castanotis*.

extreme. However, as a stimulus to further research on these interesting species, I propose a hypothetical control scheme (Figure 6) based mainly on observations and a few experiments on *Taeniopygia castanotis* (Farner & Serventy, 1960; Immelmann, 1962, 1963; Marshall & Serventy, 1958; Oksche *et al*, 1963; Serventy & Farner, unpublished experiments). My hypothesis assumes that the gonadotropin-stimulating role of the hypothalamus is essentially tonic, so that gonads are maintained in a functional state as long as the hypothalamus is not inhibited by unfavourable external information such as low environmental temperature and reduced availability of drinking water. High temperatures and availability of drinking water constitute favourable information. The hypothalamus must be relatively insensitive to negative feedback by gonadal and pituitary hormones. This hypothesis is very similar to the hypothesis of 'accelerators and inhibitors' of Marshall (1959) although not with the generality of his original proposal. The hypothesis would account for the annual periodicity in breeding in north-western Australia coinciding with the annual rains, the aperiodic breeding corresponding with the aperiodic rains of the central desert, the tendency toward 'double' breeding season (spring and fall) in the south-west, and the relatively constant breeding in irrigated regions with mild environmental temperatures. The question of an analogue of a 'refractory period' and associated histologic changes in the gonads following cessation of breeding imposed by unfavourable environmental conditions has not been resolved.

## EQUATORIAL AND TRANSEQUATORIAL MIGRANTS

Because research on these species can also contribute very significantly to a comprehensive knowledge of control of reproductive cycles, some comments are appropriate even though useful experimental information is unbelievably sparse. The general aspects of the problem, and some suggestions concerning the nature of the control system, have been discussed for *Motacilla flava* (Curry-Lindahl, 1958, 1963; Marshall & Williams, 1959) and for *Puffinus tenuirostris* (Marshall & Serventy, 1956, 1959). A limited series of experiments by Engels (1959, 1961, 1962, 1964) on *Dolichonyx oryzivorus* suggests very strongly that the control system in this species has a photoperiodic element. The experiments of Marshall & Serventy (1959) suggest that this is not the case for *Puffinus tenuirostris*. The possibility of endogenous circennial functions is often raised as a possible basis for control mechanisms in the reproductive cycles of high-latitude species with equatorial or transequatorial wintering areas. The problems associated with such endogenous periodic functions are discussed on p. 119.

## SUMMARY

The core of the control system for the timing of reproduction in birds, as in other higher vertebrates, includes the hypothalamus, anterior pituitary gland and gonads. The great variety in temporal patterns of reproduction is the result of adaptive evolution with respect to the use and processing of information, internal and external, by the hypothalamus in the control of the gonadotropic functions of the anterior pituitary gland. Species of the mid and high latitudes, as an adaptation to marked annual periodicities in the environment, have developed precise photoperiodic mechanisms as the primary basis for control. Because of their precision and the ease with which they can be manipulated quantitatively under experimental conditions, the photoperiodic mechanisms have received major attention from investigators and are the source of an overwhelming fraction of our knowledge of the timing of reproductive function in birds.

## REFERENCES

ARAI Y. (1963) Diencephalic neurosecretory centers of the passerine bird, *Zosterops palpebrosa japonica. J. Fac. Sci. Univ. Tokyo Sect. IV* **10**, 249–268.

ARAI Y., KAMBARA S. & TAKAHASHI K. (1963) The entopenduncular neurosecretory cell group in the diencephalon of the passerine bird, *Emberiza rustica latifascia. Dobutsugaku Zasshi* **72**, 84–88.

ASCHOFF J. (1953) Aktivitätsperiodik bei Gimpeln unter natürlichen und künstlichen Belichtungsverhältnissen. *Z. Vergleich. Physiol.* **35**, 159–166.

ASCHOFF J. (1955) Jahresperiodik der Fortpflanzung beim Warmblütern. *Studium Generale* **8**, 742–776.

ASCHOFF J. (1961) Biologische Uhren. In *Progress in Photobiology*, pp. 50–62. Ed. B.Chr.Christensen and B.Buchman. Amsterdam.

ASCHOFF J. (1963) Comparative physiology: Diurnal rhythms. *Ann. Rev. Physiol.* **25**, 581–600.

ASCHOFF J. & WEVER R. (1965) Resynchronisation der Tagesperiodik von Vögeln nach Phasensprung des Zeitgebers. *Z. Vergleich. Physiol.* **46**, 321–335.

ASHMOLE N.P. (1962) The Black Noddy *Anous tenuirostris* on Ascension Island. *Ibis* **103b**, 235–275.

ASSENMACHER I. (1952) La vascularisation du complexe hypophysaire chez le canard domestique. *Arch. Anat. Microscop. Morphol. Exp.* **47**, 448–572.

ASSENMACHER I. (1958) Recherches sur le contrôle hypothalamique de la fonction gonadotrope préhypophysaire chez le canard. *Arch. Anat. Microscop. Morphol. Exp.* **47**, 447–572.

ASSENMACHER I. & BAYLÉ J.D. (1964) La sécrétion prolactinique du Pigeon en réponse à differents traitements. *Compt. Rend. Soc. Biol.* **158**, 255–259.

ASSENMACHER I., TIXIER-VIDAL A. & ASTIER H. (1965) Effets de la sous-alimentation et du jeûne sur la gonadostimulation du canard. *Ann. Endocrinol. Paris* **26**, 1–26.

BAILEY R.E. (1950) Inhibition with prolactin of light-induced gonad increase in White-crowned Sparrows. *Condor* **52**, 247–251.

BAKER J.R. (1938) The relation between latitude and breeding seasons in birds. *Proc. Zool. Soc. London* **108**, 557–582.

BAYLÉ J.D. & ASSENMACHER I. (1965) Absence de stimulation du jabot du Pigeon après autogreffe hypophysaire. *Compt. Rend. Acad. Sci. Paris* **261**, 5667–5670.

BENOIT J. (1936) Facteurs externes et internes de l'activité sexuelle. I. Stimulation par la lumière de l'activité sexuelle chez le canard et la cane domestique. *Bull. biol. France Belg.* **70**, 487–533.

# Donald S.Farner

BENOIT J. (1937) Facteurs externes et internes de l'activité sexuelle. II. Étude du mécanisme de la stimulation par la lumière de l'activité testiculaire chez le Canard domestique. Rôle de l'hypophyse. *Bull. biol. France Belg.* **71**, 393-437.

BENOIT J. (1964a) The structural components of the hypothalamo-hypophyseal pathway, with particular reference to photostimulation of the gonads in birds. *Ann. N.Y. Acad. Sci.* **117**, 23-34.

BENOIT J. (1964b) The role of the eye and of the hypothalamus in the photostimulation of gonads in the duck. *Ann. N.Y. Acad. Sci.* **117**, 204-215.

BENOIT J. & ASSENMACHER I. (1953a) Rapport entre la stimulation sexuelle préhypophysaire et la neurosécrétion chez l'oiseau. *Arch. Anat. Microscop. Morphol. Exp.* **42**, 334-386.

BENOIT J. & ASSENMACHER I. (1953b) Action des facteurs externes et plus particulièrement du facteur lumineux sur l'activité sexuelle des oiseaux. *II Réunion des Endocrinologistes de Langue Française* **1953**, 33-80.

BENOIT J. & ASSENMACHER I. (1955) Le contrôle hypothalamique de l'activité préhypophysaire gonadotrope. *J. Physiol. Paris* **47**, 427-567.

BENOIT J., ASSENMACHER I. & BRARD, E. (1956) Apparition et maintien de cycles sexuels non saisonniers chez le Canard domestique placé pendant plus de trois ans à l'obscurite totalé. *J. Physiol. Paris* **48**, 388-391.

BENOIT J., ASSENMACHER I. & BRARD E. (1959) Action d'un éclairement permanent prolongé sur l'évolution testiculaire du canard Pékin. *Arch. Anat. Microscop. Morphol. Exp.* **48**, 5-11.

BERN H.A. & NISHIOKA R.S. (1965) Fine structure of the median eminence of some passerine birds. *Proc. Zool. Soc. Calcutta* **18**, 107-119.

BERN H.A., NISHIOKA R.S., MEWALDT L.R. & FARNER D.S. (1966) Photoperiodic and osmotic influences on the ultrastructure of the hypothalamic neurosecretory system of the White-crowned Sparrow, *Zonotrichia leucophrys gambelii*. *Z. Zellforsch.* **69**, 198-227.

BOUMA P.D. (1936) Broedtijden in de houtvesterij Tjiledoek (Java). *Ardea* **25**, 100-107.

BÜNNING E. (1963) *Die Physiologische Uhr.* Berlin.

BURGER J.W. (1947) On the relation of day-length to the phases of testicular involution and inactivity of the spermatogenetic cycle of the Starling. *J. Exp. Zool.* **105**, 259-267.

BURGER J.W. (1948) The relation of external temperature to spermatogenesis in the male Starling. *J. Exp. Zool.* **109**, 259-266.

BURGER J.W. (1949) A review of investigations on seasonal reproduction in birds. *Wilson Bull.* **61**, 211-230.

BURGER J.W. (1953) The effect of photic and psychic stimuli on the reproductive cycle of the male Starling, *Sturnus vulgaris*. *J. Exp. Zool.* **124**, 227-239.

CHAPIN J.P. (1932) The birds of the Belgian Congo. I. *Bull. Am. Mus. Nat. Hist.* **65**, i-x, 1-756.

COOMANS DE RUITER L. (1931) Broedtijden van vogels in de Westerafdeeling van Borneo. *Tropische Natuur (Buitenzorg)* **20**, 49-55.

CURRY-LINDAHL K. (1958) Internal timer and spring migration in an equatorial migrant, the Yellow Wagtail (*Motacilla flava*). *Arkiv Zool.* **11**, 541-557.

CURRY-LINDAHL K. (1963) Molt, body weights, gonadal development, and migration in *Motacilla flava*. *Proc. XIII Intern. Ornithol. Congr.* **2**, 960-973.

DAVIDSON J.N. (1967) Control of gonadotropin secretion in the male. In *Neuroendocrinology*, vol. 1. Ed. L.Martini and W.F.Ganong. New York (in press).

# The control of avian reproductive cycles

DISNEY H.J.deS. & MARSHALL A.J. (1956) A contribution to the breeding biology of the Weaver-finch *Quelea quelea* (Linnaeus) in East Africa. *Proc. Zool. Soc. London* **127,** 379–387.

DOLNIK V. (1963) Kolichestvennoe issledovanie zakonomernostei vesennovo rosta semennikov u nestolkikh vidov vyurkovykh ptits (Fringillidae). *Dokl. Akad. Nauk SSSR* **149,** 191–193.

DOLNIK V. (1964) O mekhanizme fotoperiodicheskovo kontrolya endogennovao ritm polovoi tsiklichnosti ptits. *Zool. Zh.* **43,** 720–733.

DOLNIK V. (1965) Rol sveta i temnoty v sezonnom izmenenii chusvitelnosti fotoperiodicheskikh regulyatorov u zyablika. *Zool. Zh.* **44,** 1423–1424.

DORWARD D.F. (1962) Comparative biology of the White-faced Booby and the Brown Booby *Sula* ssp. at Ascension. *Ibis* **103b,** 174–220.

EMME A.M. (1960) Fotoperiodicheskaya reaktsiya razmnozheniya. *Uspekhi Sovremennoi Biologii* **49,** 240–259.

ENGELS W.L. (1959) The influence of different day lengths on the testes of a transequatorial migrant, the Bobolink (*Dolichonyx oryzivorus*). In *Photoperiodism and Related Phenomena in Plants and Animals*, pp. 759–766. Ed. R.B.Withrow. Washington, D.C.

ENGELS W.L. (1961) Photoperiodism and the annual testicular cycle of the Bobolink (*Dolichonyx oryzivorus*), a transequatorial migrant, as compared with two temperate zone migrants. *Biol. Bull.* **120,** 140–147.

ENGELS W.L. (1962) Day-length and termination of photorefractoriness in the annual cycle of the transequatorial migrant *Dolichonyx* (the Bobolink). *Biol. Bull.* **123,** 94–104.

ENGELS W.L. (1964) Further observations on the regulation of the annual testicular cycle in Bobo-links (*Dolichonyx oryzivorus*). *Auk* **81,** 95–96.

ENGELS W.L. & JENNER C.E. (1956) The effect of temperature on testicular recrudescence in Juncos at different photoperiods. *Biol. Bull.* **110,** 129–137.

FARNER D.S. (1959) Photoperiodic control of annual gonadal cycles in birds. In *Photoperiodism and Related Phenomena in Plants and Animals*, pp. 717–750. Ed. R.B.Withrow. Washington, D.C.

FARNER D.S. (1961) Comparative physiology: Photoperiodicity. *Ann. Rev. Physiol.* **23,** 71–96.

FARNER D.S. (1962) Hypothalamic neurosecretion and phosphatase activity in relation to the photoperiodic control of the testicular cycle of *Zonotrichia leucophrys gambelii*. *Gen. Comp. Endocrinol.* **1** (Suppl.), 160–167.

FARNER D.S. (1964a) The photoperiodic control of reproductive cycles in birds. *Am. Scientist* **52,** 137–156.

FARNER D.S. (1964b) Time measurement in vertebrate photoperiodism. *Am. Naturalist* **98,** 375–386.

FARNER D.S. (1965) Circadian systems in the photoperiodic responses of vertebrates. In *Circadian Clocks* (Proceedings of the Feldafing Summer School, September 7–18, 1964, pp. 357–369. Ed. J.Aschoff. Amsterdam.

FARNER D.S. & FOLLETT B.K. (1966) Light and other environmental factors affecting avian repro-duction. *J. Animal Sci.* **25,** (suppl.), 90–118.

FARNER D.S. & MEWALDT L.R. (1952) The relative roles of photoperiod and temperature in gonadal recrudescence in male *Zonotrichia leucophrys gambelii*. *Anat. Record* **113,** 612–613.

FARNER D.S. & OKSCHE A. (1962) Neurosecretion in birds. *Gen. Comp. Endocrinol.* **2,** 113–147.

FARNER D.S. & SERVENTY D.L. (1960) The timing of reproduction in birds in the arid regions of Australia. *Anat. Record* **137,** 354.

FARNER D.S. & WILSON A.C. (1957) A quantitative examination of testicular growth in the White-crowned Sparrow. *Biol. Bull.* **113**, 254–267.

FARNER D.S., OKSCHE A. & LORENZEN L. (1962) Hypothalamic neurosecretion and the photoperiodic testicular response in the White-crowned Sparrow, *Zonotrichia leucophrys gambelii*. *Mem. Soc. Endocrinol.* **12**, 187–197.

FARNER D.S., WILSON F.E. & OKSCHE A. (1967) Neuroendocrine mechanisms in birds. In *Neuroendocrinology* vol. 2. Ed L.Martini and W.F.Ganong. New York (in press).

FLERKÓ B. (1963) The central nervous system and the secretion and release of luteinizing hormone and follicle stimulating hormone. In *Advances in Neuroendocrinology*, pp. 211–224. Ed. A.V. Nalbandov. Urbana, Illinois.

FLERKÓ B. (1967) Control of gonadotropin secretion in the female. In *Neuroendocrinology* vol. 2. Ed. L.Martini and W.F.Ganong. New York (in press).

FOLLETT B.K. & FARNER D.S. (1966a) The effects of daily photoperiod on gonadal growth, neurohypophysial hormone content and neurosecretion in the hypothalamo-hypophysial system of the Japanese Quail (*Coturnix coturnix japonica*). *Gen. Comp. Endocrinol.* **7**, 111–124.

FOLLETT B.K. & FARNER D.S. (1966b) Pituitary gonadotrophins in the Japanese Quail, *Coturnix coturnix japonica*, during photoperiodically induced gonadal growth. *Gen. Comp. Endocrinol.* **7**, 125–131.

FRITH H.J. & DAVIES S.J.J.F. (1961) Breeding seasons of birds in subcoastal northern territory. *Emu* **61**, 97–111.

FRITH H.J. & TILT R.A. (1959) Breeding of the Zebra Finch in the Murrumbidgee Irrigation Area, New South Wales. *Emu* **59**, 289–295.

GEORGE J.C. & NAIK D.V. (1965) The hypothalamo-hypophysial neurosecretory system of the migratory starling *Sturnus roseus* (Linnaeus). *J. Anim. Morph. Physiol.* **12**, 42–56.

GOGAN F., KORDON C. & BENOIT J. (1963) Retentissement de lésions de l'éminence médiane sur la gonadostimulation du Canard. *Compt. Rend. Soc. Biol.* **157**, 2133–2136.

GRABER J.W. & NALBANDOV A.V. (1965) Neurosecretion in the White Leghorn cockerel. *Gen. Comp. Endocrinol.* **5**, 485–492.

GREEN J.D. (1951) The comparative anatomy of the hypophysis, with special reference to its blood supply and innervation. *Am. J. Anat.* **88**, 225–311.

GRIGNON G. (1956) Développement du complexe hypothalamo-hypophysaire chez l'embryon de poulet. Thèse, Nancy. S.I.T.

HAMNER W.H. (1963) Diurnal rhythm and photoperiodism in testicular recrudescence of the House Finch. *Science* **142**, 1294–1295.

HAMNER W.H. (1964) Circadian control of photoperiodism in the House Finch demonstrated by interrupted-night experiments. *Nature* **203**, 1400–1401.

HAMNER W.H. (1965a) Avian photoperiodic response-rhythms: Evidence and inference. In *Circadian Clocks* (Proceedings of the Feldafing Summer School, September 7–18, 1964), pp. 379–384. Ed. J.Aschoff. Amsterdam.

HAMNER W.H. (1965b) Photoperiodic refractoriness: Re-evaluation and interpretation. *Am. Zoologist* **5**, 681–682.

HARRIS G.W. (1955) Neural control of the pituitary gland. *Monographs of the Physiol Soc.* **3**, i–viii, 1–298.

# The control of avian reproductive cycles

HARRIS G.W. (1960) Central control of pituitary secretion. In *Handbook of Physiology*, Section 1: Neurophysiology, vol. II, pp. 1007–1038. Washington, D.C.

HEIM DE BALSAC A. (1952) Rythme sexual et fécondité chez les oiseaux du nord-ouest de l'Afrique. *Alauda* **20**, 213–242.

HINDE R.A. (1965) Interaction of internal and external factors in integration of canary reproduction. In *Sex and Behavior*, pp. 381–415. Ed. F.A.Beach. New York.

HIRANO T., ISHII S. & KOBAYASHI H. (1962) Effects of prolongation of daily photoperiod on gonadal development and neurohypophyseal hormone activity in the median eminence and the pars nervosa of the passerine bird, *Zosterops palpebrosa japonica. Annotationes Zool. Japon.* **35**, 64–71.

IMMELMANN K. (1962) Beiträge zu einer vergleichenden Biologie australisher Prachtfinken (Spermestidae). *Zool. Jahrb. Abt. Systematik u. Oekologie* **90**, 1–196.

IMMELMANN K. (1963) Tierische Jahresperiodik in ökologischer Sicht. *Zool. Jahrb. Abt. Systematik u. Oekologie* **91**, 91–200.

JACOBS M.S. & MORGANE P.J. (1964) Retino-hypothalamic connexions in cetacea. *Nature* **203**, 778–780.

KEAST A. (1959) Australian birds: Their zoogeography and adaptations to an arid continent. *Monograph. Biol.* **8**, 89–114.

KING J.R. & FARNER D.S. (1965) Studies of fat deposition in migratory birds. *Ann. N.Y. Acad. Sci.* **131**, 422–440.

KNOCHE H. (1956) Morphologisch-experimentelle Untersuchungen über eine Faserverbindung der Retina mit den vegetativen Zentren des Zwischenhirnes und mit der Hypophyse. *Z. Zellforsch. Mikroskop. Anat.* **45**, 201–264.

KNOCHE H. (1960) Ursprung, Verlauf und Endigung der retino-hypothalamischen Bahn. *Z. Zellforsch. Mikroskop. Anat.* **51**, 658–704.

KOBAYASHI H., BERN H.A., NISHIOKA R.S. & HYODO Y. (1961) The hypothalamo-hypophyseal neurosecretory system of the Parakeet, *Melopsittacus undulatus. Gen. Comp. Endocrinol.* **1**, 545–564.

KOBAYASHI H. & FARNER D.S. (1966) Evidence of a negative feedback on photoperiodically induced gonadal development in the White-crowned Sparrow, *Zonotrichia leucophrys gambelii. Gen. Comp. Endocrinol.* **6**, 443–452.

KRAGT C.L. & MEITES J. (1965) Stimulation of pigeon pituitary prolactin release by pigeon hypothalamic extract *in vitro. Endocrinology* **76**, 1169–1176.

LACK D. (1950a) Breeding seasons in the Galapagos. *Ibis* **92**, 268–278.

LACK D. (1950b) The breeding seasons of European birds. *Ibis* **92**, 288–316.

LAWS D.F. (1961) Hypothalamic neurosecretion in the refractory and post-refractory periods and its relationship to the rate of photoperiodically induced testicular growth in *Zonotrichia leucophrys gambelii. Z. Zellforsch.* **54**, 275–306.

LAWS D.F. & FARNER D.S. (1960) Prolactin and the photoperiodic testicular response in White-crowned Sparrows. *Endocrinology* **67**, 279–281.

LEGAIT H. (1959) Contribution à l'étude morphologique et expérimentale du système hypothalamo-neurohypophysaire de la Poule Rhode-Island. Thèse, Louvain-Nancy. S.I.T.

LEHRMAN D.S. (1959a) Hormonal responses to external stimuli in birds. *Ibis* **101**, 478–496.

LEHRMAN D.S. (1959b) On the origin of the reproductive behavior cycle in doves. *Trans. N.Y. Acad. Sci.* **21**, 682–688.

LEHRMAN D.S. (1961) Gonadal hormones and parental behavior in birds and infrahuman mammals. In *Sex and Internal Secretions*, pp. 1268–1382. Ed. W.C.Young. Baltimore.

LEHRMAN D.S. (1964) Control of behavior cycles in reproduction. In *Social Behavior and Organization among Vertebrates*, pp. 143–166. Ed. W.Etkin. Chicago.

LISK R.D. & KANNWISCHER L.R. (1964) Light: Evidence for its direct effect on hypothalamic neurons. *Science* **146**, 272–273.

LOFTS B. & MARSHALL A.J. (1956) The effects of prolactin administration on the internal rhythm of reproduction in male birds. *J. Endocrinol.* **13**, 101–106.

MA R.C.S. & NALBANDOV A.V. (1963) Physiology of the pituitary gland as affected by transplantation or stalk transection: Discussion. In *Advances in Neuroendocrinology*, pp. 306–311. Ed. A.V.Nalbandov. Urbana, Illinois.

MACGREGOR W. Jr. & INLAY M. (1951) Observations on failure of Gambel quail to breed. *Calif. Fish Game* **37**, 218–219.

MARSHALL A.J. (1959) Breeding biology and physiology: Internal and environmental control of breeding. *Ibis* **101**, 456–478.

MARSHALL A.J. (1960) The environment, cyclical reproductive activity and behaviour in birds. *Symp. Zool. Soc. London* **2**, 53–67.

MARSHALL A.J. (1961) Breeding seasons and migration. In *Biology and Comparative Physiology of Birds*, vol. 2, pp. 307–339. Ed. A.J.Marshall. New York.

MARSHALL A.J. & DISNEY H.J.deS. (1957) Experimental induction of the breeding season in a xerophilous bird. *Nature* **180**, 647–649.

MARSHALL A.J. & SERVENTY D.L. (1956) The breeding cycle of the Short-tailed Shearwater, *Puffinus tenuirostris* (Temminck), in relation to transequatorial migration and its environment. *Proc. Zool. Soc. London* **127**, 489–510.

MARSHALL A.J. & SERVENTY D.L. (1958) The internal rhythm of reproduction in xerophilous birds under conditions of illumination and darkness. *J. Exp. Biol.* **35**, 666–670.

MARSHALL A.J. & SERVENTY D.L. (1959) Experimental demonstration of an internal rhythm of reproduction in a trans-equatorial migrant (the Short-tailed Shearwater *Puffinus tenuirostris*). *Nature* **184**, 1704–1705.

MARSHALL A.J. & WILLIAMS M.C. (1959) The pre-nuptial migration of the Yellow Wagtail (*Motacilla flava*) from latitude 0.04′ N. *Proc. Zool. Soc. London* **132**, 313–320.

MEDWAY Lord (1962) The relation between the reproductive cycle, moult and changes in the sublingual salivary glands of the swiftlet *Collocalia maxima* Hume. *Proc. Zool. Soc. London* **138**, 305–315.

MEIER A.H. & FARNER D.S. (1964) A possible endocrine basis for premigratory fattening in the White-crowned Sparrow, *Zonotrichia leucophrys gambelii* (Nuttal). *Gen. Comp. Endocrinol.* **4**, 584–595.

MEIER A.H., FARNER D.S. & KING J.R. (1965) A possible endocrine basis for migratory behaviour in the White-crowned Sparrow, *Zonotrichia leucophrys gambelii*. *Animal Behaviour* **13**, 453–465.

MENAKER M. (1965) Circadian rhythms and photoperiodism in *Passer domesticus*. In *Circadian*

*Clocks* (Proceedings of the Feldafing Summer School September 7–18, 1964), pp. 385–395. Ed. J.Aschoff. Amsterdam.

MERKEL F.W. (1963) Long-term effects of constant photoperiods on European robins and white-throats. *Proc. XIII Intern. Ornithol. Congr.* **2**, 950–959.

MEYER O. (1930) Uebersicht über die Brutzeiten der Vögel auf der Insel Vuatom (New Britain). *J. Ornithol.* **78**, 19–38.

MIKAMI S. (1960) The structure of the hypothalamo-hypophysial neurosecretory system in the fowl and its morphological changes following adrenalectomy, thyroidectomy and castration. *J. Fac. Agr. Iwate Univ.* **4**, 359–379.

MILLER A.H. (1962) Bimodal occurrence of breeding in an equatorial sparrow. *Proc. Nat. Acad. Sci. U.S.* **48**, 396–400.

MILLER A.H. (1963) Seasonal activity and ecology of the avifauna of an American equatorial cloud forest. *Univ. Calif. Berkely Publ. Zool.* **66**, 1–78.

MILLER A.H. (1965) Capacity for photoperiodic response and endogenous factors in the reproductive cycles of an equatorial sparrow. *Proc. Nat. Acad. Sci. U.S.* **54**, 97–101.

MOREAU R.E. (1950) The breeding seasons of African birds. 1. Land birds. *Ibis* **92**, 223–267.

MOREL G. & BOURLIÈRE F. (1956) Recherches écologiques sur les *Quelea quelea quelea* (L.) de la basse vallée du Sénégal. II. La reproduction. *Alauda* **24**, 97–122.

MOREL G., MOREL M.-Y. & BOURLIÈRE F. (1957) The Blackfaced Weaverbird or Dioch in West Africa: An ecological study. *J. Bombay Nat. Hist. Soc.* **54**, 1–15.

MORTON M.L. (1966) Diurnal feeding patterns in relation to photoperiodically induced hyperphagia and fattening. Thesis, Washington State University. Pullman.

NOVIKOV B.G. & RUDNEVA L.M. (1964) Zavisimost funktsii yaichnika u utok ot gipotalamusa. *Zh. Obshch. Biol.* **25**, 390–393.

OISHI T., KONISHI T. & KATO M. (1966) Investigations of photoreceptor mechanisms in the control of gonadal development in the Japanese Quail (in Japanese). *Environ. Control. Biol.* **3**, 37–90.

OKSCHE A. (1962a) The fine nervous neurosecretory and glial structure of the median eminence in the White-crowned Sparrow. *Mem. Soc. Endocrinol.* **12**, 199–206.

OKSCHE A. (1962b) Über die anatomische Verknüpfung des Hypothalamus mit der Hypophyse. *Anat. Anz.* **111**, 236–244.

OKSCHE A. (1965) The fine structure of the neurosecretory system of birds in relation to its functional aspects. *Proc. II Intern. Congr. Endocrinol. London 1964*, pp. 167–171.

OKSCHE A., FARNER D.S., SERVENTY D.L., WOLFF F. & NICHOLLS C.A. (1963) The hypothalamo-hypophysial neurosecretory system of the Zebra Finch, *Taeniopygia castanotis*. *Z. Zellforsch.* **58**, 846–914.

OKSCHE A., LAWS D.F., KAMEMOTO F.I. & FARNER D.S. (1959) The hypothalamo-hypophysial neurosecretory system of the White-crowned Sparrow, *Zonotrichia leucophrys gambelii*. *Z. Zellforsch.* **51**, 1–42.

OKSCHE A., MAUTNER W. & FARNER D.S. (1964) Das räumliche Bild des neurosekretorischen Systems der Vögel unter normalen und experimentallen Bedingungen. *Z. Zellforsch.* **64**, 83–100.

OKSCHE A., WILSON W.O. & FARNER D.S. (1964) The hypothalamic neurosecretory system of *Coturnix coturnix japonica*. *Z. Zellforsch.* **61**, 688–709.

# Donald S.Farner

PHILLIPS R.E. (1964) 'Wildness' in the mallard duck: Effects of brain lesions and stimulation on 'escape behavior' and reproduction. *J. Comp. Neurol.* **122**, 139–155.

PHILLIPS R.E. & VAN TIENHOVEN A. (1960) Endocrine factors involved in the failure of pintail ducks *Anas acuta* to reproduce in captivity. *J. Endocrinol.* **21**, 253–261.

PITTENDRIGH C.S. (1961) On temporal organization in living systems. *Harvey Lectures* **56**, 93–125.

PITTENDRIGH C.S. & MINIS D.H. (1964) Symposium on time measurement in photoperiodic phenomena. The entrainment of circadian oscillations by light and their role as photoperiodic clocks. *Am. Naturalist* **98**, 261–294.

RIDDLE O. (1963) Prolactin in vertebrate function and organization. *J. Nat. Cancer Inst.* **31**, 1039–1110.

SAWYER C.H. (1964) Control of secretion of gonadotropins. In *Gonadotropins*, pp. 113–170. Ed. H.H.Cole. San Francisco.

SCHARRER E. & SCHARRER B. (1963) *Neuroendocrinology*. New York.

SCHILDMACHER H. (1956) Physiologische Untersuchungen am Grünfinken, *Chloris chloris*, im künstlichen Kurztag und nach 'hormonaler Sterilisierung'. *Biol. Zentralblatt* **75**, 327–355.

SCHILDMACHER H. (1963) Photoperiodischer Effekt und spektrales Helligkeitsempfinden bei einigen Vogelarten. *Biol. Zentralblatt* **82**, 31–44.

SERVENTY D.L. & MARSHALL A.J. (1957) Breeding periodicity in western Australian birds: With an account of unseasonal nestings in 1953 and 1955. *Emu* **57**, 99–126.

SKUTCH A.F. (1950) The nesting seasons of Central American birds in relation to climate and food supply. *Ibis* **92**, 185–222.

SPATZ H. (1954) Das Hypophysen-Hypothalamus-System in seiner Bedeutung für die Fortpflanzung. *Verhandl. anat. Ges. (Mainz)* **14**, 46–85.

SZENTAGOTHAI J., FLERKÓ B., MESS B. & HALASZ B. *Hypothalamic Control of the Anterior Pituitary.* Akadémiai Kiadó, Budapest.

THREADGOLD L.T. (1960) Testicular response of the House Sparrow, *Passer domesticus*, to short photoperiods and low intensities. *Physiol. Zool.* **33**, 190–205.

VAN TIENHOVEN A. (1961) Endocrinology of reproduction in birds. In *Sex and Internal Secretion*, pp. 1088–1169. Ed. W.C.Young. Baltimore.

TIXIER-VIDAL A. (1963) Histophysiologie de l'adénohypophyse des oiseaux. *Colloques Intern. Centre Nat. Rech. Sci. Paris* **128**, 255–273.

TIXIER-VIDAL A. (1965) Caracteres ultrastructuraux des types cellulaires de l'adénohypophyse du Canard mâle. *Arch. Anat. Microscop. Morphol. Exp.* **54**, 719–780.

TIXIER-VIDAL A. & ASSENMACHER I. (1966) Étude cytologique de la prehypophyse du pigeon pendant la couvaison et la lactation. *Z. Zellforsch.* **69**, 489–519.

UEMURA H. & KOBAYASHI H. (1963) Effects of prolonged daily photoperiods and estrogen on the hypothalamic neurosecretory system of the passerine bird, *Zosterops palpebrosa japonica*. *Gen. Comp. Endocrinol.* **3**, 253–264.

VAN BRUNT E.E., SHEPHERD M.D., WALL J.R., GANONG W.F. & CLEGG M.T. (1964) Penetration of light into the brain of mammals. *Ann. N.Y. Acad. Sci.* **117**, 217–224.

VITUMS A., MIKAMI S.-I., OKSCHE A. & FARNER D.S. (1964) Vascularization of the hypothalamo-hypophysial complex in the White-crowned Sparrow, *Zonotrichia leucophrys gambelii*. *Z. Zellfessch.* **64**, 541–569.

# The control of avian reproductive cycles

Voous K.H. (1950) The breeding seasons of birds in Indonesia. *Ibis* **92**, 279–287.

Wagner H.O. & Stresemann E. (1950) Über die Beziehungen zwischen Brutzeit und Ökologie mexikanischer Vögel. *Zool. Jahrb. Abt. Systematik u. Oekologie* **79**, 273–308.

Wilson F.E. & Farner D.S. (1965) Effects of hypothalamic lesions on testicular growth. *Federation Proc.* **24**, 129.

Wingstrand K.G. (1951) *The Structure and Development of the Avian Pituitary.* Lund.

Wolfson A. (1959) Role of light and darkness in regulation of refractory period in gonadal and fat cycles of migratory birds. *Physiol. Zool.* **32**, 160–176.

Wolfson A. (1960a) Regulation of animal periodicity in the migration of birds. *Cold Spring Harbor Symp. Quant. Biol.* **25**, 507–514.

Wolfson A. (1960b) Role of light and darkness in the regulation of the annual stimulus for spring migration and reproductive cycles. *Proc. XII Intern. Ornithol. Congr. Helsinki 1958*, pp. 758–789.

Wolfson A. (1963) The role of light in the neuroendocrine system: Discussion. In *Advances in Neuroendocrinology*, pp. 402–425. Ed. A.V.Nalbandov. Urbana, Illinois.

Wolfson A. (1965) Light and endocrine events in birds: Role of the dark period and circadian rhythms in the regulation of the gonadal cycle. *Arch. Anat. Microscop. Morphol. Exp.* **54**, 579–600.

Wolfson A. & Kobayashi H. (1962) Phosphatase activity and neurosecretion in the hypothalamo-hypophyseal system in relation to the photoperiodic gonadal response in *Zonotrichia albicollis*. *Gen. Comp. Endocrinol.* **1** (Suppl.), 168–179.

Zedlitz und Trützschler, O. Graf (1911) Einiges von den Brutzeiten afrikanischer Vögel. *Verhandl. V Internat. Orn. Kongr. Berlin*, pp. 323–330.

# Aspects of the control of avian reproductive development within the breeding season

R.A.HINDE

Sub-Department of Animal Behaviour, Madingley, Cambridge

The ultimate factors limiting the breeding season are still not known precisely for any bird, but a food supply adequate to satisfy the female's heavy requirements during egg-laying, or to meet the demands of the growing young, is certainly a major issue (Lack, 1966). The proximate factors which initiate and terminate breeding have been discussed by Professor Farner in his paper to this Congress: here, the synchronization and integration of reproductive activities within the breeding season are discussed.

This problem has recently been the subject of a comprehensive review by Lehrman (1961) which is the more valuable because of the diversity of species to which it refers. It shows, however, not only that the information available for any one species refers to only limited aspects of its reproduction, but also that the mechanisms involved often differ radically between species, so that cross-species generalizations are hazardous. Clearly the need is for comprehensive studies of a few phylogenetically and ecologically diverse species: only when these are available can the limitations of generalizations be assessed with any confidence. I shall therefore attempt, not to extend Lehrman's review, but to illustrate some of the issues involved from studies of the pre-laying behaviour of the domesticated canary *Serinus canarius* which are in progress at Madingley,* drawing primarily on Lehrman's own experiments on the phylogenetically distant ring-dove *Streptopelia risoria* for a preliminary assessment of the generality of the conclusions. In concentrating on these species, I shall refer to others mainly to highlight differences, and only occasionally to extend the problems discussed.

A logical first step is to describe the behavioural changes within the breeding

* Much of the work cited here was carried out in collaboration with a number of colleagues— Elizabeth Steel, Roslyn P.Warren, R.Q.Bell, W.Baum, Rosemary Hutchison and Sheila Miller. I would also like to express my gratitude to Rosemary Hutchison for reading the manuscript, and to both her, Sheila Miller and W.Baum for agreeing to the use of previously unpublished material.

season, and then to search for temporal coincidences between these and physiological changes. The temporal association between sexual behaviour and nest-building, valid for canaries (Figure 1) as well as for many other species, provides a starting point. These two activities both regularly reach their peak some days before egg-laying: this indicates that a rather constant series of endocrine changes must be occurring at this time.

Now this period of maximum nest-building (Figure 2, a–d) and sexual behaviour is also one of rapid ovarian development. In seasonally breeding birds,

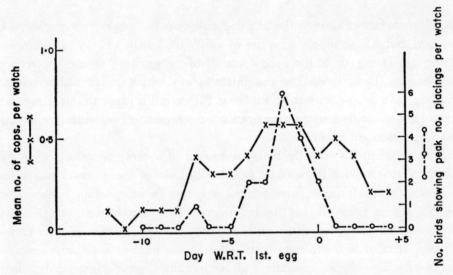

FIGURE 1. Relation of copulation and nest-building to date on which first egg was laid.

the ovarian follicles increase slowly in size during the pre-breeding and early breeding season, but then grow rapidly in the week or so before ovulation (Romanoff & Romanoff, 1949; see also Petersen, 1955; Marshall & Coombs, 1957). The coincidence between increased ovarian activity and nest-building was established directly for canaries. Females were confined singly and provided with a bare nest-pan and a supply of nest material. The number of pieces of grass which had been removed from the dispenser and placed in the nest-pan or scattered on the floor provided a sensitive measure of nest-building activity (Miller, 1965), the cup and cage being cleared daily. Females were sacrificed as certain criteria of building behaviour were reached. As shown in Figure 3, the ovaries increased little in weight between building stages 0 and 3a. However, weight is not a reliable index of the endocrine activity of the ovary. Since ovarian hormones also influence oviduct growth, the weight of the oviduct provides for some purposes a better index of ovarian endocrine activity than the weight of the ovary itself. The oviduct does in fact show an increase in weight from stage 2 of building (Figure 4).

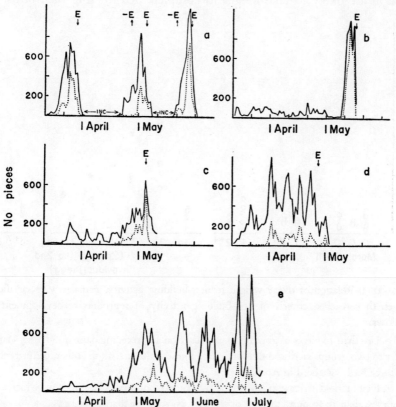

FIGURE 2. Changes in nest-building activity through the season of five individual unpaired females. The building activity was assessed in terms of the number of pieces of grass removed from the dispenser (continuous lines) or placed in the nest-pan (dotted lines), the nest-pan and cage floor being cleaned daily. E indicates date of laying of first egg of clutch. — E indicates date egg was removed by the experimenter. (a) A female which laid three times, incubating between. (b) A female which showed little building until just before she laid late in the season. (c) and (d) Females which showed marked and roughly cyclical fluctuations in building before laying. (e) A female which showed fluctuating building but did not lay.

Now the canary and many other species, but not apparently the ring-dove, develop a brood patch around the time of egg-laying: the ventral surfaces become defeathered, vascular and, later, oedematous. Since the brood patch is externally visible and its development is hormonally controlled, it provides a useful index of endocrine state. In female canaries the changes in defeathering and vascularity may start some weeks before egg-laying. Birds which lay their first egg late in the season are likely to take longer to complete defeathering than birds which

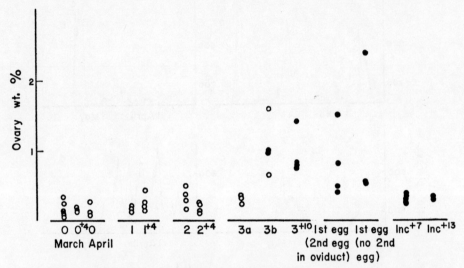

FIGURE 3. Relation of ovary weight to nest-building activity. Females were sacrificed when they reached criteria of nest-building activity or reproductive development as follows:

o. Less than 10 pieces of grass on floor of cage on all preceding days. o and o+4 March refer to two groups sacrificed in March, one four days later than the other. o April refers to three birds sacrificed in April.

1. First marked increase in amount of grass on floor of cage. The criteria were increased from less than 10 to more than 30 or less than 20 to more than 40 pieces.

$1^{+4}$. Four days after reaching criterion 1.

2. Three to five pieces placed in nest-pan on 2 successive days.

$2^{+4}$. Four days after reaching criterion 2.

3a. More than fifty pieces in nest-pan on 2 successive days.

3b. As 3a, but grass woven into a ring.

$3^{+10}$. Ten days after criterion 3a reached, but no egg laid.

1st egg, 2nd egg in oviduct. The day the first egg was laid, a second egg being found in the oviduct on autopsy.

1st egg, no 2nd egg. As previous category, but no egg in oviduct.

$Inc^{+7}$. Incubating, 7 days after the laying of the first egg.

$Inc^{+13}$. Incubating, 13 days after the laying of the first egg.

Each point refers to one individual: solid dots indicate the brood patch was completely defeathered and moderately vascular.

138

lay earlier, but also complete defeathering longer before egg-laying (Figure 5). Vascularization, to an extent that a network of vessels is clearly visible on visual inspection (stage 3 on our rating scale), usually occurs a day or two before egg-laying in birds which subsequently incubate the eggs that they lay, but again the

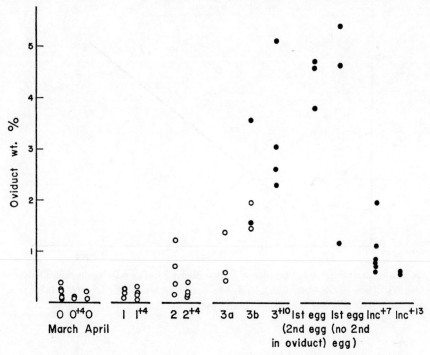

FIGURE 4. Relation of oviduct weight to nest-building activity. Conventions as in Figure 3.

interval increases the later the egg is laid (Figure 6). These changes in the relationship of brood patch development to egg-laying with the egg-laying date show that birds which lay late in the season usually do so not because their pre-breeding reproductive development started late, but because all stages of that development, at any rate up to the last few days, were prolonged.

There is, however, a rather constant relation between the completion of defeathering and vascularity stage 2 (blood vessels just visible to surface inspection). The median interval was 1.5 and −2.6 days in two studies on paired females, and −4 days for females kept without males, and in all these studies the interval was independent of the date of egg-laying (Figure 7).

Completion of defeathering and vascularity stage 2 are also closely related to the onset of intense building behaviour. In one study of paired females, where the criterion was the first record of placing material in the nest in thrice weekly 12-minute watches, no material being available at other times, the interval from

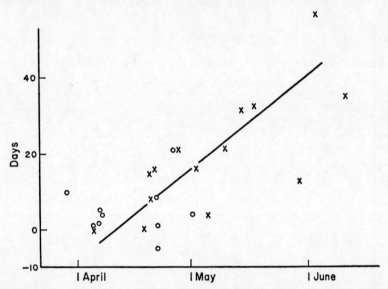

FIGURE 5. Interval between completion of defeathering and egg-laying in paired females. Abscissa—Date of 1st egg. Circles refer to first clutches which were not incubated, crosses to those which were. (From Hinde, 1962.)

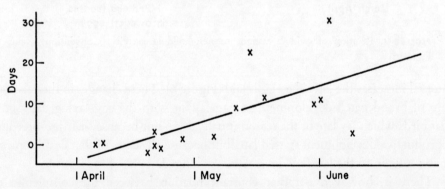

FIGURE 6. Interval between first appearance of vascularity stage 3 and egg-laying in paired females. Conventions as in Figure 5. (From Hinde, 1962.)

this criterion of building to the completion of defeathering increased only slowly with the season: once the building criterion was reached, defeathering would be completed 7-10 days later (regression line $y = 0.22x + 2.9$). In a later study unpaired females were allowed nest-building material all the time, but the material was removed from the cage floor and nest-cup daily. Here the start of intense building was taken as the mean of the day on which more than 220 pieces of material were taken from the dispenser, and that on which more than 50 pieces were found in the nest-cup, some exceptions to these criteria being made for birds whose general level of building was exceptionally low or high. Again, intense building usually started before the completion of defeathering and moderate vascularity (stage 2), and the interval changed little with the season (Figures 8 and 9, $y = -0.13x + 14$ and $y = -0.08x + 6$ respectively).

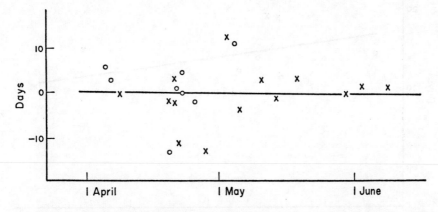

FIGURE 7. Interval between completion of defeathering and vascularity stage 2 in paired females. Conventions as in Figure 5. (From Hinde, 1962.)

The data thus indicate that the first occurrences of vascularity stage 2, complete defeathering, and intensive building, are fairly closely correlated, and mark the achievement of a certain stage of reproductive development at just that time when the oviduct is increasing in size. The date at which this is reached is, however, later, and the further interval before egg-laying longer, for birds which lay late in the season than for those which lay early. This lengthening of the phases of reproductive development, shown by birds which lay late in the season, is presumably mainly due to the levels of the relevant hormones changing more slowly in the late layers than in the early ones, so that the thresholds for the various criteria are reached at more widely spaced intervals.

However, although canaries which lay late in the season show a lengthening of most phases of reproductive development, their development is not simply progressive. Rather, many late layers show successive bursts of reproductive behaviour, followed at first by temporary regressions, and only in the end by egg-laying. This was shown clearly by data for the number of pieces of grass pulled from a dispenser by unpaired female canaries: such individuals, lacking stimulation from males, showed protracted reproductive development, and the building behaviour of many varied in an approximately cyclical fashion with a

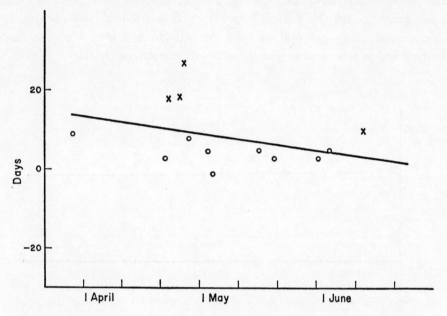

FIGURE 8. Interval between first intense building (see text) and completion of defeathering in unpaired females. The crosses refer to birds which showed nest-building fluctuating to over 200 pieces of grass removed from the dispenser per day before the building outburst in the few days before egg-laying, as in Figure 2(d).

period of 7–10 days. Some examples selected to show this are given in Figure 2, c–e.

That reproductive development may be intermittent rather than progressive was also suggested by data from a quite different source. The tactile sensitivity of the canary's brood patch increases as the date of egg-laying approaches. The increase in sensitivity is rather irregular, but large increases are especially likely to occur on days − 1/− 2, − 9/− 10 and − 18/− 19 with respect to egg-laying— again suggesting the occurrence of some underlying physiological change with a roughly regular periodicity (Hinde, Bell & Steel, 1963). There is, however, as yet no evidence of this sort for other seasonally breeding species.

# Avian reproductive development within the breeding season

Since such fluctuations are not in phase amongst the various individuals in a colony, they appear to be independent of changes in the physical environment, though of course changes in the stimuli to which the bird exposes itself may play a role. A possible hypothesis is that each incomplete burst of reproductive behaviour is correlated with the maturation of a group of ovarian follicles which cease

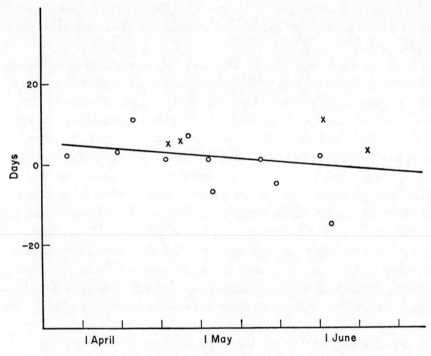

FIGURE 9. Interval between first intense building and stage 2 vascularity. Conventions as in Figure 8.

to develop and become atretic before ovulation. Such regression is known to occur with inadequate external stimulation in the ring-dove. In this species ovulation can, under certain experimental conditions, be induced by stimulation from a male. If the stimulation is of too limited duration, however, a large proportion of atretic follicles are found in the ovary (Lehrman, Wortis & Brody, 1961).

Although these fluctuations in the female canary's building behaviour seem to be independent of changes in the physical environment, the overall course of the female's development is much influenced by external factors. The roles of light and temperature in initiating breeding have already been discussed by

Professor Farner, but two types of stimulation within the breeding season itself must be mentioned. The first is that provided by the sex partner. It has long been known that female pigeons kept without males lay much later than females kept with males, if at all, and Lehrman, Brody & Wortis (1961) have shown that association with a mate induces oviduct growth, ovulation and incubation behaviour in female ring-doves. The same is true of canaries (Warren & Hinde, 1961b; Baum, unpublished). In some species, at least, the effect is reciprocal, the presence of the female also accelerating reproductive development in the male (Burger, 1953).

The precise stimuli provided by the sex partner clearly vary between species: Matthews (1939) showed that visual and auditory stimulation were sufficient and tactile stimulation unnecessary in pigeons, and in doves visual stimuli from a courting male are more effective than those from a castrated one (Erickson & Lehrman, 1964). In budgerigars sounds alone are effective (Vaugien, 1951; Ficken, van Tienhoven, Ficken & Sibley, 1960), and Brockway (1956) has shown that a particular vocalization of the male, which is normally associated with courtship, induces ovarian activity and egg-laying in females, while other vocalizations produce much smaller effects. Female canaries paired with males laid earlier than females alone in adjoining cages which could see and hear the male and female pairs: presumably it is important either that there should be tactile contact, or that the male's courtship should be directed towards the female. However, egg-laying occurred in a higher proportion of such semi-isolated females than in females caged alone in the same room and visually isolated from males (Baum, unpublished data).

A second important type of stimulation is provided by the nest material, the nest-site, and the nest which the birds build there. Canaries lay later if the material they place in the nest-cup is removed daily than if they are allowed to build normally, and later still if they are not allowed access to any source of stimulation comparable to that provided by the nest-cup (Warren & Hinde, 1961b). In ring-doves the effect of the male on readiness to incubate eggs, ovulation and oviduct growth is augmented by the presence of nest-building facilities (Lehrman, Brody & Wortis, 1961).

Here again, the precise nature of the stimuli involved varies between species. In the Red-billed Weaver *Quelea*, where the male does most of the early building, the presence of males manipulating nest material seems to be important (Marshall & Disney, 1957). In the ring-dove, where the male does most of the carrying of the material to the nest and the female most of the actual building, Lehrman

# Avian reproductive development within the breeding season

(1959) suggests it is the influence of the nest material on the behaviour of the male which is the operative factor in the stimulation of the female. In canaries the males show little building behaviour, and certain characteristics (e.g. size, texture) of the nest-cup which the female herself has constructed are important: these are effective even in the absence of males (Warren & Hinde, 1961b). The effectiveness of the stimulation which the female canary receives from the nest-cup is enhanced by the increase in the tactile sensitivity of the brood patch which occurs at this stage: so far as is known, no comparable change occurs in ring-doves.

This raises the question of the stage in the season at which these external factors produce their effects. Stimulation at any one stage of reproductive development may have ramifying effects on subsequent stages, so an effect of stimulation on any parameter of reproductive development cannot be assumed to be direct. For instance, female canaries paired with males complete the defeathering of the brood patch, nest-building and egg-laying before females kept alone. However, in those unpaired females which do achieve egg-laying, the interval between the completion of defeathering and egg-laying is similar to that in paired birds. Thus the principal influence of the male would seem to be exerted before the completion of defeathering. Since the interval between defeathering and egg-laying tends to be longer in paired birds which are not allowed to build a nest than in paired birds which are, it would seem to be stimulation from the nest which is principally important at this stage. Thus the earlier egg-laying of paired as compared with unpaired females is not solely a direct effect of stimuli from the male on the female's reproductive development, but is also due to stimulation from the nest which the male has brought the female into condition to build.

External stimuli produce both immediate effects on behaviour and longer-term effects on the female's reproductive development. For instance stimulation which the female canary receives from the nest-cup which she herself has constructed has an immediate influence on the frequency of certain nest-building movements, determines the material she selects to build with, has a longer-term influence on the amount of nest-building behaviour she shows, affects brood-patch development, and accelerates further reproductive development and egg-laying (Hinde, 1958, 1965). The long-term effects must involve changes in the endocrine state.

Now in a variety of seasonally breeding species (review by van Tienhoven, 1961), including canaries (Steel & Hinde, 1966b), many of the long-term effects on reproductive development normally induced by photostimulation, the male, and other relevant factors, can also be induced by injections of gonadotrophins.

145

In view of this, and by analogy with mammals, it is reasonable to presume that the long-term effects of external stimulation are mediated by the pituitary. Although there is evidence that gonadotrophins can influence behaviour directly in Starlings *Sturnus vulgaris* (Mathewson, 1961), they are likely to produce their main effects on behaviour indirectly, via their effects on gonad development. That gonadotrophin injections do in fact influence gonad growth in female canaries has been demonstrated directly (Steel & Hinde, 1966b). That the influence of the male on the female's reproductive behaviour is mediated partly in this way is supported by the finding that his presence makes no detectable difference to the female's building behaviour if large doses of exogenous oestrogen are provided (Warren & Hinde, 1961a).

What hormones are directly responsible for the changes in behaviour which occur as the reproductive cycle proceeds? Oestrogens undoubtedly play a major role, for not only is nest-building contemporaneous with ovarian development, but it can be induced by exogenous oestrogens in ring-doves (Lehrman, 1958) and canaries (Warren & Hinde, 1959). Rapid oviduct development occurs at the same time as nest-building, and it also can be induced by oestrogens (Brant & Nalbandov, 1956; van Tienhoven, 1961). The female sexual behaviour which also occurs at this time may be related to the same hormonal changes: it can be induced by oestrogenic hormones in domestic fowl (Adams & Herrick, 1955).

However it is far from certain that oestrogen alone is responsible for nest-building. In canaries the dose-levels required for full nest-building behaviour appear to be very high (Warren & Hinde, 1959; Steel & Hinde, 1963). Although the effect of exogenous oestrogen on nest-building is not augmented by either progesterone or prolactin, the fact that paired canaries subjected to increased day-length in winter show adequate building behaviour, while a high proportion of female canaries injected with a preparation from pregnant mare serum lay eggs without doing so (Steel & Hinde, 1966 a, b), suggests that either stimulation from an active male or secondary hormones in addition to oestrogen are normally involved.

That other hormones are playing an important role in reproductive development at this stage is shown by the influence of progesterone and prolactin on oviduct development. Both of these, as well as androgens, can augment the effect of oestrogen on oviduct development (e.g. Brant & Nalbandov, 1956; Lehrman & Brody, 1957; van Tienhoven, 1961; Steel & Hinde, 1963), and progesterone is said to be essential for the development of the albumen-secreting glands in hens (Brant & Nalbandov, 1956). Lehrman (1959) suggests that stimuli associated

146

with nest-building lead to secretion of progesterone in ring-doves. The data available for canaries are compatible with this view.

The complexity of the endocrine changes which occur shortly before egg-laying is exemplified by our present knowledge (which is of course fragmentary and undoubtedly leads to over-simplification) of the endocrine basis of brood patch development. Some results obtained with White-crowned Sparrows *Zonotrichia leucophrys* (Bailey, 1952), and canaries (Steel & Hinde, 1963, 1964; Hinde & Steel, 1964; Hutchison, Hinde & Steel, in preparation) are summarized in Table 1. Prolactin or progesterone alone are not effective in inducing any brood

TABLE I

Effects of exogenous hormones on defeathering (DEF), vascularity (VASC) and sensitivity (SENS) of brood patch in intact, hypophysectomized (-Pit) and ovariectomized (-Ovar) birds. Data on hypophysectomized birds refer to White-crowned Sparrows, those on ovariectomized birds to canaries.

| | OESTR. | | | OESTR. & PROL. | | | OESTR. & PROG. | | PROL. | | PROG. | |
|---|---|---|---|---|---|---|---|---|---|---|---|---|
| | Intact | -Pit. | -Ovar. | Intact | -Pit. | -Ovar. | Intact | -Ovar. | Intact | -Ovar. | Intact | -Ovar. |
| DEF. | + | . | + | + | + | + | + | + | . | . | . | . |
| VASC. | + | + | + | + | + | + | + | + | . | . | . | . |
| SENS. | + | . | | + | . | | + | + | . | . | . | . |

patch development. Vascularity can be induced by oestrogen even in hypophysectomized or ovariectomized birds, and so probably normally depends on oestrogen alone. Defeathering can be induced by oestrogen in both intact and ovariectomized birds, and is thus independent of ovarian hormones other than oestrogen. Since the effect of oestrogen on defeathering is augmented by prolactin (as well as by progesterone), and since in hypophysectomized White-crowned Sparrows defeathering can be induced by oestrogen in combination with prolactin but not by oestrogen alone, it probably normally depends on oestrogen and prolactin. The sensitivity changes can be induced by oestrogen alone in intact birds, but require progesterone as well in ovariectomized ones: they are thus probably normally the result of the combined action of oestrogen and progesterone.

These findings on the control of brood patch development illustrate two important points. First, it cannot be assumed that synchronous changes depend on the same endocrine factors: the different aspects of brood patch development, although overlapping in time, have different endocrine bases. Second, the level of any one of the operative hormones may be influenced by that of others. Since sensitivity changes can be induced by oestrogen alone in intact females, but require both oestrogen and progesterone in ovariectomized ones (Steel & Hinde, 1964; Hutchison *et al*, in prep.), both oestrogen and a progestin must be essential. The effectiveness of oestrogen alone in intact birds indicates either that a progestin must be already present in quantities adequate for the sensitivity changes to occur when oestrogen is administered, or that its production must be induced (directly or indirectly) by the oestrogen. By a similar argument, the data on defeathering indicate either that prolactin is present at levels adequate for defeathering through the breeding season, or that oestrogen must induce its secretion from the pituitary. The relations between progesterone and prolactin are, however, not clear: in intact canaries either can augment the effect of oestrogen on defeathering, on sensitivity of the brood patch, and on oviduct growth. It has been suggested that progesterone induces prolactin secretion, on the grounds that progesterone can cause doves to incubate, and incubation in doves is known to be associated with prolactin (Riddle & Lahr, 1944; Riddle, 1963). However, Lehrman (1958, 1963) has shown that prolactin secretion in doves (as assessed by crop growth) is a consequence of stimulation received in the course of progesterone-induced incubation, rather than of progesterone itself. Such a mechanism is unlikely to operate in canaries during brood patch formation, which starts before the female begins to sit in the nest. The alternative view, that prolactin induces progesterone secretion, is more in keeping with the natural time sequence in canaries, but it is also possible that either can affect defeathering, or that both act by eliciting a third substance which is itself effective.

The processes underlying ovulation and oviposition involve complex control processes which have not been studied in canaries or doves and cannot be discussed here. In brief, in most song-birds injections of FSH (or PMS) cause the maturation of a graded series of follicles in the ovary, which subsequently ovulate without a change in hormone treatment. PMS treatment of canaries induced egg-laying in some individuals, but others when sacrificed were found to have ovaries as heavy as those of females in the breeding season just before egg-laying, but with many equal-sized ovarian follicles (Steel & Hinde, 1966a). In domestic fowl also the follicles so produced are not graded, and additional LH injections are required for ovulation. Mechanical stimulation of the wall of the oviduct by a recently ovulated egg normally inhibits LH secretions (review by van Tienhoven, 1961).

After ovulation, special mechanisms must ensure that oviposition occurs in the nest, and not elsewhere. In the domestic hen, oviposition is preceded by an 'examination' of the nest and is often followed by a brief period of sitting (Wood-Gush, 1963). Rothchild & Fraps (1944) showed that oviposition was related to activity of the most recently ruptured follicle: removal of this follicle resulted in delayed oviposition. The 'nesting' behaviour associated with oviposition also depends on the integrity of this follicle, but it seems possible that the effect is mediated in part by the follicle's rich nerve supply, and not solely hormonally (Wood-Gush & Gilbert, 1964).

The sitting which is associated with egg-laying, and which later merges into full incubation behaviour, may be important in limiting clutch size in some species. In certain gulls (*Larus*) the effect of removal of eggs during egg-laying on the laying of additional ones depends on the extent to which the female has incubated: incubation for 2–4 days is associated with degeneration of the additional follicles which had previously been maturing in the ovary (Paludan, 1951; Weidmann, 1956).

The hormonal basis of incubation has already been alluded to briefly. In doves, it can be induced by exogenous progesterone (though in other species the effect of exogenous progesterone may vary with the level already in the blood (van Tienhoven, 1958)): after several days of progesterone-induced incubation the crop is enlarged (an index of prolactin secretion), although progesterone does not induce prolactin in doves which are not given opportunity to incubate. It thus seems that prolactin secretion is induced by stimuli received in the course of progesterone-initiated incubation (Lehrman, 1963, and references cited; see also Riddle, 1963, for a divergent view). Although prolactin injections do not initiate incubation in doves, they can (and probably normally do) maintain it once it has started (Lehrman & Brody, 1961). In hens, too, prolactin levels remain high for so long as the bird continues to incubate (Saeki & Tanabe, 1955). However, it is not clear how far the mechanism whereby prolactin secretion is initiated in doves can be generalized to other species. Attempts to induce incubation behaviour in canaries with both progesterone and prolactin have so far proved unsuccessful, and no data are available for other Passerines. Furthermore, as we have seen, prolactin seems to play a part in the defeathering of the brood patch. Since this starts some time before incubation, prolactin secretion up to the levels necessary for brood-patch formation cannot be incubation-induced.

The studies cited illustrate various aspects of the problem of the integration of the female's reproductive behaviour within the breeding season. Taken together they show that her reproductive development can be understood only in terms of a constantly changing interaction between the external stimuli to which she is exposed, her own physiological condition, and her behaviour. For instance, nest-building depends in part on oestrogen, itself produced in response to external stimulation by a hypothalamic/pituitary/gonad mechanism. Nest-building also depends on immediate external factors, including a nest-site and nest-material. It results in the formation of a new source of stimulation, the nest. The effectiveness of this depends in part on the hormone-induced increase in tactile sensitivity of the brood patch. Stimulation from the nest has both positive and negative effects on nest-building behaviour, and influences the selection of material. It also influences longer-term reproductive development, and thus further changes in behaviour and exposure to fresh stimulus situations. These and other interactions between behaviour, external stimuli and endocrine factors acting both peripherally and centrally, have been discussed in more detail elsewhere (Hinde, 1965; Hinde & Steel, 1966).

So far we have neglected the role which experience may play in these interactions, but there is evidence that it may be important. Lehrman (1953) found that ring-doves which had had previous experience of rearing young would feed squabs after prolactin treatment, but adult ring-doves without such experience would not. The prolactin produced the same physiological effects, including enlargement of the crop, in both cases. Now the effect on the parental feeding behaviour of the experienced birds could be eliminated by application of a local anaesthetic to the crop region, but not elsewhere. The prolactin thus affected parental feeding by its effect on the sensory input from the enlarged crop, and it seems that the role of experience lies in ensuring a proper response to this stimulation in the presence of stimuli from the young. Similarly, experienced birds show incubation after progesterone treatment more readily than do inexperienced ones (Lehrman, 1962).

These results show that experience is likely to play a large part in the integration of reproductive development. Since there are endocrine differences between first- and second-year birds (e.g. canaries; Steel & Hinde, 1966 a, b), the task of differentiating between learning and other effects of experience will need precise experimental control. It is, however, clearly essential for further understanding of the integration of breeding behaviour.

In conclusion, this review perhaps demonstrates some of the complexities which are met in an attempt to analyse the control of reproduction in one sex of one species at a relatively superficial level, and emphasizes the constant interaction between stimuli, behaviour and endocrine state. In view of these data it would seem that at present further progress requires not studies of limited aspects of reproduction in diverse species, but comprehensive studies of a few carefully chosen ones, with the analysis pushed gradually to a more refined level than has here been achieved.

## REFERENCES

ADAMS J.L. & HERRICK R.B. (1955) Interaction of the gonadal hormones in the chicken. *Poultry Sc.* **4,** 117-121.

BAILEY R.E. (1952) The incubation patch of passerine birds. *Condor* **54,** 121-136.

BRANT, J.W.A. & NALBANDOV A.V. (1956) Role of sex hormones in albumen secretion by the oviduct of chickens. *Poultry Sci.* **35,** 692-700.

BROCKWAY B.F. (1965) Stimulation of ovarian development and egg laying by male courtship vocalization in Budgerigars (*Melopsittacus undulatus*). *Anim. Behav.* **13,** 575-578.

BURGER J.W. (1953) The effect of photic and psychic stimuli on the reproductive cycle of the male Starling (*Sturnus vulgaris*). *J. Exper. Zool.* **124,** 227-240.

ERICKSON C.J. & LEHRMAN D.S. (1964) Effect of castration of male ring doves upon ovarian activity of females. *J. Comp. Physiol. Psychol.* **58,** 164-166.

FARNER D.S. (1966) The control of avian reproductive cycles. *Proc. XIV Internat. Orn. Congr.,* 107-133.

FICKEN R.W., VAN TIENHOVEN A., FICKEN M.S. & SIBLEY F.C. (1960) Effect of visual and vocal stimuli on breeding in the Budgerigar (*Melopsittacus undulatus*). *Anim. Behav.* **8,** 104-106.

HINDE R.A. (1958) The nest-building of domesticated canaries. *Proc. zool. Soc. Lond.* **131,** 1-48.

HINDE R.A. (1962) Temporal relations of brood patch development in domesticated canaries. *Ibis* **104,** 90-97.

HINDE R.A. (1965) Interaction of internal and external factors in integration of canary reproduction. In *Sex and Behavior.* Ed. F.A.Beach. Wiley, New York.

HINDE R.A., BELL R.Q. & STEEL E.A. (1963) Changes in sensitivity of the canary brood patch during the natural breeding season. *Anim. Behav.* **11,** 553-560.

HINDE R.A. & STEEL E.A. (1962) Selection of nest material by female canaries. *Anim. Behav.* **10,** 67-75.

HINDE R.A. & STEEL E.A. (1964) Effect of exogenous hormones on the tactile sensitivity of the canary brood patch. *J. Endocrin.* **30,** 355-359.

HINDE R.A. & STEEL E.A. (1966) Integration of the reproductive behaviour of female canaries. *Sym. Soc. exp. Biol.* **20,** 401-426.

HUTCHISON R.E., HINDE R.A. & STEEL E.A. (in preparation) Effect of exogenous hormones on brood patch development in ovariectomized canaries.

LACK D. (1966) *Population Studies of Birds.* Oxford.

LEHRMAN D.S. (1955) The physiological basis of parental feeding behavior in the ring dove (*Streptopelia risoria*). *Behaviour* **7,** 241-286.

LEHRMAN D.S. (1958) Induction of broodiness by participation in courtship and nest-building in the ring dove (*Streptopelia risoria*). *J. Comp. Physiol. Psychol.* **51,** 32-36.

# R.A.Hinde

Lehrman D.S. (1958) Effect of female sex hormones on incubation behavior in the ring dove (*Streptopelia risoria*). *J. Comp. Physiol. Psychol.* **51**, 142–145.

Lehrman D.S. (1959) Hormonal responses to external stimuli in birds. *Ibis* **101**, 478–496.

Lehrman D.S. (1961) Gonadal hormones and parental behavior in birds and infrahuman mammals. In *Sex and Internal Secretions*. Ed. W.C.Young. Williams & Wilkins, Baltimore.

Lehrman D.S. (1962) Interaction of hormonal and experiential influences on development of behavior. In *Roots of Behavior*. Ed. E.L.Bliss. Hoeber, New York.

Lehrman D.S. (1963) On the initiation of incubation behaviour in doves. *Anim. Behav.* **11**, 433–438.

Lehrman D.S. & Brody P. (1957) Oviduct response to estrogen and progesterone in the ring dove (*Streptopelia risoria*). *Proc. Soc. exp. Biol., N.Y.* **19**, 373–375.

Lehrman D.S. & Brody P. (1961) Does prolactin induce incubation behaviour in the ring dove? *J. Endocrin.* **22**, 269–275.

Lehrman D.S. & Brody P. N. (1964) Effect of prolactin on established incubation behavior in the ring dove. *J. Comp. Physiol. Psychol.* **57**, 161–165.

Lehrman D.S., Brody P.N. & Wortis R.P. (1961) The presence of the mate and of nesting material as stimuli for the development of incubation behavior and for gonadotropin secretion in the ring dove (*Streptopelia risoria*). *Endocrinology* **68**, 507–516.

Lehrman D.S. & Wortis R.P. (1960) Previous breeding experience and hormone-induced incubation behavior in the ring dove. *Science* **132**, 1667–1668.

Lehrman D.S., Wortis R.P. & Brody P. (1961) Gonadotropin secretion in response to external stimuli of varying duration in the ring dove (*Streptopelia risoria*). *Proc. Soc. exp. Biol., N.Y.* **106**, 298–300.

Marshall A.J. & Coombs C.J.F. (1957) The interaction of environmental, internal and behavioural factors in the rook (*Corvus f. frugilegus* L.) *Proc. zool. Soc. Lond.* **128**, 545–589.

Marshall A.J. & Disney H.J.deS. (1957) Experimental induction of the breeding season in a xerophilous bird. *Nature, Lond.* **180**, 647–649.

Matthews L.H. (1939) Visual stimulation and ovulation in pigeons. *Proc. Roy. Soc.* **126B**, 557–560.

Mathewson S.F. (1961) Gonadotrophic control of aggressive behavior in Starlings. *Science* **134**, 1522.

Miller S. (1965) Nest-building activity in the ring dove (*Streptopelia risoria*). Ph.D. thesis, Rutger's University, New Brunswick, N.J., U.S.A.

Paludan K. (1951) Contributions to the breeding biology of *Larus argentatus* and *Larus fuscus*. *Vidensk. Medd. Dansk naturh. Foren. Kbh.* **114**, 1–128.

Petersen A.J. (1955) The breeding cycle in the Bank Swallow. *Wilson Bull.* **67**, 235–286.

Riddle O. (1963) Prolactin or progesterone as key to parental behavior: a review. *Anim. Behav.* **11**, 419–432.

Riddle O. & Lahr E.L. (1944) On broodiness of ring doves following implants of certain steroid hormones. *Endocrinology* **35**, 255–260.

Romanoff A.L. & Romanoff A.J. (1949) *The Avian Egg*. Wiley, New York.

Rothchild I. & Fraps R.M. (1944) Relation between light–dark rhythms and hour of lay of eggs experimentally retained in the hen. *Endocrinology* **35**, 355–362.

Saeki Y. & Tanabe Y. (1955) Changes in prolactin content of fowl pituitary during broody periods and some experiments on the induction of broodiness. *Poult. Sci.* **34**, 909–919.

# Avian reproductive development within the breeding season

STEEL E.A. & HINDE R.A. (1963) Hormonal control of brood-patch and oviduct development in domesticated canaries. *J. Endocrin.* **26**, 11–24.

STEEL E.A. & HINDE R.A. (1964) Effect of exogenous oestrogen on brood patch development of intact and ovariectomized canaries. *Nature, Lond.* **202**, 718–719.

STEEL E.A. & HINDE R.A. (1966a) Effect of artificially increased day-length in winter on female domesticated canaries. *J. Zool.* **149**, 1–11.

STEEL E.A. & HINDE R.A. (1966b) Effect of exogenous serum gonadotrophin (PMS) on aspects of reproductive development in female domesticated canaries. *J. Zool.* **149**, 12–30.

VAN TIENHOVEN A. (1958) Effect of progesterone on broodiness and egg production of turkeys. *Poult. Sci.* **37**, 428–433.

VAN TIENHOVEN A. (1961) Endocrinology of reproduction in birds. In *Sex and Internal Secretions*. Ed. W.C.Young. Williams & Wilkins, Baltimore.

VAUGIEN L. (1951) Ponte induite chez la Perruche ondulée maintenue à l'obscurité et dans l'ambience des volières. *C.R. Acad. Sci. Paris* **232**, 1706–1708.

WARREN R.P. & HINDE R.A. (1959) The effect of oestrogen and progesterone on the nest-building of domesticated canaries. *Anim. Behav.* **7**, 209–213.

WARREN R.P. & HINDE R.A. (1961a) Does the male stimulate estrogen secretion in female canaries? *Science* **133**, 1354–1355.

WARREN R.P. & HINDE R.A. (1961b) Roles of the male and the nest-cup in controlling the reproduction of female canaries. *Anim. Behav.* **9**, 64–67.

WEIDMANN U. (1956) Observations and experiments on egg-laying in the Black-headed Gull (*Larus ridibundus*). *Brit. J. Anim. Behav.* **4**, 150–161.

WOOD-GUSH D.G.M. (1963) Control of the nesting behaviour of the domestic hen. I. The role of the oviduct. *Anim. Behav.* **11**, 293–299.

WOOD-GUSH D.G.M. & GILBERT A.B. (1964) The control of the nesting behaviour of the domestic hen. II. The role of the ovary. *Anim. Behav.* **12**, 451–453.

# Clutch-size in the Pied Flycatcher

## LARS VON HAARTMAN

The present paper is a revision of some earlier publications on the clutch-size of the Pied Flycatcher *Ficedula hypoleuca*, which all date from the 'fifties (v. Haartman, 1951, 1954, 1956). The ample data accumulated during a quarter of a century, and the advent of an appropriate device to analyse such data—the electronic computer —have made such a revision desirable.

The average size of 1124 complete clutches of the Pied Flycatcher in 1941–65 in my study area Lemsjöholm in south-western Finland, as calculated with the electronic computer, was $6.288256 \pm 0.030322$. 460 nest-cards from all over Finland, but mainly from the south, gave an average of 6.38. The agreement between these figures indicates that the information obtained through the nest-cards is reliable.

The variation of the clutch-size is shown in Table 1. Clutches known to have been laid by two females (9 and 11 eggs) were not included. The c/11 was laid

TABLE I

Clutch-size of the Pied Flycatcher at Lemsjöholm

| Clutch-size | 1 | 2 | 3 | 4 | 5 | 6 | 7 | 8 | 9 |
|---|---|---|---|---|---|---|---|---|---|
| No. of clutches | 2 | 6 | 13 | 32 | 117 | 455 | 425 | 69 | 5 |

by two females simultaneously, whereas in the c/9 one female laid 7 eggs and was incubating them when the other female, having lost the first eggs of her own clutch, started to lay in her nest. In the case of the c/11 one female disappeared, whereas the c/9 was incubated by the two females side by side, the nest-bowl becoming considerably enlarged as incubation proceeded. These females seemed to ignore each other completely, leaving the nest and returning independently of each other. It is possible that some of the c/9 included in Table 1 were laid by two females.

## Lars von Haartman

Though its clutch-size varies considerably, the Pied Flycatcher is a determinate layer. Removing eggs continuously or adding eggs before or immediately after laying started did not influence the number of eggs laid by the female (Figure 1).

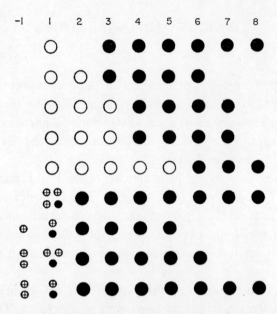

FIGURE I. Number of eggs laid by nine female Pied Flycatchers after removal or addition of eggs. 1, 2, 3, etc. = first, second, third, etc. day of laying. − 1 = the day before commencement of laying. Empty circles = eggs removed immediately after laying. Gap = no egg laid. Dark circles = eggs not removed. Circles with a cross = additional eggs. For instance, the first horizontal row shows a clutch where the first egg was removed, no egg was laid on the second day, and one egg was laid daily during the third to eighth day. Thus, the female in question laid seven eggs.

As in a number of other species studied, the 1-year-old Pied Flycatchers (age known through ringing) laid smaller clutches than older females (Table 2). It ought to be stressed that some of the 1-year-old females probably fail to nest (v. Haartman 1951, p. 21). Together with an astonishingly low return percentage (v. Haartman, 1960), this explains why 25 years of ringing has yielded so few 1-year-old females. The comparatively small number of 1-year-old females in the nesting population also explains why the mean clutch-size of females of unknown age is nearly the same as in females known to be old.

The clutch-size of the Pied Flycatcher decreases continuously throughout

# Clutch-size in the Pied Flycatcher

the nesting-season. This is true at least of clutches started from May 26 onwards; until this date the clutch-size seems to remain stable. Both the records from Lemsjöholm and the nest-cards show about the same decrease (Figure 2). This

TABLE 2

Clutch-size of young and old Pied Flycatchers at Lemsjöholm

| Clutch-size | 1 | 2 | 3 | 4 | 5 | 6 | 7 | 8 | 9 | n | M |
|---|---|---|---|---|---|---|---|---|---|---|---|
| Age unknown | 1 | 5 | 11 | 24 | 101 | 384 | 358 | 55 | 5 | 944 | 6.29±0.03 |
| 2 or more years | 1 | 1 | 2 | 6 | 14 | 58 | 67 | 14 | — | 163 | 6.33±0.09 |
| 1-year-old | — | — | — | 2 | 2 | 13 | — | — | — | 17 | 5.65±0.17 |

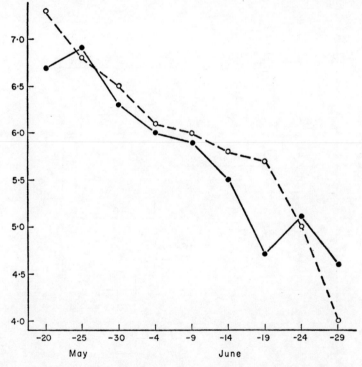

FIGURE 2. The decrease of the clutch-size of the Pied Flycatcher throughout the nesting season. Average size of clutches begun during periods of 5 days according to observations at Lemsjöholm (black line) and nest-cards from Finland south of 62° N (broken line).

applies at least to the period May 21–June 14 when records are plentiful. During the period May 26–June 14 the mean clutch-size decreases by 0.07 eggs daily, according to the Lemsjöholm records.

# Lars von Haartman

Most, if not all, Finnish Passerines show a corresponding decrease of the clutch-size throughout the nesting season. But in no other species studied so far does the decrease seem to be so rapid as in the Pied Flycatcher. In the Redwing *Turdus iliacus*, for instance, the clutch-size remains more or less unchanged throughout 1½ months, then decreases during the very end of the season (Figure 3). The

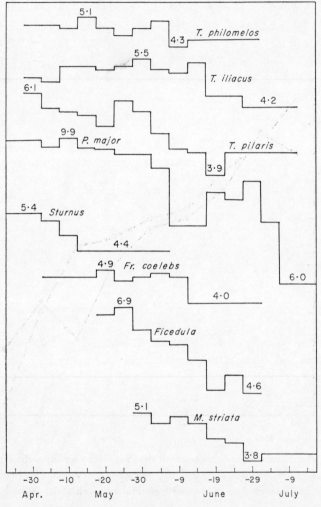

FIGURE 3. The clutch-size of a number of Passerines in southern Finland (60°–62° N) during their nesting season. Average size of clutches begun during periods of 5 days according to nest-cards (except the Pied Flycatcher, which is based on observations at Lemsjöholm).

causes of the decrease in clutch-size may vary to some extent from species to species, but the amount and quality of the food are probably involved. The curves for the Pied Flycatcher and the Great Tit *Parus major*, a species which, like the Pied Flycatcher, uses a great number of larvae for feeding its young, run parallel; in both species the marked decrease of clutch-size starts after May 25.

Besides the food situation, another ultimate factor may have influenced the size of late clutches in the Pied Flycatcher. Through the successive polygamy of some of the males (v. Haartman, 1951), a considerable number of late-nesting

TABLE 3

| Clutches commenced | No. of broods | Broods fed by: | | |
|---|---|---|---|---|
| | | ♂♀ | ♀ | ♂ |
| May 14–25 | 116 | 94% | 2.6% | 3.5% |
| May 26–30 | 169 | 91.7% | 4.7% | 3.6% |
| May 31–June 4 | 103 | 83.5% | 14.6% | 2.0% |
| June 5–29 | 58 | 60.3% | 34.5% | 5.2% |

females will have to feed their young unaided (Table 3). As shown earlier (v. Haartman, 1954), the female Pied Flycatcher can to some extent compensate for the work normally performed by her mate. With broods of 4–5 or more young this is no longer the case, however, and the young receive fewer meals than broods fed by both parents. This fact may also contribute to the poor result of late broods of the Pied Flycatcher (cf. Table 5).

The proximate factors causing the decrease of clutch-size are poorly understood. It has been maintained (e.g. for the Caspian Tern *Hydroprogne caspia*, Bergman, 1953) that the increasing number of young individuals laying towards the end of the season should explain the decrease of the average. This may be true with respect to some species; with the Pied Flycatcher it is not. First, the differences in laying date between young and old females are very small in Finnish Pied Flycatchers:

| Age of female | Average date of laying |
|---|---|
| Unknown | 29.7±0.22 May |
| 2 or more years | 28.7±0.50 May |
| One year | 31.9±1.35 May |

(This does not, of course, exclude the possibility that the difference may be larger in southerly populations of the species, where the nesting season is less compressed and the females can 'afford' to postpone their laying.) Secondly, the curves for 1-year-old and 2-year-old or older females, treated separately, show exactly the same trend (Figure 4).

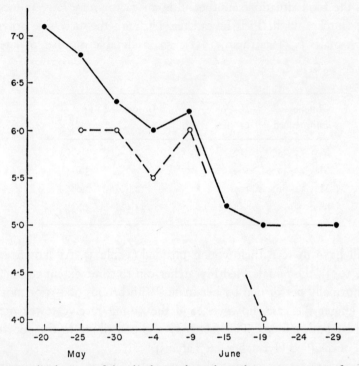

FIGURE 4. The decrease of the clutch-size throughout the nesting season of 1-year-old (broken line) and older (black line) female Pied Flycatchers at Lemsjöholm. Averages of clutches begun during periods of 5 days.

Another popular belief is that repeat clutches have to be smaller than original clutches because of exhaustion of the females and that, therefore, their increasing number towards the end of the nesting season will cause the mean clutch-size to decrease. In England, where in a number of Passerines the average size of clutches laid actually increases during the beginning of the season (Lack, 1954), this belief may be difficult to maintain. Nor is it, of course, applicable to a species like the Redwing in Finland, where clutch-size remains unchanged for 1½ months, in spite of frequent repeat layings. Also, one may point to the existence of 'indeterminate' layers, which by continuous removal of eggs may be caused to lay an abnormally large number without becoming physiologically exhausted. As for the Pied Flycatcher, we may point to the small number of clutches lost and repeated, and further to the fact that no repeat clutch, to my knowledge, was commenced before June 5, whereas the decrease of the average clutch-size starts as early as about May 26.

It is quite true that repeat clutches are generally smaller than the original clutches of the same females (Table 4). But it is reversing cause and effect to assume that the repeat clutches cause the decrease of the clutch-size towards the end of the

TABLE 4

Size of repeat clutches compared with original clutch-size

|  |  | Repeat clutch | | | |
|---|---|---|---|---|---|
|  |  | 6 | 5 | 4 | 3 |
|  | 8 | 1 |  |  |  |
| Original | 7 | 3 | 1 |  |  |
| clutch | 6 | 2 | 2 |  | 1 |
|  | 5 |  |  | 1 |  |

nesting season. On the contrary, repeat clutches are probably small because they are laid late. The average date of commencement of the original clutches summarized in Table 4 is May 27, and the corresponding average of the repeat clutches June 16. The mean clutch-sizes are 6.45 and 5.27 respectively. This implies a decrease of the average clutch-size by 0.06 a day, which corresponds well to the daily decrease of 0.07 found to be typical of the clutch-size of the Pied Flycatcher after May 25.

The decrease of the clutch-size may take place in either of two ways. Either a certain average clutch-size is connected with the date ('calendar reaction') or the reaction is 'relative', the earliest laying females having a certain mean irrespective of the date when they start to lay, and the mean of the later-laying females depending upon how early or late they are in relation to these. To decide between these alternatives the years were divided into early, average and late years, and the relation between clutch-size and date was calculated separately for the early and the late years. The early years were 1945, 46, 48, 52, 53, 54, 62, the late ones 1944, 50, 51, 55, 56, 57, 65. In the early years the average date of commencement of all clutches in the population varied from May 26 to May 28, in the late years between May 30 and June 2. The result is shown in Figure 5. If, now, the average clutch-size were determined 'relatively' the curve of the late years should be shifted towards the right. But this is not the case. The curves of the late and early years seem to be more or less identical. Thus, the average clutch-size seems in some way to be determined 'by the calendar'.

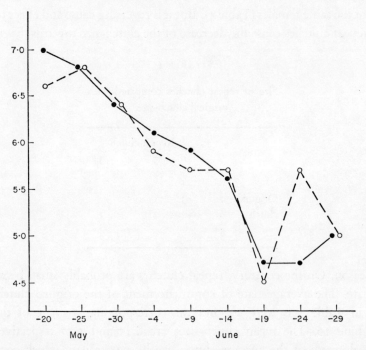

FIGURE 5. The decrease of the clutch-size of the Pied Flycatcher at Lemsjöholm throughout the nesting season, early years (broken line) and late years (black line) separated. Average of clutches begun during periods of 5 days.

If a certain average clutch-size corresponds to a certain date, and the time of laying varies from year to year, late years ought to have a smaller average clutch-size than early ones. This seems, on the whole, to be true (Figure 6), although there are exceptions which I cannot explain at the present moment.

Lack (1954) has shown that the percentage of ringed nestlings recovered after reaching a certain age may give information on post-fledging survival. In the case of the Pied Flycatcher, the percentage recovery decreases as the season progresses, showing that late-hatched birds survive less well than those hatched earlier (Table 5). Similarly, we can test whether relatively fewer young birds reach

# Clutch-size in the Pied Flycatcher

maturity from abnormally large broods than from broods of normal size (Table 6). In making this calculation it has to be taken into account that as the season

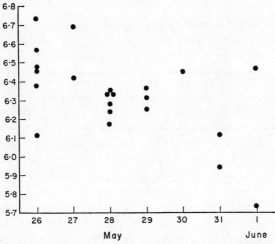

FIGURE 6. Correlation between the average clutch-size of the Pied Flycatcher at Lemsjöholm 1943–65 (1941, 1942 and 1958 were excluded because of scarce or incomplete data) and the earliness of nesting, expressed as the date when half of the females had begun to lay.

TABLE 5

Pied Flycatchers ringed at Lemsjöholm as nestlings and recovered in the study area in a later year or found during migration abroad (only a few cases)

| Clutches commenced | Young ringed | Found |
|---|---|---|
| May 14–25 | 1314 | $37 = 2.81\% \pm 0.45$ |
| May 26–June 4 | 2821 | $57 = 2.02\% \pm 0.26$ |
| June 5–29 | 358 | $4 = 1.12\% \pm 0.55$ |

advances the 'normal' size of a brood decreases. The figures, like Curio's (1960) from a study area in Germany, give no support* to the view that members of

* After the manuscript was finished, D.Lack (*Population Studies of Birds*, Oxford, 1966) published B.Campbell's data on the survival of young Pied Flycatchers in an English forest. If treated in the same way as above, these data yield the following figures: subnormally large broods, 5.1% recovered; normally large, 4.5%; supernormally large, 4.6%.

abnormally large broods are weaker and yield relatively fewer mature individuals than broods of the usual size.

TABLE 6

Pied Flycatchers ringed as nestlings at Lemsjöholm and recovered in the area in a subsequent year or found during migration abroad (few cases). The b/9 and b/10 were the result of artificial enlargement of broods.

| Clutches commenced | | 1 | 2 | 3 | 4 | 5 | 6 | 7 | 8 | 9 | 10 |
|---|---|---|---|---|---|---|---|---|---|---|---|
| | | | | | | Brood size | | | | | |
| May 14–25 | Ringed | 1 | 8 | 15 | 64 | 145 | 432 | 483 | 80 | 36 | 30 |
| | Found | | | 1 | 1 | 7 | 16 | 10 | 2 | | |
| May 26–June 4 | Ringed | 11 | 36 | 93 | 224 | 555 | 1212 | 553 | 24 | 72 | |
| | Found | | | 1 | 2 | 11 | 26 | 15 | | 2 | |
| June 5–29 | Ringed | 2 | 2 | 24 | 92 | 105 | 84 | 21 | 16 | | |
| | Found | | | | 1 | 3 | | | | | |
| All periods | Ringed | | 625 | | | 2879 | 916 | | | | |
| | Found | | 12 | | | 67 | 19 | | | | |
| | per cent | 1.91±0.55 | | | | 2.33 ±0.26 | 2.07±0.47 | | | | |

REFERENCES

BERGMAN G. (1953) Verhalten und Biologie der Raubseeschwalbe (*Hydroprogne tschegrava*). *Acta Zool. Fenn.* **77**, 1–50.

CURIO E. (1960) Lebenserwartung und Brutgrösse beim Trauerschnäpper (*Muscicapa h. hypoleuca* Pallas). *Proc. XII Internat. Orn. Congr.*, 158–161.

v. HAARTMAN L. (1951) Der Trauerfliegenschnäpper. II. Populationsprobleme. *Acta Zool. Fenn.* **67**, 1–60.

v. HAARTMAN L. (1951) Successive polygamy. *Behaviour* **3**, 256–274.

v. HAARTMAN L. (1954) Der Trauerfliegenschnäpper. III. Die Nahrungsbiologie. *Acta Zool. Fenn.* **83**, 1–96.

v. HAARTMAN L. (1956) Finska Vetenskaps-Societetens fenologiska undersökningar. Några synpunkter och nya arbetsuppgifter. *Soc. Scient. Fenn. Årsbok XXXIII B:* **3**, 1–23.

v. HAARTMAN L. (1960) The ortstreue of the Pied Flycatcher. *Proc. XII Internat. Orn. Congr.*, 266–273.

LACK D. (1954) *The Natural Regulation of Animal Numbers.* Oxford.

# Aspects of the population ecology of the Short-tailed Shearwater *Puffinus tenuirostris*

D.L.SERVENTY

C.S.I.R.O. Division of Wildlife Research,
Perth, Western Australia

## INTRODUCTION

There can be no large group of birds on which there has been added in recent years such a substantial body of new information as the Procellariiformes. The pioneers of the modern studies on the life-histories of petrels, such as R.M. Lockley, R.A.Falla and L.E.Richdale, have been followed by many investigators throughout the world and the group is now under active and continuous attention.

It has now been revealed that the Procellariiformes have a very complex life-history as far as the terrestrial phase is concerned; and not only complex but remarkably stereotyped. What is discovered about one species is found to be true in many others. This suggests that features of the basic reproductive cycle were developed fairly early in the evolution of the order and have been retained with little modification under the varied ecological conditions in which the species now live, despite the fact that the environmental pressures have created a tremendous range of body-size and feeding patterns.

The data for the present account of the Short-tailed Shearwater *Puffinus tenuirostris* were accumulated from the study of a small population, ranging from about 75 to 150 pairs, on Fisher Island, near Flinders Island in eastern Bass Strait, Tasmania (lat. 40° 13′ S, long. 148° 14′ E). The study began in a preliminary way in 1947, gathered impetus in 1950 and is still continuing.

## THE BREEDING CYCLE

*Arrival*

Breeding adults make their first landfall in the last week of September, after a transequatorial migration in the Pacific Ocean. The only first-hand information I have of the birds' arrival on the nesting islands refers to my field survey of September 1952 at Fisher Island. Our party established itself on the island on September 22 when there was no sign of the shearwaters and no evidence of 'scratching out' of the past season's nesting burrows. The first birds were seen on the evening of September 25 when two birds, both males, were captured in the rookery. On the following evening very many more birds were present both in the burrows and on the surface. In each of three burrows examined two ringed birds were present, male and female, and from their history were ascertained to be mated pairs. On succeeding nights the population built up rapidly.

A sample collected on September 29 for histological examination of the gonads showed that the males had attained spermatogenesis and in the females the oocytes were beginning the steep increase in size which is preliminary to egg production (Marshall & Serventy, 1956, 1957). There are few other direct eye-witnesses' reports of the first landfall of the breeding adults but they are in conformity with the information just given—e.g. Littler (1910) and Perryman (1937).

*Scratching-out Period*
The interval between the landfall of the adult birds, at the end of September, and the pre-egg-laying exodus at the beginning of November, may conveniently be referred to as the 'scratching-out' period, to borrow a term used by the commercial mutton-bird operatives in the Flinders Island region. This term is descriptive of one of the more obvious activities of the newly arrived birds during these 4 weeks, namely, the refurbishing and digging-out of the old burrows. Histologically the period is marked by the completion of spermatogenesis in the male, for at the end of the period the testes reach their peak in size and development and the sperms are shed. The end of the period is apparently marked by the insemination of the female.

*Pre-laying Exodus*
Egg-laying takes place in late November and the first few days of December, being remarkably constant from year to year and telescoped to a few days on either side of the mean date, November 25–26 (Serventy, 1963). Just prior to egg-laying the population abandons the nesting islands for a period of about 3 weeks. The deserted rookeries present a strange contrast from the animated conditions reigning up to the beginning of November, for not a bird will be seen flying around at night, nor a sound heard. The birds do not reappear until the actual nights of egg-laying, when there is a sudden resumption of activity in the rookeries.

This phenomenon was well known to the operatives of the commercial mutton-birding islands from the earliest days and was referred to by visiting naturalists, including Davies (1846, p. 13), Elwes (1859, p. 399), Montgomery (1898, p. 210), A.J.Campbell (1901, p. 885), Littler (1910, p. 167), Lord & Scott (1924, p. 138) and Perryman (1937, p. 15). However, except in the most recent literature, this pre-laying disappearance of the birds has not been commented on as a phase of the life cycle of other petrels. Lockley (1942) gives no hint that it may occur in *Puffinus puffinus* and Richdale (1950) found nothing analogous to it in his review of the pre-egg stage in the albatross family. Fisher (1952, p. 337) does not mention anything of this nature obtaining in the Fulmar *Fulmarus glacialis*, but a suggestion that the birds temporarily vacate the nesting islands before laying is given in an appendix by Venables to Fisher's book (p. 483). He provides data showing a pronounced drop in Fulmar populations at nesting sites in the Shetlands, concluding that 'many fulmars appear to go off to sea just before laying'. Tickell (1962, pp. 15, 21) discovered that the phenomenon also occurs in the prion *Pachyptila desolata*, with the interesting variation that the 'honeymoon' flight of about 10 days was confined to the female. His very logical explanation is that the presence of the male is required at the burrow to prevent snow accumulating and consolidating at the entrance. He also draws attention to an overlooked report by Valette (1906) that Cape Pigeons depart on a 'honeymoon' flight for about 10 days prior to laying.

To obtain more precise information on the sequence of events in *Puffinus tenuirostris* particular attention was paid to this problem during the 1952–53 nesting season. The results showed that the nightly influx of birds began to diminish in the first days of November and by the night of November 6/7 it had virtually ceased. Thereafter no birds were observed at the island until the evening of November 20, when there was a considerable influx coinciding with the onset of egg-laying. The interval between the middle of the pre-laying exodus (the night of November 3/4) and the peak of egg-laying (November 25/26, *vide* Serventy, 1963, p. 341) is 3 weeks, though the period during which the rookeries are virtually untenanted is less, extending from about the nights of November 6/7 to November 19/20, i.e. about 2 weeks. It would be natural for the first birds leaving on the exodus to be the earliest to return for the egg-laying and this is suggested by the history of the male bird in Burrow 404. The screens were erected at this burrow on October 31, but they remained intact each night until November 17/18 when ♂ 15013 was found. Apparently he had left some time prior to October 31, but despite his early return his mate did not lay the egg until after November 23.

From the histological data in Marshall & Serventy (1956) it is evident that the final growth and maturation of the egg take place during this pre-laying exodus.

Insemination, however, probably occurs in the burrow just prior to the exodus, though it has not been observed in our species. Rowan (1952, p. 102) was able to observe copulation in *P. gravis* in the rookeries at Nightingale Island but unlike *P. tenuirostris*, which is wholly nocturnal and subterranean in its behaviour, *P. gravis* 'has a strongly developed diurnal habit during the breeding season' and may display openly on the surface. Tickell (1962, p. 16) observed copulation in *Pachyptila desolata* on numerous occasions both in the open and in the burrow, 'just prior to the departure of the females on their "pre-laying" flight'.

To what extent the pre-laying exodus takes place in petrel species other than those just named is not known, but the likelihood is that it is a general phenomenon in the group. The observations of V.N.Serventy (1952, p. 11) suggest that it may occur in *Puffinus carneipes*, and R.A.Falla (in litt., November 23, 1954) believes it occurs in *P. griseus*. The phenomenon would be more readily detected in those species which have a short well-defined egg-laying period, such as the migratory *P. tenuirostris*, *P. griseus* and *P. carneipes*, than in forms where the period is protracted and consequently the various phases of the nesting cycle tend to become blurred when observed in the mass.

*Incubation and Fledging Periods*
The male and female incubate the egg in alternate and lengthy shifts of duty, the male taking the first, though the female will usually remain with the egg until the male arrives. The duration of the incubation shifts varies from 10 to 16 days, and the frequencies of duty are summarized in Table 1. Adequate data are available only for the first shifts of male and female.

The male's first shift is most frequently 12 or 13 days, and the female's 11–13 days. There is occasionally a fifth shift but usually the egg hatches when the female is incubating during the fourth shift and she broods the chick for the few days it is attended in the burrow. Sometimes, however, the female has to be relieved by the male parent who undertakes the fifth shift. In January 1954 there were twenty-seven cases under observation at which the role of the parents could be exactly determined. In twenty-three burrows the female was incubating when the egg hatched, but in eight of these she left immediately and the day-time brooding of the chick was left to the male. In five burrows the male incubated the egg for the final stages (for 1, 2, 2, 3 and 5 days respectively) and continued to brood the chick afterwards.

The off-duty mate does not revisit the islands and the incubating bird receives no food and does not go to sea during this period. The incubation period varies between 52 and 55 days, with an average of 53 days (based on twenty-four cases).

The chick is hatched between January 10 and 23 and is brooded by one of the parents for about 2 days and then left alone during the day. Both parents share in the feeding, which may be nightly for the first week or so (range 3–12 days) and thereafter at intervals, with several days (up to 16) elapsing between meals. The last feeding (corresponding to the final visit of the parents to the nesting

TABLE I

Incubation shifts of male and female parents

| | Frequency of shifts of different lengths (days) | | | | | | | | Mean length in days |
| --- | --- | --- | --- | --- | --- | --- | --- | --- | --- |
| | 9 | 10 | 11 | 12 | 13 | 14 | 15 | 16 | |
| 1st shift ♂ | — | 1 | 6 | 31 | 29 | 10 | 1 | 1 | 12.6 |
| 2nd shift ♀ | — | 2 | 6 | 5 | 4 | 1 | — | — | 11.8 |
| 3rd shift ♂ | — | — | — | — | — | — | 2 | — | — |
| 4th shift ♀ | 1 | — | 1 | — | — | — | — | — | — |

burrow) is 1–23 days (average of 14 days for twenty cases studied) before the departure of the young birds. This is the 'starvation' or 'desertion' period of authors.

These lengthy absences from the nesting islands enable the adult birds to forage for great distances. Unusual evidence of the extent of these travels has recently been provided in a very neat way by Sutherland (1965) in his investigation of the movement of pumice fragments ejected from a submarine eruptive centre near the South Sandwich Islands in March 1962. It was possible to trace the course of the 'front' of this pumice raft in the Southern Ocean as it was dispersed eastwards under the influence of the West Wind Drift. It first arrived in western Tasmania in December 1963. However, most interestingly, pumiceous balls, identical in chemical and petrological character with the South Sandwich pumice, were identified in stomach contents of nestling mutton-birds at Great Dog Island, near Flinders Island, collected on March 29, 1963, i.e. about 9 months earlier. It was calculated that at the time of the recovery of the pumiceous balls from the nestlings the front of the raft was probably at least 1200 miles west of Macquarie Island, and the parent birds must have flown about 1000 miles to the south-west of their breeding ground to have picked up the pumice. On the most conservative estimate the south-west flight could not have been less than 500 miles.

There is ample opportunity for the breeding adults to cover these distances. At twenty-one Fisher Island nests for which the relevant data are available, in the period immediately preceding the end of March the nestlings remained unfed for intervals of from 3 to 15 days (averaging 9 days). This refers, of course, to the absences of either parent; it was not possible to ascertain which one had come to feed the nestling. So one or other parent could conceivably have been away very much longer than these figures indicate.

It does not necessarily follow that the adult birds are constantly searching for food for the nestlings during these periods of absence. In fact, the evidence points to the contrary. The food items present in the stomachs of the young birds are usually identifiable as to species and show little indication of prolonged decomposition or breakdown. On March 21, 1964, very early in the morning, I collected a series of food samples from well-filled stomachs of nestlings at Great Dog Island and these were examined by the late Dr Keith Sheard, of the C.S.I.R.O. Division of Fisheries and Oceanography. He reported that about one-quarter of the material was at the stage of digestion of food found in the stomachs of feeding birds which are shot at sea. Much of the material must have been taken within several hours of landing to feed the chicks. Dr Sheard pointed out that the food was so comparatively fresh that it appeared that the adult birds collected it only just before heading for the rookeries. It would appear that their previous hunting was for their own needs. The organisms present in this sample were part of the indigenous fauna of seas adjacent to the rookeries—the Euphausiid *Nyctiphanes australis*, Alima larvae of Stomatopods, Brachyuran Megalopids (including those of the shore crab *Leptograpsus*) and clupeoid remains. Earlier samples of stomach contents examined for me by Dr Sheard were also of local organisms.

Data on the times when the breeding adults cease visiting the rookeries are available from two surveys at Fisher Island, in 1954 and 1961. In 1954 fledglings were studied daily at twenty-one burrows and, as judged from the date of the last feeding, the parents made their last visits over a period of some 3 weeks. The earliest date for a 'last visit' was March 29/30 and the latest April 20/21. Most of the birds (six individuals) made their 'last visit' at about the mid-point of this period, i.e. the night of April 9/10. The last time a breeding adult bird was actually seen on the surface at night during this survey was on April 12/13. The last four birds to be encountered about this time (April 8 to 12) were males. In the 1961 survey the last birds seen on the surface were three males on the night of April 13/14 and another male on April 15/16. Surface adults become extremely scarce, however, after the end of March.

A sample of thirty birds collected for experimental purposes in the Furneaux group on the nights of April 9/10 and 10/11, 1957, consisted of twenty males and ten females. A similar sample on the night of April 9/10, 1958, of thirty-five birds was made up of twenty-two males and thirteen females. From all these records, it would appear that the male parents are usually the ones to give the final feed to the chicks.

It can be readily understood that during incubation, where a narrowly defined egg-laying period exists, and with a comparatively lengthy shift system obtaining, flocks sampled at sea should be predominantly one or other sex. Attention was drawn to this many years ago by Stuart-Sutherland (1922, p. 58). Referring to casualties of *Puffinus griseus* at lighthouses between December and March, he noted that a 'curious fact in connection with the Mutton Birds is that one night all the specimens killed against the lantern will be males, whilst on another night all will be females'. There are not enough data available to make a definite generalization, but it does appear that the shift system, involving a sexual segregation in the flocks at sea, prevails well before the incubation period and persists after it during the care of the young. Thus I have the following suggestive records. Before egg laying: October 13, 1939, of five birds shot from a large flock off Maria Island, Tasmania, four were females and one a male; three birds shot on November 1, 1939, near Jervis Bay, N.S.W., were all males. After hatching: four birds shot on February 9, 1939, out of a flock near Cliffy Island, Victoria, were all males. In fledgling birds and migrating pre-breeders on the southward migration the sex ratio is even.

*Occurrence of the Non-breeding Age-groups*

As detailed later, Short-tailed Shearwaters do not usually make a landfall until they are 3 or 4 years of age, though a minute proportion may appear briefly at the age of 2 years. These earlier age groups tend to appear at the rookeries relatively later in the season, after the eggs have hatched; the older non-breeding individuals arrive earlier. The first- and second-year birds, though they do not make a landfall, frequent the neighbouring seas, as is indicated by the recoveries of ringed birds.

In Table 2 are tabulated the occurrences ashore of non-breeding marked shearwaters of various age-classes. The figures are grouped in half-monthly totals and represent the accumulated records from January 1953 to March 1965 of 487 separate appearances of 211 individuals. Unfortunately the data in this table cannot be used for an exact assessment of the relative frequency of visits to the rookery of the various categories of birds, as the periods of observation were not constant over the whole period represented in the table. Up to the start of egg-laying (c. November 18) there were only very limited opportunities for observing the presence of non-breeding immatures, and the period between the third week in December and mid-January has only been sketchily covered. Observation in late February and early March was also restricted. However, some generalizations may be made from the data.

Young birds at age 4 are more frequently encountered than any other pre-breeding class. The drop in numbers of the older immatures, from age 5 onwards, is clearly due either to their joining the ranks of the breeding birds or to their disappearance from the island. The fewer numbers of 3-year-old birds must mean that only a proportion of these birds make a landfall at that age and the rest either stay at sea or come ashore only comparatively briefly. (It may be assumed that there is an equal chance of missing or overlooking individuals of all age-groups.) Using the number of 4-year-old birds as a basis, only 40 per cent of 3-year-old birds make a landfall and only 2 per cent of 2-year-old birds. If the comparison is restricted to the number of individuals recorded per season (last column of Table 2), rather than the number of occasions on which the birds were recorded, the respective percentages are 47 and 4.

Two-year-old birds have only been seen during February. Three-year-old birds mostly appear from the second week in January until early March. Four-year-old birds may start appearing in late November but the bulk are seen during January and February, and they are not recorded after mid-March. Five-year-old and older pre-breeders arrive with the breeding adults at egg-laying time and may quite conceivably arrive with the adults at their initial landfalls from late September onwards. These older immatures usually cease coming ashore by the end of February.

There are indications that the non-breeding birds tend to visit the island more freely at biologically exciting stages in the cycles of the breeding adults. Thus no birds at all, not even immatures, visit the island at the pre-egg-laying exodus (p. 166). On the other hand there is an increase of visits by the immature groups, with a heightened tempo of nocturnal activity, during the egg-laying and hatching periods (see also Warham, 1960, p. 83).

Most of these pre-breeders are encountered on the surface at night. Relatively few stay over, in unoccupied burrows, by day. Those that are found in burrows

TABLE 2

Occurrences of pre-breeders at Fisher Island. Records are arranged in half-monthly periods

| Age | Oct. 1 | Oct. 2 | Nov. 1 | Nov. 2 | Dec. 1 | Dec. 2 | Jan. 1 | Jan. 2 | Feb. 1 | Feb. 2 | Mar. 1 | Mar. 2 | Total number of records | Total number of individuals |
|---|---|---|---|---|---|---|---|---|---|---|---|---|---|---|
| 2 | | | | | | | | | 2 | 2 | | | 4 | 4 |
| 3 | | | 1 | 1 | 14 | 2 | 3 | 10 | 24 | 23 | 3 | 4 | 68 | 57 |
| 4 | | | 14 | 14 | 45 | 12 | 13 | 43 | 52 | 33 | 10 | | 168 | 121 |
| 5 | | | 45 | 16 | 20 | 5 | 7 | 21 | 27 | 7 | | | 133 | 81 |
| 6 | | 2 | 20 | 4 | 8 | 5 | 3 | 10 | 7 | 4 | 2 | | 69 | 39 |
| 7 | 1 | | 8 | 1 | 8 | 3 | 3 | 8 | 6 | 1 | | | 36 | 20 |
| 8 | | | 3 | 1 | 3 | 1 | 1 | 1 | 3 | | | | 9 | 4 |
| Totals | | | | | | | | | | | | | 487 | 326 |

are usually the older age-groups, of 5 years and older. Only two 3-year-old birds have been found in a burrow by day and one 4-year-old bird.

*Fledgling Birds—Emergence and Departure*

With the disappearance of the adult breeding birds from the rookeries at night the current crop of nestlings starts to emerge from the burrows and becomes conspicuous on the surface. They may be seen near their own burrows, frequently exercising their wings by a succession of rapid beats. The earliest date on which such a young bird was seen on the surface was on the night of April 2/3, 1961, but the main emergence started on the night of April 11/12. This was also the date of the first emergence in the 1954 season. After April 12 in 1954 and April 15 in 1961 only the current season's fledglings were seen at the surface. The young birds first are readily recognizable as such through carrying varying amounts of down. Towards the end of the month, however, when the down has been largely lost, to the casual observer there is nothing to distinguish them from adults. They finally disappear on their first exodus migration by the first week of May. The seasonal composition of the population frequenting the nesting islands is shown diagrammatically in Figure 1.

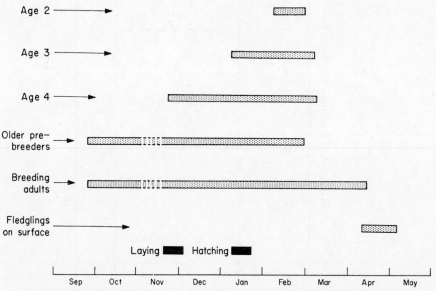

FIGURE 1. Seasonal composition of Short-tailed Shearwaters at Fisher Island, according to age categories. The break in the bars of the older pre-breeders and breeding adults represents the pre-laying exodus.

# Population ecology of the Short-tailed Shearwater

Though some at least of the birds in their first and second year revisit the seas around the breeding area (as proved by the recovery of marked individuals) they do not make a landfall ordinarily until they are 3 or 4 years old. A few precocious individuals make a landfall at 2 years of age, but they represent less than $1\frac{1}{2}$ per cent of the total.

As the composition of the non-breeding birds present on the island can at the best be only imperfectly sampled, owing to lengthy intervals between the observing periods, it is impossible to assert positively that any particular individual first

TABLE 3

First return of marked fledglings to Fisher
Island (data to 1960–61 season)

| Age at first recorded return, years | Number of individuals |
|---|---|
| 2 | 3 |
| 3 | 48 |
| 4 | 99 |
| 5 | 35 |
| 6 | 20 |
| 7 | 4 |
| 8 | 0 |

recorded when it was, say, 5 or 6 years of age, may not really have made a landfall at a much earlier age but escaped detection. Table 3 gives the age 'at first recorded return' of marked fledglings to Fisher Island.

Whilst the figures for 6- and 7-year-old birds have dubious value, owing to the possibility that many of them had been previously overlooked, the table demonstrates that substantial numbers of immature birds make their first landfall at 4 years of age and in lesser proportion at 3 years of age. In round figures we may say that immature birds have 2 years of experience of the nesting terrain before they pass into the ranks of the breeding stock.

The percentage survival of the young birds to the immediate pre-breeding stage is remarkably high. In Table 4 is set out the number of young birds known to have been successfully fledged and the number which have been checked back at the island after 3 years or more of life.

The figures of returning birds, of course, are only a minimum. They could conceivably be higher, as some birds which make only a temporary sojourn after landfall could be overlooked during the sampling surveys and others might not come back at all to the island, but go to rookeries on neighbouring islands. Nevertheless, they do indicate a substantial survival of immatures.

TABLE 4

Return of Fisher Island progeny

| Natal year | Escapement number | Number returned | Percentage returned |
|---|---|---|---|
| 1950 | 20 | 9 | 45 |
| 1951 | 63 | 18 | 29 |
| 1952 | 22 | 13 | 59 |
| 1953 | 35 | 12 | 34 |
| 1954 | 81 | 29 | 36 |
| 1955 | 26 | 13 | 50 |
| 1956 | 30 | 6 | 20 |
| 1957 | 71 | 32 | 45 |
| 1958 | 58 | 13 | 22 |
| 1959 | 65 | 22 | 34 |
| 1960 | 51 | 22 | 43 |
| Total | 522 | 189 | Mean = 37 |

Most of the losses occur in the first year, but even these are relatively low considering the size of the population involved (Serventy, 1957, p. 58; 1961, p. 53). Too few recoveries are available from fledglings marked at Fisher Island to give a true picture of the mortality pattern: one bird died just after leaving the island, another died in the Bering Sea at 3 years of age, and the third was a victim of the spring mortality in eastern Australia at 6 years of age.

However, recourse may be had to the results of the extensive ringing programme on other islands. In Table 5 are set out the numbers of birds marked as fledglings between 1950 and 1964 in various rookeries in south-eastern Australia which were found dead or injured, the data being separated according to age at death and geographical area.

The number of fledglings marked with monel metal rings during the period on which the data of Table 5 are based (1950–64) totalled 36,797. The percentage recovery is, therefore, quite minute. In the vulnerable first year or so of life

TABLE 5

Mortality pattern of birds marked as fledglings

| Age at death, years | Recovery area | | | |
|---|---|---|---|---|
| | Within breeding area | North Pacific | Eastern Australia and New Zealand | Total |
| 0 | 9 | 17 | 26 | 52 |
| 1 | 2 | 2 | 6 | 10 |
| 2 | — | 1 | 3 | 4 |
| 3 | 1 | 1 | 2 | 4 |
| 4 | 5 | — | 1 | 6 |
| 5 | — | — | — | — |
| 6 | — | — | 1 | 1 |
| 7 | — | — | — | — |
| 8 | — | — | — | — |
| 9 | — | — | 1 | 1 |
| 10 | — | — | — | — |
| 11 | — | — | 1 | 1 |
| Total | 17 | 21 | 41 | 79 |

(combining age-classes 0 and 1 in the above table) a total of sixty-two dead or injured birds were reported, i.e. 0.17 per cent. In the period before landfall at the natal islands (i.e. the age-groups 0, 1 and 2 in the table), the recovered rings totalled sixty-six, i.e. 0.18 per cent. If the data in Table 4 can be accepted as correct, then the true average mortality in these age-groups should approach 63 per cent. The difference gives an indication of the number of dead marked birds that are not recovered, not surprising in the case of this species whose migratory circuit around the Pacific Ocean is largely over areas where there is no possibility of knowledge-able observers recovering rings from the casualties which occur.

Nevertheless, the low rate of ring recovery along the beaches of eastern and south-eastern Australia, where during the southward migration in spring and summer a very considerable mortality may occur, involving thousands of birds in a season, is rather striking. It attests to the huge aggregate population of the species. We have teams of observers examining certain of these beaches each year, searching for marked birds, in particular Cronulla Beach south of Sydney, New South Wales. Between 1950 and 1964 our observers have counted 22,086 dead shearwaters of this species on the beach. Among them there were only two ringed birds, which were not, however, ringed as fledglings, but as breeding adults. This programme will continue and when a significantly large number of birds (ringed as fledglings) *are* eventually recovered, a method will be available of making an approximate assessment of the total population of the species by the Petersen (or Lincoln) Index technique.

### HOMING OF YOUNG BIRDS TO THE NATAL ISLAND

It has been found that a substantial number of young birds, reared on Fisher Island, return to the island in the pre-breeding years and some settle down as nesting birds. In Table 6 is set out a statistical summary of the numbers of birds returning as pre-breeders and those staying on to breed, in comparison with the numbers fledged each year.

It will be seen that the number of young birds which homed back to the natal island in the pre-breeding years averages (for the period covered in this particular table) 38 per cent of the escapement number, and as explained on p. 176, this must be a minimal number as some individuals were very probably overlooked in the surveys. Only 13 per cent of those that were fledged, and 31 per cent of those that returned, remained as breeders on their natal island. Both sexes behaved simi-larly. The balance of the birds presumably sought breeding sites on other islands, and this is definitely proved for several individuals which were subsequently found on Little Green Island slightly more than half a mile away.

Return to the natal islands has no hereditary basis. Eggs have been transferred from other islands to Fisher and the fledged young have returned to Fisher Island. At what stage, then, does the young bird form an attachment to the piece of land to which it tends to home in later life? Our first experiment to find an answer was to transfer fifty fledglings from other islands to Fisher Island at the end of the

# Population ecology of the Short-tailed Shearwater

desertion period (when they would no longer require parental feeding) but before they left on their initial exodus migration. Not one of these birds subsequently returned to Fisher Island, but 36 per cent of the eighty-one native Fisher Island birds did so. It was evident that the transferred birds had already become 'imprinted' on their own home island.

It was thought that the most likely sensitive period for this 'locality imprinting'

TABLE 6
Homing details of Fisher Island progeny

| Natal year | Escapement number | Number returned | Number remaining to breed | Percentage remaining to breed: of escapement number | of number returned | Sex ratio of breeding birds ♂ | ♀ |
|---|---|---|---|---|---|---|---|
| 1950 | 20 | 9 | 3 | 15 | 33 | 1 | 2 |
| 1951 | 63 | 18 | 8 | 13 | 44 | 6 | 2 |
| 1952 | 22 | 13 | 5 | 23 | 38 | 1 | 4 |
| 1953 | 35 | 12 | 5 | 14 | 42 | 2 | 3 |
| 1954 | 81 | 29 | 8 | 10 | 28 | 4 | 4 |
| 1955 | 26 | 13 | 2 | 8 | 15 | — | 2 |
| 1956 | 30 | 6 | 0 | — | — | — | — |
| 1957 | 71 | 32 | 13 | 18 | 41 | 9 | 4 |
| Total | 348 | 132 | 44 | 13 | 31 | 23 | 21 |

was when the chick first emerged from its burrow at night to exercise its wings. This emergence usually starts in mid-April, coinciding with the beginning of the 'desertion' or 'starvation' period. So from 1961 onwards batches of young fledglings have been transferred from other islands to Fisher Island at this period. Thus far, results have only been possible from the 1961 experiment and the returns cannot yet be regarded as complete. However, the results to date are as follows:

| | Escapement number | Returned birds | Percentage return |
|---|---|---|---|
| Fisher Island 'control' birds | 61 | 17 | 28 |
| Transferred birds | 16 | 3 | 19 |

The results may be considered as distinctly encouraging for the hypothesis. The percentage return is certainly below that of the native (control) chicks, but one should not expect otherwise. It is impossible, in an experiment of this sort, to ensure that none of the experimental birds is already imprinted.

The hypothesis of locality imprinting was first put forward by Thorpe in 1944 (p. 67) from studies on the higher Hymenoptera. Various observations on birds, giving results similar to those reported here on shearwaters, have been summarized by Drost (1951, p. 228) who comments: 'Experiments with young birds show the same result: they do not return to their proper home but to the place where they have grown up and were liberated.' This generalization is not wholly true of *Puffinus tenuirostris* where quite clearly a locality imprinting is involved and the sensitive period is restricted.

Those individuals which have finally settled down to nest on Fisher Island have chosen a burrow site in the particular rookeries in which they themselves were hatched and raised. Thus of the three rookeries on the island no chick has settled on other than its own natal rookery. In the case of the largest rookery—Home Rookery—the distances between the birth burrow and the first breeding burrow were as follows:

12 ♂♂—average distance, 22 feet, varying from 2 to 60 feet.
12 ♀♀ —average distance, 25 feet, varying from 4 to 60 feet.

Usually once a bird settles on a nest site it persists there throughout life.

The incoming young birds are absorbed into the nesting community mainly as partners to established breeding birds who have lost, or have changed, their mates. Of forty-nine Fisher Island-raised young birds on which the relevant data are available, 76 per cent have mated up with 'aged' birds, 20 per cent with young birds breeding for the first time, and 4 per cent with young birds breeding for the second time.

### AGE AT FIRST BREEDING

In the circumstances existing at Fisher Island it would appear to be a simple matter to obtain a large amount of precise data on the age at which individual birds, marked as fledglings, begin to breed. In actual fact it is often uncertain when particular individuals do start. Apart from being possibly overlooked—surprisingly easy even in such a small colony as this—one cannot always satisfactorily distinguish preliminary association, between birds, burrows and mates, from the genuine start of reproduction. Table 7 summarizes the data on twenty-three females (based on egg-laying) and twenty-one males (first mated with productive females), whose breeding history could not have been previously

TABLE 7
Age at first breeding

| Age of bird | Number of females | Number of males |
|---|---|---|
| 4 | 0 | 0 |
| 5 | 9 | 2 |
| 6 | 9 | 9 |
| 7 | 5 | 6 |
| 8 | 0 | 4 |

overlooked. It will be seen that females tend to begin breeding slightly earlier than males, the mean commencing age for females being 5.3 years and for males 6.6 years. The mean age for both sexes combined is 5.9 years.

The span of ages at which breeding commences is from 5 to 8 years. It is interesting that no non-breeding Fisher Island-raised birds continue to visit Fisher

TABLE 8
Age at which non-breeding young
were last seen

| Age | Number of individuals |
|---|---|
| 3 | 12 |
| 4 | 36 |
| 5 | 26 |
| 6 | 12 |
| 7 | 8 |
| 8 | 1 |

Island after these ages. Table 8 sets out the ages at which young birds, which did not settle down on Fisher Island as breeders, were last recorded at the island. It could well be that birds of the younger ages (3 and 4 years) continue to visit at older ages (5 and 6) and were overlooked but it is unlikely that the frequencies at the older ages (7 and 8) will be significantly altered by further observations.

The disappearance of these birds from Fisher Island can scarcely be attributed to mortality, but is plainly a case of exodus to other breeding grounds. Of the eight birds last seen at Fisher Island at 7 years of age half were picked up on Little Green Island, just over half a mile away, at ages varying from 10 to 14 years when they were obviously breeding there. Altogether eleven Fisher Island young birds have been seen at the Little Green Island promontory after they ceased visiting Fisher Island.

It is clear that despite their strong tendency to home back to the natal area (see p. 180) these shearwaters cease to frequent it after the normal span of ages at which breeding starts (5–8 years) if they do not succeed in finding a mate or a home burrow, and move to other rookeries. In the particular case of Fisher Island a contributing factor in the exodus may be human disturbance or the increasingly unfavourable nature of the peripheral parts of the rookeries.

### EGG SIZE IN RELATION TO AGE

Richdale (1957, p. 112) has shown that young females of the Yellow-eyed Penguin *Megadyptes antipodes* laying for the first time produce narrower eggs than when they are older, and later suggests (Richdale, 1963, p. 19) that this may be true also of *Puffinus griseus*.

Measurements of eggs laid by females of *P. tenuirostris* of known age support Richdale's suggestion, but our data are not extensive enough as yet. Females in their first breeding year lay narrow eggs which, moreover, are longer than eggs of older birds, and the mean width of eggs increases up to about the sixth or seventh breeding season, as shown in Table 9.

The mean width of eggs of marked females which have been breeding for upwards of ten seasons is 47.6 mm (twenty eggs in sample). The mean width of two random samples of twenty-five and one hundred eggs in burrows has in both cases been 47.1 mm.

The data for marked females have been examined by Dr D.W.Goodall of the Division of Mathematical Statistics, C.S.I.R.O. The regression of egg width on breeding age is highly significant ($r = 0.4440$, $n = 48$). Differences between individuals in the regression of egg width on breeding age did not reach significance (see Table 10).

In Table 11 the data are slightly recast, to show the mean egg widths of females at their actual ages, irrespective of their breeding history. The significance here is less ($r = 0.3279$), indicating that the important factor determining egg width is not so much the actual age of the female, but the number of times she has laid an egg.

These results lead to a consideration of the problem of eggs found on the surface of rookeries and not in burrows (Richdale, 1963, p. 18). Though occasional

TABLE 9
Egg widths at successive breeding intervals

| Year of breeding | Number of eggs in sample | Mean width of egg (mm) |
|---|---|---|
| 1st | 7 | 44.4 |
| 2nd | 7 | 46.1 |
| 3rd | 5 | 46.8 |
| 4th | 4 | 46.8 |
| 5th | 2 | 47.4 |
| 6th | 4 | 47.2 |
| 7th | 5 | 47.6 |
| 8th | 3 | 46.8 |
| 9th | 3 | 47.7 |

TABLE 10
Analysis of variance, regression of egg width on breeding age

| | Degrees of freedom | Sum of squares | Mean square | Variance ratio |
|---|---|---|---|---|
| Common regression | 1 | 14.6770 | 14.6770 | |
| Between regressions | 9 | 9.3129 | 1.0348 | 1.53 |
| Between means (corrected for common regression) | 15 | 49.6780 | 3.3119 | |
| Deviations | 23 | 15.5935 | 0.6780 | |

eggs may be found on the surface of any mutton-bird rookery every season, in some years there may be very large numbers, referred to as 'gluts' by the islanders in the Furneaux group. At one such occurrence, at Great Dog Island in November–December 1959, I measured a sample of fifty-two surface eggs.

The mean width was 46.5 mm, which differs significantly from the mean of those in random samples from the breeding burrows (47.1 mm). These narrow surface eggs, therefore, are probably laid by young birds though not solely by individuals in their first breeding year.

TABLE II
Egg widths at particular ages

| Age of female in years | Number of eggs in sample | Mean width of egg (mm) |
|---|---|---|
| 5 | 6 | 45.4 |
| 6 | 6 | 45.7 |
| 7 | 11 | 46.3 |
| 8 | 8 | 46.6 |
| 9 | 8 | 47.2 |
| 10 | 5 | 47.6 |
| 11 | 5 | 47.0 |

MIGRATION MORTALITIES

Adults and young birds appear to follow the same migratory circuit in the Pacific Ocean (Serventy, 1958). There are two areas where large numbers of marked shearwaters are regularly recovered: (a) in the North Pacific Ocean where many first-year birds become entangled in salmon-fishing nets during their exodus migration, and (b) along the eastern Australian coast where again many first-year birds perish at the end of their return migration, the cause here being starvation. Included in the predominantly first-year victims on this Australian section are, in some seasons, a number of older birds. This is not the case in the North Pacific where only pre-breeding birds have so far been reported as casualties.

The east Australian migration deaths occur from October to December, sometimes lasting into January. Since 1938 we have been conducting counts along a 4-mile stretch of beach between Cronulla and Boat Harbour, south of Botany Bay, N.S.W., to assess the yearly fluctuations. In some years the mortality may be very low and less than ten birds may be counted during the entire season. In years of peak mortality the count may reach nearly 4000 individuals. There may be 10 years or more with continuously low mortalities, as happened between 1943 and 1953, or there may be a rapid succession of bad mortality years. The number of dead birds in high-mortality years arouses public attention and there are references to the phenomenon in popular and scientific literature. Thus mortalities on a scale to arouse public comment occurred in 1851, 1880, 1883, 1895, 1919, 1934 and 1935. The mortality of 1934 was particularly severe and extended from southern Queensland to Tasmania, and dead birds were washed up on the other side of the Tasman Sea, in New Zealand, where, interestingly enough, the local breeding species, *Puffinus griseus*, was not affected. In more recent years there were heavy-mortality years in 1938, 1940, 1941, 1942 (very severe), 1954 (very severe), 1958, 1960 and 1962 (particularly on the south coast).

During the various mortality periods a number of birds have been examined by pathologists, but no obvious indications of disease could be found. All the dead birds are invariably in an emaciated condition, with empty stomachs. Weak live birds at the time are frequently reported as voraciously attacking the baited hooks of anglers and line fishermen and are plainly desperate for food. All the evidence attests to the deaths being due to starvation through a temporary short-age of surface food (small pelagic fish and euphausiid crustacea) just after the birds have battled through the trade winds barrier when nearing the end of their return migration (Serventy, 1958, p. 331).

Details of the age classification of the birds figuring in the Australian mortalities are set out in Table 12. Adult birds are not ordinarily conspicuous in these morta-lities. Their absence in the table up to 1959 is primarily due to the comparative fewness of marked adult birds at large. Latterly the banding of adult birds, parti-cularly of birds known to be breeders, has been stepped up, accounting for the increased recoveries since 1960 (see Table 13).

The mortality among birds of this category was particularly pronounced in the early summer of 1962, when a number of birds known to be breeding adults succumbed. This mortality began about November 7 and lasted only a few days. Of the eleven birds known to be breeders it was possible to sex four of them; all were males. Dr R.Mykytowycz, pathologist of the C.S.I.R.O., was able to visit the south coast beaches shortly afterwards and dissected 536 carcases; of these 435 (81 per cent) were males, almost all with well-enlarged gonads.

This mortality took place during the 'pre-laying exodus' when both sexes are at sea. However, the shift system, which is obvious among breeding birds during the incubation period (which starts about November 20), is in being long before egg-laying and persists after hatching. In other words the two sexes are segregated for a large part of the period they are at the breeding grounds. Therefore, an aggregation which comprised mainly male breeding birds (known breeding

TABLE 12

Mortality in eastern Australia and New Zealand

| Year of mortality | Age classes of marked dead birds of known age | | | | | | | Marked dead birds of partially known ages | | Grand total |
|---|---|---|---|---|---|---|---|---|---|---|
| | 0+ | 3 | 4 | 6 | 9 | 11 | Total | Adults of unknown age when banded | Breeding adults when banded | |
| 1951–52 | 1 | — | — | — | — | — | 1 | — | — | 1 |
| 1952–53 | — | — | — | — | — | — | — | — | — | — |
| 1953–54 | 1 | 1 | — | — | — | — | 2 | — | — | 2 |
| 1954–55 | — | — | — | — | — | — | — | — | — | — |
| 1955–56 | — | 1 | — | — | — | — | 1 | — | — | 1 |
| 1956–57 | — | — | — | — | — | — | — | — | — | — |
| 1957–58 | — | — | — | — | — | — | — | — | — | — |
| 1958–59 | — | — | 1 | — | — | — | 1 | — | — | 1 |
| 1959–60 | 3 | — | — | 1 | — | — | 4 | — | — | 4 |
| 1960–61 | 7 | — | — | — | — | — | 7 | 1 | — | 8 |
| 1961–62 | 7 | — | — | — | — | — | 7 | 6 | 3 | 16 |
| 1962–63 | 12 | 1 | — | — | — | — | 13 | 15 | 11 | 39 |
| 1963–64 | 3 | 1 | 1 | — | — | 1 | 6 | 5 | — | 11 |
| 1964–65 | 3 | 6 | 4 | — | 1 | — | 14 | 1 | 1 | 16 |
| Total | 37 | 10 | 6 | 1 | 1 | 1 | 56 | 28 | 15 | 99 |

# Population ecology of the Short-tailed Shearwater

localities among the victims included the Furneaux group and the Tollgates Islands) encountered hostile physical conditions and succumbed on a large scale.

These 'hostile factors' in the Tasman Sea environment stem from the basic instability of the marine conditions there, the complex hydrological character of the water bodies leading to wide fluctuations in plankton and pelagic fish abundance (cf. Serventy, 1956, p. 38). Thus adequate surface stores of food may

TABLE 13

Number of birds ringed as adults (breeding adults and
adults of unknown status combined)

| Season | Number ringed each season | Progress total |
|---|---|---|
| 1949–50 to 1955–56 | 458 | 458 |
| 1956–57 | 50 | 508 |
| 1957–58 | 51 | 559 |
| 1958–59 | 294 | 853 |
| 1959–60 | 827 | 1,680 |
| 1960–61 | 4,442 | 6,122 |
| 1961–62 | 1,566 | 7,688 |
| 1962–63 | 1,994 | 9,682 |
| 1963–64 | 1,009 | 10,691 |
| 1964–65 | 2,306 | 12,997 |

not be regularly available. Here we may have one of those rare situations where the normal hypothesis, of randomness of death after the immature mortality, may not strictly hold. In the western portion of the Tasman Sea we have dense concentrations of shearwaters on traditional but unreliable feeding areas, where in some seasons a dearth of food may put severe and unusual stress on the two ends of the population—the young and inexperienced, and the ageing ones. In ordinary mortality situations the deaths of the ageing birds may be expected to be spread out over many years. Here in the unusual Tasman Sea environment deaths appear to be clumped at (though not of course confined to) the two vulnerable ends of the life-span.

This suggestion—for it can be no more than that at the moment—of an 'old age' effect in the local shearwater population cannot be substantiated until a great many more data are forthcoming. Fortunately the local situation is most advantageous for their accumulation: the ringing programme on fledglings and breeding adults is going on apace, a large fraction of the dead birds are washed up on accessible beaches and observing teams are being organized for their inspection.

## SUMMARY

Breeding Short-tailed Shearwaters make their first landfall in the last week of September. The phenomenon of the 'pre-laying exodus' is particularly conspicuous in this species because of the short, well-defined laying period, and the nesting islands are entirely deserted for about a fortnight at this time.

The parents have lengthy incubation shifts, the male taking the first, of about 12–14 days. The shift system, involving a sexual segregation in the flocks at sea, appears to prevail before the incubation period and persists during the care of the young.

The young are fed at lengthening intervals, with several days elapsing between meals. These long absences enable the parents to undertake long-distance foraging, and one piece of evidence is cited suggesting that they may pick up food 1000 miles away, though examination of stomach contents of young birds indicates that much of the material fed to them may be freshly taken in neighbouring seas.

Survival of the fledged young to the immediate pre-breeding stage is high, the mean percentage return being 37 per cent, which must be a minimal measure of the real survival over this period. The homing of the young birds back to the natal area has no hereditary basis, but 'locality imprinting' appears to take place during a restricted sensitive period when the young begin their nocturnal emergences from the burrows in mid-April, at the start of the 'desertion period'.

Pre-breeding birds home back to their natal islands, but do not make a landfall until their third or fourth year. The earlier age-groups of pre-breeders come ashore at about the hatching time of the eggs and cease their visits by the end of February. Pre-breeders of 5 years or older arrive with the breeding adults at the end of September.

Both sexes may start breeding at 5 years of age, but the mean starting age for males is 6.6 years and for females 5.3 years. Young females lay narrower eggs than do older birds, and the surface eggs found on some breeding islands are laid by young individuals.

Recoveries of ringed birds indicate two areas in the extensive migratory circuit where heavy mortality of first-year birds is known to occur: in the north-west Pacific and the east coast of Australia.

### REFERENCES

CAMPBELL A.J. (1901) *Nests and Eggs of Australian Birds*. Published by the author, Sheffield.

DAVIES R.H. (1846) Some account of the habits and natural history of the Sooty Petrel. *Tasmanian J. Nat. Sc.* **2**, 13–16.

DROST R. (1951) Study of bird migration 1938–1950. *Proc. Xth Int. Ornith. Congr. Uppsala 1950*, pp. 216–240.

ELWES R. (1859) Note on the breeding and mode of capture of the Short-tailed Petrel, or Mutton-bird (*Puffinus obscurus*), in the islands in Bass's Straits. *Ibis* (1st ser.) **1**, 397–399.

FISHER J. (1952) *The Fulmar*. Collins, London.

LITTLER F.M. (1910) *A Handbook of the Birds of Tasmania*. Published by the author, Launceston.

LOCKLEY R.M. (1942) *Shearwaters*. J.M.Dent, London.

LORD C.E. & SCOTT H.H. (1924) *A Synopsis of the Vertebrate Animals of Tasmania*. Oldham, Beddome & Meredith, Hobart.

MARSHALL A.J. & SERVENTY D.L. (1956) The breeding cycle of the Short-tailed Shearwater, *Puffinus tenuirostris* (Temminck), in relation to trans-equatorial migration and its environment. *Proc. Zool. Soc. Lond.* **127** (4), 489–510.

MONTGOMERY H.H. (1898) On the habits of the Mutton-bird of Bass Strait, Australia (*Puffinus tenuirostris*). *Ibis* (7th ser.) **4**, 209–216.

PERRYMAN C.E. (1937) Notes from Althorpe Islands. *South Austral. Ornithol.* **14** (1), 14–19.

RICHDALE L.E. (1950) The pre-egg stage in the albatross family. *Biol. Monogr.*, N.Z. No. **3**, 1–92.

RICHDALE L.E. (1957) *A Population Study of Penguins*. Oxford University Press.

RICHDALE L.E. (1963) Biology of the Sooty Shearwater *Puffinus griseus*. *Proc. Zool. Soc. Lond.* **141** (1), 1–117.

ROWAN M.K. (1952) The Great Shearwater, *Puffinus gravis*, at its breeding grounds. *Ibis* **94** (1), 97–121.

SERVENTY D.L. (1956) The Southern Bluefin Tuna, *Thunnus thynnus maccoyii* (Castelnau), in Australian waters. *Austr. Journ. Mar. Freshw. Res.* **7**, (1), 1–43.

SERVENTY D.L. (1957) The banding programme on *Puffinus tenuirostris*. I. *C.S.I.R.O. Wildlife Research* **2**, 51–59.

SERVENTY D.L. (1958) Recent studies on the Tasmanian Mutton-bird. *Austr. Mus. Mag.* **12** (10), 327–332.

SERVENTY D.L. (1961) The banding programme on *Puffinus tenuirostris*. II. *C.S.I.R.O. Wildlife Research* **6**, 42–55.

SERVENTY D.L. (1962) Slender-billed Shearwater. In *Handbook of North American Birds*, vol. 1, pp. 179–186. Ed. R.S.Palmer. Yale University Press, New Haven and London.

SERVENTY D.L. (1963) Egg-laying timetable of the Slender-billed Shearwater. *Proc. XIIIth Int. Ornithol. Congr.* **2**, 338–343.

SERVENTY V.N. (1952) The Archipelago of the Recherche. Part 2, Birds. *Austr. Geog. Soc. Rep.* No. **1**.

STUART-SUTHERLAND R. (1922) Round the lamp. *Emu* **22** (1), 54–59.

SUTHERLAND F.L. (1965) Dispersal of pumice, supposedly from the 1962 South Sandwich Islands eruption, on southern Australian shores. *Nature* **207** (5004), 1332–1335.

# D.L.Serventy

THORPE W.H. (1944) Types of learning in insects and other invertebrates. Part III. *Brit. Journ. Psychol. (General Section)* **34**, 66–76.

TICKELL W.L.N. (1962) The Dove Prion, *Pachyptila desolata* Gmelin. *Falkland Islands Dependencies Survey Sc. Repts.* No. **33**, 1–55.

VALETTE L.H. (1906) Viaje á las Islas Orcadas Australes. *An. Secc. Vet. Zool.* **3**, No. 2, Pt. 1, 3–38 (cited from Tickell, 1962).

VENABLES L.S.V. (1952) Appendix VII in J.Fisher, *The Fulmar*. Collins, London.

WARHAM J. (1960) Some aspects of breeding behaviour in the Short-tailed Shearwater. *Emu* **60** (2), 75–87.

# Populationsdynamik des Weissen Storchs, *Ciconia ciconia*, in Mitteleuropa

GERHARDT ZINK

Vogelwarte Radolfzell, 7761 Schloss Möggingen, Germany

Der Weisse Storch ist seit langer Zeit das bevorzugte Untersuchungsobjekt unseres Instituts. Seit Thienemann im Jahre 1906 die ersten Störche beringte (Thienemann, 1907), ist eine lange Reihe von Veröffentlichungen erschienen, die sich mit dieser Art befassen (Schüz & Zink, 1955). Zahlreiche Untersuchungen anderer Autoren wurden angeregt. Als Folge davon gehört unser Vogel im westlichen Teil seines Verbreitungsgebiets zu den am vielseitigsten untersuchten Vogelarten. Brutbiologie, Verhalten, Nahrung, Zug, Orientierung, Parasiten und andere Teilgebiete seiner Lebensgeschichte wurden gründlich durchleuchtet. Wenn hier eine Zusammenfassung über Fragen der Populationsdynamik gegeben werden kann, dann ist das in erster Linie zwei Forschern zu danken: Der eine ist Richard Tantzen, der von 1928 bis 1965 alljährlich den Storchbestand in Oldenburg (NW-Deutschland) erfasste und damit die bisher längste Populations-untersuchung, die sich mit einer Vogelart beschäftigte, unternommen und ihre Ergebnisse veröffentlicht hat (Tantzen, 1962). Es ist gewährleistet, dass diese Be-standsaufnahmen auch nach seinem Tode am 30.1.1966 weitergeführt werden. Der andere ist Ernst Schüz, der einen grossen Teil zur gegenwärtigen Kenntnis vieler Teilgebiete aus der Biologie des Weissen Storches beigetragen und viele andere veranlasst hat, an diesem Forschungsprogramm mitzuarbeiten. Auch die inter-nationalen Bestandsaufnahmen der Jahre 1934 and 1958 gehen auf seine Anregung zurück.

Zwei verschiedene Untersuchungsmethoden und ihre Ergebnisse bilden die Grundlage für diesen Bericht:

1. Jährliche Bestandsaufnahmen erfassen die Brutpopulation in vielen Teilen Mitteleuropas. Dabei werden nicht nur die Zahl der brütenden Paare und die Nichtbrüter, die ein Nest besetzen, sondern auch der Zeitpunkt der Ankunft am Nest, die Zahl der ausgeflogenen Jungen, die Gründe für Verluste und andere Einzelheiten festgestellt.

Diese Zusammenfassung kann keine vollständige Übersicht geben, sondern nur Beispiele bringen. Die Quellen bis 1959 wurden in bisher vier Übersichten zusammengestellt und ausgewertet (Schüz, 1936 und 1940; Sauter & Schüz, 1954; Schüz & Szijj, 1960b). Eine fünfte Übersicht aus der Feder von Schüz & Szijj ist in Vorbereitung. Sie wird auch den Einzeldank an die vielen verdienten Mitarbeiter aussprechen und die veröffentlichten und unveröffentlichten Quellen nennen, die z. T. schon für diesen Bericht zur Verfügung standen.

2. In besonderen Untersuchungsgebieten werden jährlich alle brütenden Altvögel kontrolliert und die Ringinschrift bei beringten Vögeln mit dem Fernrohr abgelesen (Abbildung der dafür verwendeten Spezialringe bei Zink, 1963). Auf diese Weise werden u.a. Unterlagen über das Alter bei der ersten Brut, über Alter und Verhalten von Vögeln, die nicht zur Brut schreiten, über die Entfernung zwischen Geburtsort und Brutort, die Ortstreue nach der ersten Brut und die Sterblichkeitsrate der Altvögel gesammelt.

### BESTANDSSCHWANKUNGEN

Die Bestände des Weissen Storchs in Mitteleuropa sind gekennzeichnet durch erhebliche Schwankungen über längere Zeiträume. Nach einem Gipfel am Ende des letzten Jahrhunderts nahmen die Brutpaarzahlen in den ersten zehn bis fünfzehn Jahren dieses Jahrhunderts stark ab. Dabei wurden Zahlen erreicht, die nur noch ein Drittel bis ein Viertel der ursprünglichen Höhe ausmachten. Danach verlangsamte sich der Rückgang bis zum Ende der zwanziger Jahre. Für diesen ganzen Zeitraum stehen allerdings nur gelegentliche Zählungen in verschiedenen Gebieten zur Verfügung. Jährliche Bestandsaufnahmen gibt es erst seit 1928 und zunächst nur für Oldenburg. Sie mögen daher als Beispiel für die weitere Entwicklung dienen (Abb. 1, mittlere Kurve). Von einem Tiefpunkt im Jahre 1929 nimmt der Bestand bis 1940 zu mehr als doppelter Höhe zu. Dann fallen die Zahlen bis zum Jahre 1950. Der Tiefststand ist 1953 erreicht. Die Zahl der ausgeflogenen Jungen (Abb. 1, obere Kurve) schwankt mehr als die der Paare. Sie hängt ab nicht nur vom Wetter in der Aufzuchtzeit, vom Nahrungsangebot, von der Zahl der bei intraspezifischen Kämpfen zerstörten Eier oder getöten Jungen, sondern auch vom Anteil der Paare, die Junge erfolgreich aufziehen. Den Anteil der jungenlosen Paare zeigt Abb. 1 (untere Kurve). Es ist deutlich, dass ein Tief in der Jungenzahl immer mit einem hohen Anteil jungenloser Paare zusammenhängt und umgekehrt. Auf das Phänomen der nichtbrütenden Paare wird später noch einzugehen sein.

Dieses Bild für das Auf und Ab des Storchbestands gilt recht allgemein für ganz Mitteleuropa: Abnahme vom Beginn dieses Jahrhunderts bis etwa 1929,

# Populationsdynamik des Weissen Storchs in Mitteleuropa

dann starke Zunahme bis 1940, in SW-Deutschland bis 1948, dann wieder Abnahme, die meist weit unter die Zahlen für 1929 geht. In diesem Zeitraum haben Schweden und die Schweiz ihre Störche ganz verloren. Die beiden internationalen Bestandsaufnahmen der Jahre 1934 und 1958 zeigen eine allgemeine Abnahme

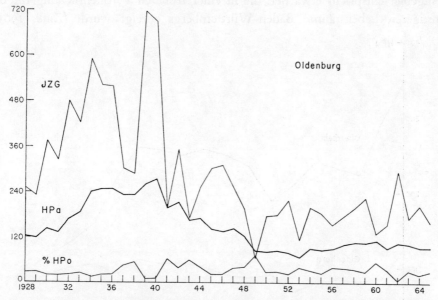

ABB. 1. Der Bestand des Weissen Storchs in Oldenburg—The population of the White Stork in Oldenburg (north-west Germany) 1928–65.

JZG    = Zahl der ausgeflogenen Jungstörche—Numbers of young raised.
HPa    = Zahl der Paare mit Nestbindung—Numbers of pairs attached to a nest.
% HPo = Prozentsatz der jungenlosen Paare—Percentage of pairs without young.

in Mitteleuropa von etwa 50%, die aber im Nordwesten (vor allem in den Niederlanden und in Dänemark) erheblich stärker (bis 80%), im Südosten (Bayern, Österreich) aber kaum bemerkbar ist oder gar umgekehrte Vorzeichen hat (Schüz & Szijj, 1960a und 1962).

Vergleicht man nun verschiedene Gebiete, für die seit 1948 genaue Unterlagen vorliegen, so ergeben sich z. T. erhebliche Unterschiede in der Bestandsentwicklung. Abb. 2 stellt zunächst Oldenburg dem Rheintal nördlich von Basel (= Oberrheingebiet) gegenüber. Beide Kurven zeigen einen starken Abfall im Jahre 1949, das in ganz Mitteleuropa eines der schlechtesten Brutjahre überhaupt war. Dann schwanken die Zahlen in Oldenburg nur noch wenig. Ungünstige Jahre sind auch 1953 und 1961. Die Zahl für 1965 liegt aber um 10% höher als die für

193

1949. Im Oberrheingebiet verläuft die Entwicklung bis 1961 ähnlich. Ungünstige Jahre treten allerdings immer paarweise auf (1949/50, 1953/54 und 1961/62). Im Gegensatz zu Oldenburg nehmen die Zahlen nach 1961 aber ständig ab. Sie fielen bis 1965 auf 34% des Bestands von 1949.—Diese Kurve für das Oberrheingebiet entspricht etwa der, die in einer früheren Veröffentlichung für die günstigeren Lebensräume Baden-Württembergs gezeigt wurde (Zink, 1963).

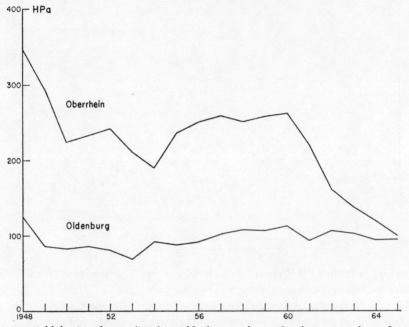

ABB. 2. Zahl der Storchpaare (HPa) in Oldenburg und am Oberrhein—Numbers of pairs (HPa) in Oldenburg and in the upper Rhine valley, 1948-65.

Auch dort hatte der Bestand in den Jahren 1949–60 nicht abgenommen. Hier sind die Zahlen für das Elsass hinzugefügt. Damals konnte darauf hingewiesen werden, dass die Abnahme in den ungünstigeren hügeligen oder trocken gelegten Teilen Baden-Württembergs über den ganzen Zeitraum hinweg ziemlich stetig war. Der Nullpunkt ist jetzt (1965) nahezu erreicht. Der Unterschied zwischen den beiden Lebensraum-Gruppen wurde damit erklärt, dass die im günstigeren Oberrheintal geborenen Vögel sich später nahezu ausschliesslich im gleichen Gebiet ansiedeln, während diejenigen aus den ungünstigeren Gebieten grossenteils in günstigere Räume abwandern, die im Osten oder Westen angrenzen. Seitdem diese ungünstigen Lebensräume fast ganz aufgegeben sind, nimmt der Bestand auch im Oberrheingebiet ab.

# Populationsdynamik des Weissen Storchs in Mitteleuropa

Abbildung 3 vergleicht die Bestandsbewegungen für den gleichen Zeitraum in anderen Gebieten. Wie in Oldenburg gibt es im Bezirk Osnabrück (Niedersachsen) und in der Landschaft Stapelholm (Schleswig-Holstein) keine Abnahme. Man sieht die gleichen Einschnitte wie dort in den Jahren 1949, 1953 and 1961. Recht

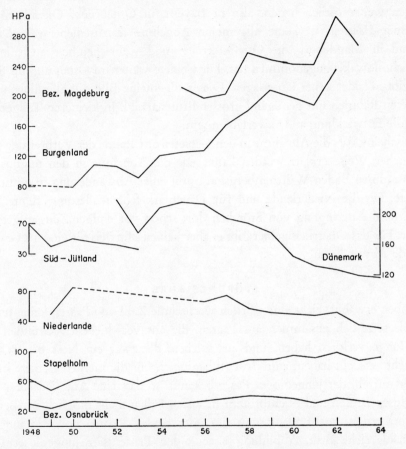

ABB. 3. Zahl der Storchpaare (HPa) in anderen Gebieten—Numbers of pairs (HPa) in other districts, 1948–64.

erheblich ist die Abnahme dagegen in den Niederlanden und in Dänemark, während weiter im Osten im Bezirk Magdeburg und im Burgenland (Österreich) eine beträchtliche Zunahme zu verzeichnen ist. Zusammenfassend kann man sagen, dass der Bestand in den letzten achtzehn Jahren nur am Rand der mitteleuropäischen Verbreitung im Oberrheingebiet, in den Niederlanden und in Dänemark zurückgegangen ist. In Dänemark ist das Bild für die Inseln und die nördlichen Teile Jütlands noch ungünstiger als für den Süden Jütlands. In den fünf südjütländischen Ämtern Vejle, Ribe, Haderslev, Tonder und Aabenraa beträgt der Rückgang in den Jahren 1952 bis 1964 nämlich nur 36,5%, während er im übrigen Land 59,8% ausmacht. In den Gebieten, die vom Rande der Verbreitung aus gesehen weiter östlich liegen, also in Bayern, in Osnabrück, Oldenburg und Schleswig-Holstein ist keine allgemeine Abnahme festzustellen, während der Bestand in Magdeburg, in Ost-Österreich und wahrscheinlich auch in der Tschechoslowakei zugenommen hat. Für Gebiete weiter im Osten und im Südosten gibt es leider keine Unterlagen. Dieses allgemeine Bild gilt allerdings nur in grösseren Räumen mit genügend grosser Brutpaarzahl. In kleineren Teilgebieten kann die Entwicklung anders verlaufen sein.

Es scheint, dass die Abnahme in den Gebieten am Rande der Verbreitung nicht in gleicher Weise erklärt werden kann, wie die Abnahme in den ungünstigen Lebensräumen Baden-Württembergs, also mit einer Abwanderung in günstigere Gebiete. Für die Niederlande und für Dänemark fehlen allerdings Unterlagen dafür, da die Beringung von Störchen dort schon vor einiger Zeit aufgegeben wurde. Für das Oberrheingebiet gibt es aber keinen Hinweis für eine ins Gewicht fallende Abwanderung.

### STÖRUNGSJAHRE

Wie oben erwähnt, zieht eine jährlich wechselnde Zahl von Paaren keine Jungen auf. Sie setzt sich zusammen aus Paaren, die aus verschiedenen Gründen Eier oder Junge verloren haben, und aus solchen, die zwar ein Nest besetzt, aber gar nicht versucht haben, eine Brut zu beginnen. Für die meisten Gebiete ist nur die Gesamtzahl der jungenlosen Paare bekannt, so dass eine Aufgliederung nach erfolglosen Bruten und Nichtbrütern in vielen Fällen nicht möglich ist. Bei den Nichtbrütern ist meist wenigstens einer der beiden Partner noch zu jung für eine erfolgreiche Brut. Abbildung 4 zeigt den Prozentsatz jungenloser Paare (% HPo) für Oldenburg, Baden-Württemberg und das Elsass. Es fällt sofort ins Auge, dass die Prozentzahlen in Oldenburg wesentlich höher liegen als in den beiden anderen Gebieten. In Oldenburg fällt der Prozentsatz nur in einem Jahr (1962) unter 20%, während er in fünf Jahren über 40% beträgt. Im Elsass gibt es in zehn Jahren weniger als 20%, nur in einem mehr als 30% und in keinem mehr als 40%. Die Zahlen für Baden Württemberg liegen etwas höher als die für das Elsass. Die senkrechten Pfeile der Abbildung bezeichnen die sogenannten Störungsjahre (Kuhk & Schüz, 1950). Sie sind gekennzeichnet:

# Populationsdynamik des Weissen Storchs in Mitteleuropa

1. durch einen hohen Anteil jungenloser Paare (=% HPo—im Elsass und in Baden-Württemberg mindestens 20%, in Oldenburg mindestens 40%),

2. davon abhängig durch eine niedrige Durchschnittszahl der je Paar aufgezogenen Jungen (JZa-Zahl),

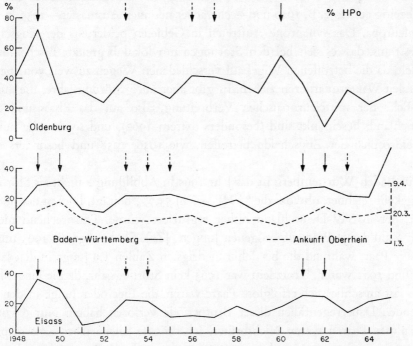

ABB. 4. Prozensatz der jungenlosen Paare (%HPo) im Elsass, in Baden-Württemberg und in Oldenburg—Percentage of pairs without young in Alsace, in Baden-Württemberg and in Oldenburg, 1948–65. Pfeile bezeichnen Störungsjahre, gestrichelte Pfeile schwache Störungsjahre—Arrows indicate disturbed years, broken arrows less markedly disturbed years. Die gestrichelte Linie unter der Kurve für Baden-Württemberg nennt die mittlere Ankunftszeit an den Nestern auf der badischen Oberrheinseite—The broken line below the curve for Baden-Württemberg gives the mean arrival dates at the nests of the east side of the upper Rhine valley.

3. meist auch durch verspätete Frühjahrsankunft am Nest und
4. durch gegenüber dem Vorjahr verringerte Zahl der Paare.

Die Abhängigkeit der % HPo-Zahl vom Zeitpunkt der Ankunft am Nest ist deutlich zu sehen bei der Kurve für Baden-Württemberg, der die durchschnittlichen Ankunftsdaten im badischen Oberrheingebiet als gestrichelte Linie beigefügt sind.

# Gerhardt Zink

Die Gründe, die zu diesen Störungsjahren führen, sind noch immer unbekannt. Die Störung muss offensichtlich im Winterquartier oder auf den Zugwegen eintreten, da die Vögel verspätet und meist in verminderter Anzahl an den Brutplätzen ankommen. Dies gilt sowohl für Altvögel wie für Erstbrüter, wie weiter unten gezeigt werden wird. Die Störungsjahre treten oft in weiten Gebieten gleichzeitig auf, so z. B. 1949 und—schwächer in seinen Ausmassen—1953 in ganz Mitteleuropa. Das synchrone Auftreten in Gebieten beiderseits der Zugscheide schliesst aus, dass es sich bei den Störungen um lokal begrenzte Erscheinungen handelt, da die betroffenen Vögel auf verschiedenen Wegen zu weit voneinander liegenden Winterquartieren ziehen. Es gibt aber auch Störungsjahre, die auf die SW-Ecke der mitteleuropäischen Verbreitung, also auf das Elsass und SW-Deutschland, beschränkt sind (besonders extrem 1962), und solche, die nur die Gebiete östlich der Zugscheide betreffen, wie 1956, 1958 und besonders stark 1960.

Für Baden-Württemberg ist das Jahr 1965 in Abbildung 4 nicht als Störungs-jahr gekennzeichnet, obwohl die % HPo-Zahl 53,7% beträgt. Dies ist der höchste Wert, der in SW-Deutschland bisher registriert wurde. Entsprechend niedrig ist die Zahl der je Paar aufgezogenen Jungen (JZa). Sie beträgt für 1965 nur 1,1 Junge je Paar, während die bis dahin niedrigsten Zahlen 1,9 Junge in den Jahren 1950 und 1962 waren. Trotzdem war 1965 kein Störungsjahr, da die jungenlosen Paare fast ausschliesslich erfolglose Paare waren, die Eier oder Junge in den ver-heerenden Dauerregenfällen dieser Brutperiode verloren haben. Nur 6 von 36 jungenlosen Paaren waren Nichtbrüter. Ich möchte solche Jahre Katastrophen-jahre nennen, da ihre Ursachen im Gegensatz zu den Störungsjahren bekannt sind und in den ökologischen Verhältnissen des Brutgebiets liegen. Wir kennen solche Katastrophenjahre auch aus anderen Gebieten, z. B. 1958 aus dem Bur-genland (Österreich) mit 48,9% HPo und einer JZa-Zahl von 1,24 (Aumüller, 1959). Dort war allerdings eine stark verspätete Heimkehr, also eines der Kenn-zeichen für ein Störungsjahr, mit verheerenden Wetterbedingungen in der Aufzuchtzeit, nämlich extremer Dürre und später heftigen Gewitterregen, den Kennzeichen für ein Katastrophenjahr, zusammengefallen.

In Baden-Württemberg liegen die % HPo-Zahlen auch 1964, im Elsass 1964 und 1965 über 20%. Auch diese Jahre gelten nicht als Störungsjahre, da die JZa-Werte 1965 dem Durchschnitt entsprechen, 1964 sogar wesentlich darüber liegen. In Oldenburg war 1960 die % HPo-Zahl hoch (54,9%), die Ankunft aber normal und auch die Zahl der Paare höher als 1959. Diese Beispiele zeigen, wie vielfältig die Einflüsse sind, die auf die Bestandsentwicklung einwirken, und

# Populationsdynamik des Weissen Storchs in Mitteleuropa

wie schwierig es ist, festzustellen—besonders wenn das nachträglich und ohne genaue Unterlagen geschehen muss—ob eine hohe HPo-Zahl und ein schlechter Bruterfolg auf eine Störung ausserhalb des Brutgebiets zurückgehen oder in den ökologischen Verhältnissen des Brutgebiets (z.B. Wetterbedingungen, Nahrungsangebot, intraspezifische Kämpfe) ihre Ursachen haben.

### BRUTERFOLG

Wie im vorhergehenden Abschnitt gezeigt wurde, hängt der Bruterfolg entscheidend davon ab, wie gross der Prozentsatz jungenloser Paare in den einzelnen Jahren und in den verschiedenen Gebieten ist. Die grossen Unterschiede in der % HPo-Zahl zwischen dem Elsass und Baden-Württemberg einerseits und Oldenburg andererseits wurden in Abbildung 4 dargestellt. In Tabelle 1 sind die Zahlen für weitere Gebiete zusammengefasst, soweit sie für grössere Räume und für die gleichen Jahre zur Verfügung stehen. Ausser in Baden-Württemberg und im Elsass ist die % HPo-Zahl auch im bayerischen Bezirk Schwaben und im Bezirk Magdeburg niedrig, während sie im Nordwest-Teil der mitteleuropäischen Verbreitung und im Burgenland (Österreich) hoch ist, am höchsten in Oldenburg, Stapelholm (Schleswig-Holstein) und in Dänemark. Es scheint danach, dass die Zahlen vom Südwesten her nach Norden und Osten ansteigen. Natürlich sind nur die Extreme statistisch gesichert. Entsprechend den Werten für die % HPo-Zahl ist der Bruterfolg, d.h. die Zahl der je Paar ausgeflogenen Jungen (JZa), am höchsten im Elsass, am niedrigsten in NW-Deutschland, in den Niederlanden und in Dänemark. Den niedrigsten Durchschnittswert hat die Landschaft Stapelholm in Schleswig-Holstein, möglicherweise deshalb, weil in diesem dichtbesiedelten Gebiet Kämpfe zwischen Artgenossen besonders häufig sind und dabei oft Eier zerstört oder Junge getötet werden. Auffällig ist auch der trotz niedriger % HPo-Zahl niedrige Wert für den Bezirk Magdeburg.

Vergleicht man die Durchschnittswerte für die erfolgreichen Paare (JZm), so findet man ähnliche Unterschiede. Wieder hat das Elsass die höchste, Stapelholm die niedrigste Durchschnittszahl. Daraus ist ersichtlich, dass für den durchschnittlichen Bruterfolg nicht nur die % HPo-Zahl massgebend ist, sondern dass auch andere Einflüsse berücksichtigt werden müssen. Der Unterschied zwischen dem Elsass und dem benachbarten Baden-Württemberg könnte darauf beruhen, dass die Zahlen für Baden-Württemberg nicht nur das Oberrheingebiet, sondern auch die höher gelegenen Brutgebiete im Donau-Bodensee-Raum enthalten. Man sollte denken, dass sich die Verhältnisse auf beiden Seiten des Rheintals gleichen. Die Gegenüberstellung in Tabelle 2 zeigt, dass die Unterschiede bestehen

# Gerhardt Zink

bleiben. Die Differenz bei den JZm-Zahlen 1948–65 ist statistisch hoch gesichert. Hier spielen die klimatischen Bedingungen, die beiderseits des Rheins recht verschieden sind, eine entscheidende Rolle. Das Elsass liegt im Regenschatten der

TABELLE I

Brutpaar-Zahlen und Bruterfolg—Numbers of pairs and of young raised

| | HPa | HPo | % HPo | JZG | JZm | JZa |
|---|---|---|---|---|---|---|
| **1948–65** | | | | | | |
| Elsass | 2105 | 367 | 17,4 | 5724 | 3,29 | 2,72 |
| Baden-Württemberg | 2517 | 506 | 20,1 | 6023 | 2,99 | 2,39 |
| Oldenburg | 1725 | 603 | 35,0 | 3214 | 2,86 | 1,86 |
| Stapelholm | 1359 | 446 | 32,8 | 2332 | 2,55 | 1,72 |
| **1955–63** | | | | | | |
| Elsass | 1096 | 169 | 15,4 | 3061 | 3,30 | 2,79 |
| Baden-Württemberg | 1217 | 235 | 19,3 | 2897 | 2,95 | 2,38 |
| Bez. Schwaben | 420 | 92 | 21,9 | 1002 | 3,05 | 2,39 |
| Bez. Osnabrück | 313 | 90 | 28,8 | 615 | 2,77 | 1,96 |
| Niederlande, 1956–64 | 450 | 129 | 28,7 | 820 | 2,55 | 1,82 |
| Bez. Hildesheim und Bez. Braunschweig | 306 | 103 | 33,7 | 548 | 2,69 | 1,79 |
| Oldenburg | 914 | 311 | 34,0 | 1695 | 2,81 | 1,85 |
| Stapelholm | 763 | 261 | 34,2 | 1243 | 2,48 | 1,63 |
| Dänemark | 1518 | 527 | 34,7 | 2643 | 2,67 | 1,74 |
| Bez. Magdeburg | 2161 | 396 | 18,3 | 4470 | 2,53 | 2,07 |
| Burgenland, 1954–62 | 1529 | 437 | 28,6 | 2981 | 2,73 | 1,95 |

HPa = Zahl der Paare mit Nestbindung (mit und ohne Bruterfolg)—Pairs occupying a nest.

HPo = Paare ohne Bruterfolg—Pairs without young.

% HPo = Anteil der Paare ohne Bruterfolg (HPo) an der Gesamtzahl der Paare (HPa)—Percentage of pairs without young.

JZG = Zahl der aufgezogenen Jungen—Numbers of young raised.

JZm = Aufgezogene Junge je erfolgreiches Paar—Young per successful pair.

JZa = Aufgezogene Junge je Paar, alle Paare (HPa) gerechnet—Young per pair, all pairs (HPa) considered.

Vogesen. Die Stadt Kolmar hat in normalen Jahren nur etwa 55% der jährlichen Regenmenge, die in Freiburg am Fusse des Schwarzwalds niedergeht. Selbst in regenreichen Jahren hat das Elsass meist weniger Regen als die andere Rheinseite in Normaljahren. Besonders deutlich ist der Einfluss der Witterung im Jahre 1965, das für die Ostseite des Rheintals ein Katastrophenjahr war (siehe S. 198). In den entscheidenden Monaten der Brutzeit, nämlich im Mai und Juni, betrug die Niederschlagsmenge in Kolmar 172,6 mm, in Mengen Kreis Freiburg (Baden) aber 259,3 mm, in Legelshurst Kreis Kehl (Baden) sogar 287,9 mm. Das langjährige Mittel für Mengen ist 165 mm, für Legelshurst 158 mm. Die badische Rheinseite hatte deshalb 1965 mehr als doppelt soviel jungenlose Paare wie das Elsass. Erfolglose Paare, also solche, die eine Brut begonnen, aber Eier oder Junge

TABELLE 2

Vergleich zwischen Elsass und badischem Oberrheingebiet—Comparison between Alsace and the eastern side of the Rhine valley in Baden

| | Elsass | Baden |
|---|---|---|
| Abnahme—Decrease 1948–65 | 68% | 74% |
| Paare ohne Junge—Pairs without Young (% HPo) 1948–65 | 17,4% | 19,2% |
| Junge je Paar—Young per pair (JZa) 1948–65 | 2,72 | 2,39 |
| Junge je erfolgreiches Paar—Young per successful pair (JZm) 1948–65 | 3,29 | 2,96 |
| % HPo 1965 | 24% | 53% |
| JZa 1965 | 2,58 | 1,07 |
| JZm 1965 | 3,38 | 2,29 |

verloren haben, gab es im Elsass 11 unter 55 Paaren, auf der badischen Rheinseite 22 unter 45 Paaren. Der Bruterfolg ist deshalb im Elsass nahezu normal, bei den erfolgreichen Paaren (JZm) sogar etwas besser als normal, während Baden das schlechteste Brutergebnis seit 1948, also seit Beginn der regelmässigen Bestandsaufnahmen, aufweist. Die Verluste sind dabei nicht durch Nahrungsmangel eingetreten, sondern dadurch, dass die regennassen Altvögel nicht in der Lage waren, den Jungen die notwendige Wärme zu vermitteln. Es sind zwei Fälle bekannt, in denen ein Altvogel dermassen durchnässt war, dass er im Flug nicht genügend Höhe gewinnen konnte, um das Nest zu erreichen. Er musste deshalb in Nestnähe in einem Hof landen und konnte dort eingefangen werden. In anderen Fällen mag das Wasser aus den kompakten Nestern nicht mehr abgelaufen sein, so dass Eier oder Junge im Wasser lagen und unterkühlten. So krass sind die Verhältnisse natürlich nur in Ausnahmejahren. Aber auch in Normaljahren ist das Elsass gegenüber der badischen Rheinseite klimatisch begünstigt. In achtzehn

Jahren war der Bruterfolg im Elsass nur einmal (1949) schlechter als auf der Ostseite des Rheins, sonst immer besser. Die Störche scheinen kein Gefühl für die klimatische Begünstigung der Westseite des Rheintals zu haben, sonst müssten sich mehr in Baden geborene Vögel im Elsass ansiedeln als umgekehrt. Von 4,4 badischen Störchen siedelt sich aber nur einer im Elsass an, und umgekehrt von 4 elsässischen einer in Baden.

Dieses Beispiel zeigt klar, wie verschieden die Bedingungen in eng benachbarten Gebieten sein können, und wie vorsichtig wir sein müssen, wenn wir für einen Vergleich nur wenige Jahre oder Populationen von geringer Grösse zur Verfügung haben.

### TODESURSACHEN

Die Wiederfunde beringter Vögel liefern Material über die Todesursachen, denen eine Vogelart ausgesetzt ist. Sie können in den verschiedenen Teilen der Jahresverbreitung eines Vogels recht verschieden sein. Störche werden im allgemeinen in den Brutgebieten von Menschen nicht verfolgt. Auf den Zugwegen und in den Überwinterungsgebieten werden sie aber in erheblichem Ausmass getötet. Einzelheiten vermittelt Tabelle 3. Unbekannt ist die Todesursache in allen Fällen, in denen der Finder nur 'tot gefunden' mitgeteilt hat. Zu den Drahtanflügen sind auch die Funde gerechnet, bei denen 'unter Hochspannung tot gefunden' gesagt ist. Andere Unfälle sind Anflüge gegen Autos oder andere Verkehrsmittel, Tod in Schornsteinen oder unbeabsichtige Vergiftungen. Unter 'natürlichen Ursachen' sind Todesarten gemeint, die nicht mittelbar oder unmittelbar durch Menschen verursacht sind, wie Tod bei Kämpfen zwischen Artgenossen, Tod durch Unwetter (Blitzschlag, Hagel) oder durch natürliche Feinde. Kämpfe zwischen Artgenossen sind nur aus den Brutgebieten bekannt. Es geht dabei offensichtlich fast immer um den Nestbesitz, nicht um Partner oder gar um Nahrungsreviere.

Betrachtet man die prozentualen Anteile der verschiedenen Todesursachen, so ergibt sich eine recht ähnliche Verteilung auf beiden Seiten der Jahresverbreitung. In den Brutgebieten überwiegen die Unfälle, vor allem die Drahtanflüge. In SW-Deutschland und im Elsass gehen etwa 8 von 10 Verlusten auf Drahtleitungen zurück. Die Verfolgung durch Menschen ist am höchsten in W-Afrika, sehr hoch auch in Spanien, im Balkan, in Vorderasien und in Ostafrika. In den Ländern, die unter diesen Begriffen zusammengefasst sind, ist die Verfolgung allerdings nicht überall gleich intensiv. In der Türkei z. B. werden Störche fast gar nicht geschossen, während die Jagd auf diese Vögel in den benachbarten Ländern Syrien und Libanon besonders eifrig betrieben wird.

# Populationsdynamik des Weissen Storchs in Mitteleuropa

**TABELLE 3**

Todesursachen nach deutschen Ringfunden nach 1945—Causes of death based on German ringing recoveries after 1945

| Fundgebiet—Country of recovery | A | % | B | % | C | D | % C+D | E | F | % E+F | Summe sum A–F | Summe sum B–F |
|---|---|---|---|---|---|---|---|---|---|---|---|---|
| SW-Deutschland, Elsass, Schweiz | 44 | 27,0 | 2 | 1,7 | 92 | 10 | 85,7 | 5 | 10 | 12,6 | 163 | 119 |
| Frankreich ohne Elsass | 51 | 44,7 | 25 | 39,7 | 29 | 2 | 49,2 | 3 | 4 | 11,1 | 114 | 63 |
| Spanien, Portugal | 49 | 48,0 | 39 | 73,6 | 13 | — | 24,5 | — | 1 | 1,9 | 102 | 53 |
| NW- und W-Afrika | 33 | 46,5 | 34 | 89,5 | — | — | — | 4 | — | 10,5 | 71 | 38 |
| Bayern, Mitteldeutschland Österreich, Ungarn, | 53 | 34,9 | 10 | 10,1 | 74 | 5 | 79,8 | 4 | 6 | 10,1 | 152 | 99 |
| Tschechoslowakei | 18 | 28,1 | 3 | 6,5 | 35 | 1 | 78,3 | 1 | 6 | 15,2 | 64 | 46 |
| Balkan | 29 | 51,8 | 19 | 70,4 | 7 | — | 26,0 | — | 1 | 3,7 | 56 | 27 |
| Vorderasien | 38 | 53,5 | 23 | 69,7 | 4 | 3 | 21,2 | 2 | 1 | 9,1 | 71 | 33 |
| Ostafrika (Ägypten—Kapland) | 125 | 61,0 | 56 | 70,0 | 7 | 2 | 11,2 | 6 | 9 | 18,8 | 205 | 80 |

A = Todesursache unbekannt—Cause of death unknown.
B = Von Menschen getötet—Killed by man.
C = Drahtanflüge—Flew into overhead wires.
D = Andere Unfälle—Other accidents.
E = Tot durch Erschöpfung—Died of exhaustion.
F = Andere natürliche Ursachen—Other natural causes.

Die Prozentzahl von A ist auf die Summe A–F, alle anderen Prozentzahlen sind auf die Summe B–F bezogen—The percentage of A is calculated for the sum A–F, all other percentages are calculated for the sum B–F. Die gestrichelte Linie trennt Westwanderer und Ostwanderer—The broken line separates storks migrating west of the Mediterranean from those migrating east.

# Gerhardt Zink

Die vorgelegten Zahlen sind natürlich relativ. Sie sagen etwas aus über den Anteil der verschiedenen Todesursachen in den einzelnen Gebieten der Jahresverbreitung. Sie geben aber keinen Anhalt für die tatsächlichen Verluste, die die mitteleuropäische Storchpopulation in diesen Gebieten erleidet, da die Aussicht auf Wiederfundmeldungen von Land zu Land recht verschieden ist und auch die unterschiedliche Aufenthaltsdauer in den einzelnen Ländern berücksichtigt werden muss. Die grosse Zahl von Funden mit unbekannter Todesursache ist ein weiterer Unsicherheitsfaktor. Es ist deshalb äusserst schwierig, Gründe dafür zu finden, dass bei manchen Populationen der Bestand stark zurückgeht. Alle vorstellbaren Faktoren, die auf menschliche Einflüsse zurückgehen—Abschuss entlang der Zugwege und in den Winterquartieren, die Errichtung von Drahtleitungen, die Trockenlegung von Feuchtgebieten, die Verwendung von Insektiziden in den Brutgebieten und in den Winterquartieren—gelten nicht nur für die abnehmenden Populationen, sondern auch für diejenigen, deren Bestand sich auf gleicher Höhe hält oder gar zunimmt. Störche finden dort die besten Lebensbedingungen, wo es unter kontinentalen Klimaeinflüssen Feuchtgebiete gibt. Klimatische Faktoren haben deshalb auf die Bestandsentwicklung sicherlich einen Einfluss. Mitteleuropa erfuhr einen Höhepunkt maritimen Wetters während der ersten drei Dekaden dieses Jahrhunderts. Dann trat ein Wechsel zu einer mehr kontinentalen Phase ein (Seilkopf, 1951). Wie wir gesehen haben, nahmen die Bestände des Weissen Storchs bis 1929 stark ab, um dann bis 1940 bzw. 1948 wieder erheblich zuzunehmen. Johansen & Bjerring (1955) stellen für Dänemark fest, dass der Klimawechsel zu kalten und nassen Frühjahrsmonaten und damit zu ungünstigen Brutbedingungen von grösstem Einfluss auf die Abnahme der dänischen Population in den Fünfziger Jahren war. Dieser Zusammenhang ist nicht immer so augenfällig. In SW-Deutschland war die starke Abnahme in den Jahren 1948–54 begleitet von einer Serie trockener und heisser Sommer. In diesem Zeitraum von sieben Jahren fallen aber vier Störungsjahre, die den Einfluss günstiger klimatischer Bedingungen durchaus zunichte machen können. Die Störungsjahre sind für einen Rückgang nicht unmittelbar verantwortlich. Sie kommen ebenso in Perioden der Zunahme vor. Sie können aber die Abnahme in einer abnehmenden Population wesentlich beschleunigen.

### ALTER BEI DER ERSTEN BRUT

Zu den Fragen, die durch die jährliche Kontrolle beringter Altvögel geklärt werden konnten, gehört die nach dem Alter bei der ersten Brut. In unserem Untersuchungsgebiet im südlichen Teil des Oberrheintals kennen wir nunmehr

# Populationsdynamik des Weissen Storchs in Mitteleuropa

119 Erstbrüter. Die Verteilung auf die einzelnen Altersklassen zeigt Tabelle 4. Etwa die Hälfte der Vögel ist bei der ersten Brut zwei oder drei Jahre, die andere Hälfte vier bis sechs Jahre alt. In den ersten beiden Altersklassen überwiegen die Männchen, dann die Weibchen. Im Durchschnitt brüten die Männchen ein halbes Jahr früher als die Weibchen. Dieser Unterschied ist statistisch gesichert ($P<0,01$). Die Tabelle zeigt, dass das Erstbrutalter für 54 Männchen, aber nur für 37 Weibchen

TABELLE 4
Alter bei der ersten Brut—Age of first breeding

| | | | | |
|---|---|---|---|---|
| 2-jährig—2 years old: | 7 | ( 3♂ | 1♀) | ⎫ 51% |
| 3-jährig—3 years old: | 54 | (31♂ | 13♀) | ⎭ |
| 4-jährig—4 years old: | 38 | (14♂ | 13♀) | ⎫ |
| 5-jährig—5 years old: | 16 | ( 5♂ | 8♀) | ⎬ 49% |
| 6-jährig—6 years old: | 4 | ( 1♂ | 2♀) | ⎭ |

| | | | |
|---|---|---|---|
| | 119 | (54♂ | 37♀) |

Durchschnittliches Alter bei der ersten Brut—

| | |
|---|---|
| Average age of first breeding: | 3,6 Jahre/years |
| Durchschnitt für ♂—Average for ♂: | 3,4 Jahre/years (n = 54) |
| Durchschnitt für ♀—Average for ♀: | 3,9 Jahre/years (n = 37) |
| Durchschnitt/Average 1955–60: | 3,4 Jahre/years (n = 58) |
| Durchschnitt/Average 1961–65: | 3,8 Jahre/years (n = 61) |

bekannt ist. Dieser Unterschied beruht wahrscheinlich auf zwei Gründen: 1. auf der Sterblichkeit, der die Weibchen in dem halben Jahr ausgesetzt sind, um das sie später zur Brut schreiten als die Männchen, 2. auf einem höheren Anteil an Abwanderern in Gebiete ausserhalb des Kontrollbezirks bei den Weibchen. Die durchschnittliche Entfernung zwischen Geburtsort und Ansiedlungsort beträgt nämlich 33 km bei den Männchen, 61 km bei den Weibchen. Die Tabelle weist ausserdem auf einen Unterschied zwischen den Jahren 1955–60 einerseits und 1961–65 andererseits hin. In der erstgenannten Periode war die Storchpopulation im Oberrheintal verhältnismässig stabil. Zweijährige Erstbrüter treten nur in diesen Jahren auf. Nach 1960 hat der Bestand im Untersuchungsgebiet ständig abgenommen. In diese Jahre der Abnahme fallen ausserdem zwei Störungsjahre (1961 und 1962), die offenbar für das Auftreten jugendlicher Erstbrüter besonders ungünstig sind. Bis 1960 sind 62% aller Erstbrüter zwei- und dreijährig, in den Jahren 1961–65 nur noch 41%. In die zweite Periode fallen 9 der 16 fünfjährigen und

3 der 4 sechsjährigen Erstbrüter. Bei abnehmendem Bestand ist ausserdem die Chance für einen brutwilligen Storch, schon in jungen Jahren einen geeigneten Partner zu finden, geringer als bei stabilem oder bei zunehmendem Bestand.

In einer früheren Veröffentlichung (Schnetter & Zink, 1960) wurde darauf hingewiesen, dass das Erstbrutalter in Ostpreussen erheblich höher ist als in SW-Deutschland. Es mag im Durchschnitt um etwa ein Jahr verschoben sein. Da vergleichbare Unterlagen für die dazwischen liegenden Gebiete fehlen, muss vorläufig offen bleiben, ob der Übergang von höherem zu niedrigerem Erstbrutalter von Nordosten nach Südwesten allmählich erfolgt, oder ob es irgendwo im Zwischengebiet eine mehr oder weniger scharfe Grenze gibt, die möglicherweise sogar mit der Grenzlinie zusammenfällt, die die beiden Zugrichtungen trennt, also mit der Zugscheide.

Der durchschnittliche Bruterfolg bei der ersten Brut beträgt für

> 7 zweijährige Erstbrüter: 1,85 Junge
> 54 dreijährige Erstbrüter: 2,35 Junge
> 38 vierjährige Erstbrüter: 2,60 Junge
> 20 fünf- und sechsjährige Erstbrüter: 2,70 Junge.

Aus diesen Zahlen könnte man einen besseren Bruterfolg bei höherem Erstbrutalter ablesen. Der Unterschied zwischen den Drei- und Vierjährigen hat seine Ursache aber fast ausschliesslich im Katastrophenjahr 1965 mit seinen ungewöhnlich ungünstigen Aufzuchtbedingungen. Die fünf dreijährigen Erstbrüter haben in diesem Jahr keinen einzigen, die beiden vierjährigen aber zwei Jungvögel zum Ausfliegen gebracht. Lässt man die Brutergebnisse von 1965 unberücksichtigt, so beträgt der Durchschnitt für

> 49 dreijährige Erstbrüter: 2,63 Junge.
> 36 vierjährige Erstbrüter: 2,70 Junge.

Einen deutlich geringeren Bruterfolg haben also nur die zweijährigen Erstbrüter. Zwischen den Drei- bis Sechsjährigen und auch zwischen diesen Erstbrütern und den Altvögeln, die schon früher gebrütet haben, gibt es keine gesicherten Unterschiede. Im Gegensatz dazu wurden solche Unterschiede zwischen drei-, vier- und fünfjährigen Erstbrütern in Ostpreussen gefunden (Schüz, 1957). Dabei waren die Fünfjährigen am erfolgreichsten und auch die Vierjährigen erfolgreicher als die Dreijährigen. Es scheint deshalb, wie Lack (1966) vermutet, dass die Aufzuchtbedingungen in Baden einfacher sind als in Ostpreussen.

# Populationsdynamik des Weissen Storchs in Mitteleuropa

Andere Ergebnisse der gleichen Untersuchungsmethode wurden schon früher vorgelegt (Zink, 1963). Sie sollen hier nur kurz zusammengefasst werden. Störche besetzen im Jahr vor der ersten Brut häufig schon ein Nest, ohne zu brüten. Diese Vögel findet man meist am Rand der lokalen Verbreitung oder an sonstwie verhältnismässig ungünstigen Stellen. Diese Nichtbrüter siedeln dann für ihre erste Brut nach günstigeren Brutplätzen um. Nach der ersten Brut sind Umsiedlungen recht selten. Sie kommen bei etwa 15% der im nächsten Jahr zurückkehrenden Altvögel vor und führen meist in Nachbarorte. Die mittlere Umsiedlungsentfernung beträgt 10 km. Nur 10% überschreiten 20 km. Die mittlere Entfernung zwischen Geburtsort und Brutort beträgt 44 km. 70% der Altvögel bleiben innerhalb eines Umkreises von 50 km vom Geburtsort. Die Ansiedlungsentfernung ist aber bei den Vögeln, die in den ungünstigeren hügeligen oder trockengelegten Teilen des Landes geboren sind, grösser, da diese Vögel für ihre erste Brut meist in günstigere Lebensräume abwandern. Die Ansiedlungsentfernung ist bei Weibchen fast doppelt so gross wie bei Männchen (siehe S. 205).

### STERBLICHKEIT DER BRUTVÖGEL

Die jährliche Kontrolle der Brutvögel liefert Zahlen für die Rückkehrquote bei den Altvögeln, die einen guten Anhalt für das Verhältnis zwischen Sterblichkeit und Fortpflanzungsrate geben. Die Unterlagen sind in Tabelle 5 zusammengestellt. Wieder sind die Ergebnisse der Jahre mit gleichbleibendem Bestand (1955–59) denen mit abnehmendem Bestand (1960–64) gegenübergestellt. In der ersten 5-Jahres-Periode beträgt die jährliche Sterblichkeit 24%, in der zweiten 37%. Dieser Unterschied ist wieder hauptsächlich durch die beiden Störungsjahre 1961 und 1962 verursacht. In diesen beiden Jahren beträgt die Rückkehrrate nur 52%! Die hier wiedergegebenen Zahlen für die jährliche Sterblichkeit sind wahrscheinlich etwas zu hoch, da bei den älteren Vögeln durch verlorene Ringe Verluste vorgetäuscht sein können. Berücksichtigt man nur die Vögel bis zum siebenten Lebensjahr aus allen Jahren ausser den beiden Störungsjahren, so ergibt sich ebenfalls eine Sterblichkeit von knapp 24%. Wenn man diesen Wert als Normalwert ansieht, bedeutet das, dass bei gleichbleibendem Bestand unter 100 Brutvögeln 24 Erstbrüter sein müssen. Für die Berechnung der Fortpflanzungsrate darf man die in Tabelle 1 angeführten Werte JZa und JZm nicht verwenden. Der eine (JZa) ist zu niedrig, da auch die Nichtbrüter mitgerechnet sind, der andere (JZm) zu hoch, da er die erfolglosen Paare nicht berücksichtigt. Eine Neuberechnung für alle Brutvögel der Jahre 1955–59 ergibt einen Durchschnittswert von 2,74 Jungen je Paar. Dabei sind auch die Paare mitgerechnet, die Eier

TABELLE 5

Rückkehrrate der im Oberrheingebiet kontrollierten Brutstörche und Zahl der Umsiedlungen—Return rate of breeding storks in the upper Rhine valley and numbers of changes in the breeding place

| | Kontrolliert Examined | Zurückgekehrt Returned | Davon im nächsten Jahr—Of these in the next year | | | |
| --- | --- | --- | --- | --- | --- | --- |
| | | | Im gleichen Nest In the same nest | In anderem Nest In another nest | Tot Dead | Verschollen Presumed dead |
| 1955 | 7 | 6 | 4 | 2 | — | 1 |
| 1956 | 12 | 11 | 11 | — | 1 | — |
| 1957 | 36 | 28 | 26 | 2 | 4 | 4 |
| 1958 | 38 | 28 | 22 | 6 | 5 | 5 |
| 1959 | 47 | 33 | 30 | 3 | 2 | 12 |
| 1955–59 | 140 | 106 = 75,7% | 93 = 87,7% | 13 | 12 | 22 |
| 1960 | 49 | 28 | 25 | 3 | 2 | 19 |
| 1961 | 47 | 22 | 18 | 4 | 2 | 23 |
| 1962 | 44 | 31 | 25 | 6 | 3 | 10 |
| 1963 | 41 | 30 | 24 | 6 | 2 | 9 |
| 1964 | 46 | 32 | 26 | 6 | 3 | 11 |
| 1960–64 | 227 | 143 = 63,0% | 118 = 82,5% | 25 | 12 | 72 |
| 1955–64 | 367 | 249 = 67,6% | 211 = 84,7% | 38 | 24 | 94 |

oder Junge verloren haben, und ebenso diejenigen Vögel, die in einem Jahr mit der Brut ausgesetzt, aber vorher schon einmal gebrütet haben. Dies bedeutet, dass 100 Altvögel im Mittel 137 Junge haben. Von diesen Jungen müssen bei einer jährlichen Alters-Sterblichkeit von 24% 24 oder 17,5% das Brutreifealter erreichen, wenn der Bestand sich auf gleicher Höhe halten soll. Tabelle 6 nennt

### TABELLE 6

Zahl der in Südbaden beringten Jungstörche und Anteil der Rückkehrer und Totfunde—Numbers of ringed nestling storks in southern Baden and rates of returns and recoveries

| | Beringt Ringed | Als Brutvogel kontrolliert Returned for breeding | % | % Totfunde % Recovered |
|---|---|---|---|---|
| 1948–53 | 344 | 29 | 8,4 | |
| 1954 | 95 | 15 | 15,8 | |
| 1955 | 120 | 10 | 8,3 | 11,1 |
| 1956 | 124 | 20 | 16,1 | |
| 1957 | 195 | 21 | 10,8 | 8,7 |
| 1958 | 195 | 20 | 10,3 | 7,2 |
| 1959 | 237 | 7 | 2,9 | 6,7 |
| 1960 | 203 | 6 | 2,9 | 7,9 |
| 1961 | 106 | 6 | 5,7 | 9,4 |

Die Rückkehr-Zahlen oberhalb der gestrichelten Linie müssen in Wirklichkeit etwas höher sein, da erst in den Jahren unterhalb dieser Linie das ganze Gebiet kontrolliert wurde und so der eine oder andere Vogel der Kontrolle vorher entgangen sein kann—The figures for the returns above the broken line actually should be somewhat higher as we have covered the whole area only in the years below this line. Thus some birds may have been missed in the former time.

die tatsächlichen Rückkehrquoten für die beringten Jungvögel. Nur zwei Jahre kommen den geforderten 17,5% nahe: 1954 und 1956. Wenn man 1 oder 2% Abwanderer in Gebiete ausserhalb des Untersuchungsgebiets annimmt, haben beiden Jahre die für einen gleichbleibenden Bestand notwendigen Werte für Sterblichkeit und Fortpflanzungsrate. Nach 1956 ist wieder der Einfluss der Störungsjahre zu sehen. Vögel, die 1957 oder 1958 aufgewachsen sind, waren 1961 vierjährig bzw. dreijährig. Ihr Anteil an den Rückkehrern liegt erheblich unter dem Normalstand. Noch niedriger ist der Anteil bei den beiden Jahrgängen unmittelbar vor den Störungsjahren. Nur 3% konnten später als Brutvögel festgestellt werden. Diese beiden Jahrgänge sind also nahezu völlig verschwunden. Bei den Jahrgängen 1957 bis 1960 ist auch die Wiederfundrate toter Vögel beträchtlich niedriger als vorher. Wenn—wie wir annehmen—die Verluste durch Störungen im Winterquartier muss eintreten, also in Gebieten mit den niedrigsten Wiederfund-Aussichten, dadurch die Gesamt-Wiederfundquote verringert werden.

Aus Unterlagen, die Schüz (1955) vorgelegt hat, errechnete Lack (1966) eine jährliche Altvogel-Sterblichkeit von 21%. Er meint dazu, dass dies ein ungewöhnlich hoher Wert ist für eine Vogelart, bei der die Brutreife erst im Alter von drei, vier oder fünf Jahren eintritt. Die noch höhere Sterblichkeitsrate von 24% scheint für SW-Deutschland durchaus normal zu sein. Sie muss in den letzten Jahren sogar noch erheblich höher gewesen sein, da der Bestand dort stark zurückgeht, obwohl die davon betroffene Population das niedrigste Brutreifealter hat, das bisher bekannt ist, und eine höhere Fortpflanzungsrate als die anderen mitteleuropäischen Populationen. Es wäre wünschenswert, wenn vergleichbare Ergebnisse aus Gebieten östlich der Zugscheide und bei zunehmendem Bestand gewonnen werden könnten. Es besteht einige Hoffnung, dass dieser Wunsch für ein Gebiet in der Tschechoslowakei in absehbarer Zeit in Erfüllung geht. In unserem eigenen Untersuchungsgebiet wird die Arbeit fortgesetzt und vor allem durch die Verwendung dauerhafterer Ringe verbessert werden.

## SCHRIFTTUM

AUMÜLLER S. (1959) Statistik des Weißstorchenbestandes im Burgenland in den Jahren 1956, 1957 und 1958. *Burgenländische Heimatblätter* **21**, 195–207.

JOHANSEN H. & BJERRING A. (1955) Bestanden af Stork (*Ciconia ciconia* (L.)) i Danmark 1952–54. *Dansk Orn. Foren. Tidsskr.* **49**, 114–126.

KUHK R. & SCHÜZ E. (1950) 1949 Störungsjahr im Bestand des Weiss-Storchs, *Ciconia ciconia*. *Orn. Beob.* **47**, 93–97.

LACK D. (1966) *Population Studies of Birds*, pp. v+341. Clarendon Press, Oxford.

SAUTER U. & SCHÜZ E. (1954) Bestandsveränderungen beim Weißstorch: Dritte Übersicht, 1939–1953. *Vogelwarte* **17**, 81–100.

SCHNETTER W. & ZINK G. (1960) Zur Frage des Brutreifealters südwestdeutscher Weiss-Störche (*C. ciconia*). *Proc. XII Internat. Orn. Congr.*, 662–666.

SCHÜZ E. (1936) Internationale Bestands-Aufnahme am Weissen Storch 1934. *Orn. Monatsber.* **44**, 33–41.

SCHÜZ E. (1940) Bewegungen im Bestand des Weissen Storches seit 1934. *Orn. Monatsber.* **48**, 1–14.

# Population dynamics of the White Stork

Schüz E. (1955) Über den Altersaufbau von Weißstorch-Populationen. *Acta XI Congr. Internat. Orn.*, 522–528.

Schüz E. (1957) Das Verschlingen eigener Junger (Kronismus) bei Vögeln und seine Bedeutung. *Vogelwarte* **19**, 1–15.

Schüz E. & Szijj J. (1960a) Vorläufiger Bericht über die Internationale Bestandsaufnahme des Weißstorchs 1958. *Vogelwarte* **20**, 253–257.

Schüz E. & Szijj J. (1960b). Bestandsveränderungen beim Weißstorch: Vierte Übersicht, 1954 bis 1958. *Vogelwarte* **20**, 258–273.

Schüz E. & Szijj J. (1962) Report on the International Census of the White Stork 1958. *Bull. Internat. Council Bird Preservation* **8**, 86–98.

Schüz E. & Zink G. (1955) Bibliographie der Weißstorch-Untersuchungen der Vogelwarte Rossitten-Radolfzell und Helgoland. *Vogelwarte* **18**, Beiheft, 81–85.

Seilkopf H. (1951) Änderungen des Klimas und der Avifauna in Mitteleuropa. *Beitr. Naturkde. Niedersachsens* **4**, 97–110.

Tantzen R. (1962) Der Weisse Storch *Ciconia ciconia* (L.) im Lande Oldenburg. *Oldenburger Jb.* **61**, 105–213.

Thienemann J. (1907). VI. Jahresbericht (1906) der Vogelwarte Rossitten der Deutschen Ornithologischen Gesellschaft. *J. Orn.* **55**, 481–548.

Zink G. (1963). Populationsuntersuchungen am Weissen Storch (*Ciconia ciconia*) in SW-Deutschland. *Proc. XIII Internat. Orn. Congr.*, 812–818.

## SUMMARY

### POPULATION DYNAMICS OF THE WHITE STORK IN CENTRAL EUROPE

*Ciconia ciconia* is in the western part of its range one of the best known of all species of birds, and its breeding biology, behaviour, feeding habits, migration, orientation, parasites and other aspects of its biology have been the subject of numerous thorough studies. This paper deals with its population dynamics. It is based on yearly censuses of the breeding population in many parts of the range, together with the times of arrival in spring, the numbers of young raised, and other details, also on the examination of all breeding adults in special study areas, as a result of which data have been obtained on the age of first breeding, the behaviour of non-breeding subadults, the area of first settlement in relation to the area of origin and the mortality rate of breeding birds.

*Fluctuations in numbers.* The populations of the White Stork in Central Europe are characterized by big changes in numbers. After a peak at the end of the last century a considerable decline took place until the end of the 'twenties, to about one-quarter to one-third of the initial numbers. Then the numbers increased until 1940 (SW. Germany up to 1948), followed again by a decline which goes in most areas far below the level of 1929 (Figure 1). In this period Switzerland and

# Gerhardt Zink

Sweden lost their storks entirely. A comparison between several districts, from which exact numbers are available for the years after 1948, reveals marked differences (Figures 2 and 3). After a decline in 1949, which was one of the worst years all over Central Europe, numbers changed only slightly in some areas. This is true for Oldenburg and Osnabrück (Lower Saxony), for Schleswig-Holstein and also for Bavaria. By contrast, numbers decreased in the areas at the edge of the bird's range in the upper Rhine valley north of Basle, in the Netherlands and in Denmark. In Oldenburg the figure for 1965 is 10 per cent higher than that for 1949, whereas in the upper Rhine valley it is only 34 per cent of that for 1949. In contrast to these western areas a considerable increase can be observed farther east, in Magdeburg and in Burgenland (Austria), and an evident increase also in Czechoslovakia. No comparable figures are available for areas farther east and south-east.

*Störungsjahre (years of disturbance).* The percentage of pairs that fail to raise young varies annually. They consist of pairs which have lost eggs or young for various reasons and of pairs which occupy nests but do not even try to breed (Figure 4). In most cases at least one bird of these non-breeding pairs is not old enough for successful breeding. Years with a high percentage of pairs without young are the so-called *Störungsjahre* (years of disturbance). Besides the high percentage of pairs without young which differs in different districts (at least 20 per cent in Baden-Württemberg and Alsace, at least 40 per cent in Oldenburg), these *Störungsjahre* are characterized by low figures for young raised per pair, in most cases also by late arrival in spring, and by a lower return rate than usual of both first-breeders and adults.

The reason for these years of disturbance is still unknown. The disturbance may have its origin in the winter-quarters or on the migration routes, as the birds come back later than usual from migration and in smaller numbers. The 'disturbance' often affects wide areas on both sides of the *Zugscheide*, so that local causes can be excluded. Other years are called *Katastrophenjahre* (years of catastrophe). In contrast to the years of disturbance the causes for the catastrophes are known, and are usually attributable to unfavourable ecological factors in the breeding area.

*Breeding success.* The numbers of young raised per pair depend not only on the weather in the breeding season, on the availability of food and on the number of eggs destroyed or young killed during intraspecific fights, but also on the percentage of non-breeding birds. As has been shown, this percentage varies greatly year by year and from district to district. Table 1 gives details for several districts.

# Population dynamics of the White Stork

In southern Germany and Alsace, the percentage of pairs without young (per cent HPo) is low and thus the number of young raised per pair (JZa) high. The figures for Oldenburg, Schleswig-Holstein and Denmark show the opposite extreme. There are some indications that the figures for per cent HPo increase from the south-west corner of the stork's range in Central Europe to the east and to the north. Differences exist, too, in the numbers of young per successful pair (JZm). They are highest again in Alsace and lowest in the Netherlands, Magdeburg and Schleswig-Holstein.

The figures for Baden-Württemberg presented in Table 1 consist of those for the Rhine valley and for other parts of the country. One would think that the figures for the Rhine valley alone should not differ from those for Alsace on the other side of the river, but Table 2 shows that they differ markedly. This is a clear result of climatic differences: Alsace lies in the rain shadow of the Vosges Mountains. The annual rainfall at Colmar is only about 55 per cent of that at the foot of the Black Forest. Even in rainy years Alsace has less rain than the right side of the river in normal years. 1965 was a catastrophic year for Baden due to heavy rain during the whole breeding season. The east side of the river had more than twice as many failures as Alsace, where the figures for the number of young per pair were almost normal, and those for young per successful pair even higher than normal. In Baden both were far below the normal level. This example shows how much conditions may differ in neighbouring areas, and how careful we have to be in comparing single years or small numbers. Storks seem to be unaware of this difference between the two sides of the Rhine valley as there is no preference for the Alsatian side.

*Causes of mortality*. Ringing results have provided data on the causes of mortality. They are extremely different in the different parts of the stork's range throughout the year. Storks are generally not persecuted by man in the breeding grounds but are killed to a great extent on migration and in the winter-quarters (Table 3). In the breeding areas accidental death predominates (mostly caused by flying into overhead wires). Natural causes include death through being struck by lightning, through hailstones and during intraspecific fights. The figures, of course, are relative, and say nothing about the exact numbers of birds killed in the different parts of the range throughout the year.

It is, therefore, extremely difficult to find the reasons for the decline in numbers in some populations. All imaginable human factors—shooting, the drainage of damp ground, the erection of wires, the use of insecticides—involve not only the decreasing populations but also those which are stable or even increasing. As the

White Stork finds the best conditions for life in damp parts of continental climate, climatic factors surely have an influence. Central Europe experienced a peak of maritime weather during the first three decades of this century when numbers of storks decreased. Then the weather passed into a more continental phase, and stork populations increased. In Denmark the prevalence of cold and moist springs, and thus unfavourable breeding conditions, was said to be the main factor in the decrease of the 'fifties; but elsewhere this correlation is not always so obvious. In south-west Germany the marked decrease from 1948 to 1954 was accompanied by a series of dry and hot summers. But in this period 4 out of 7 years have been years of disturbance, which may override the effect of favourable climatic conditions. These disturbed years are not in themselves responsible for a decrease as they occur also in increasing populations, but they can speed up the decrease in a decreasing population.

*Age of first breeding.* In the southern part of the Rhine valley the age of first breeding is known for 119 birds (Table 4). About half of the birds started breeding when 2 or 3 years old, the other half when 4, 5 or even 6 years old. Males predominate in the first 2 years, females from 4 to 6 years. The different numbers for males and females may be due partly to the mortality of females in the 6 months after males start breeding, partly to a higher rate of abmigration in females. The mean distance between birth place and place of first breeding is 33 km in males, 61 km in females. The difference between the years 1955–60 and 1961–65 is due mostly to the 2 years of disturbance (1961 and 1962) in the second period. There were no cases of 2-year-old birds breeding in this period, and the figures for the older year classes have been higher immediately following the years of disturbance.

The age of first breeding is considerably higher (by approximately 1 year) in East Prussia than in south-west Germany. As comparable figures are not available for other areas it is not known if the age of first breeding changes gradually from north-east to south-west or if there is a break somewhere in between, perhaps at the boundary between the different migration routes (the *Zugscheide*).

The breeding success for the first brood is smaller than usual in the few 2-year-old breeders, with an average of 1.85 young per pair, whereas the older age classes have figures between 2.63 and 2.70. There is no significant difference between the success of 3- to 6-year-old first-breeders, nor between these and experienced birds. This is contrary to findings in East Prussia, where younger parents have been less efficient in raising young than older ones. Other results of this method of examining the breeding adults of a given area each year have been published earlier (Zink, 1963).

# Population dynamics of the White Stork

*Mortality rate.* The return rate of breeding birds, shown in Table 5, indicates a mortality of 24 per cent from 1955 to 1959, and of 37 per cent from 1960 to 1964. Most of this difference in fact depends on the two disturbed years 1961 and 1962, which had a return rate of 52 per cent only. The figures may be somewhat lower than the true ones as some of the older birds may have lost their rings. If the mortality rate for the first period, when numbers were not decreasing, is taken as normal, it means that, in a stable population, out of one hundred breeding birds twenty-four should be first-breeders. The reproduction rate is 2.74 young per pair in these years. One hundred breeding birds produce, therefore, 137 young. Of these twenty-four or 17.5 per cent should reach maturity to keep numbers stable. Table 6 gives the actual return rate of birds ringed as nestlings. The figure for 1956 is just about what is needed for a stable population, if 1 or 2 per cent are added to allow for abmigration to places outside the study area. After 1956 the influence of the 2 years of disturbance becomes obvious again. In 1961 the birds born in 1957 and 1958 would have been 4- and 3-year-old first-breeders respectively; they came back at a considerable lower rate than is normal. Lower again are the figures for the 2 years immediately preceding the years of disturbance. The storks born in these 2 years were almost all lost, only 3 per cent returning to breed. In all of these years the recovery rate of dead birds was also smaller than usual. As the disturbances are likely to occur in the winter-quarters, where the recovery rate is always lower than in Europe, a higher mortality in Africa will lower the overall recovery rate.

Lack (1966) considered a mortality rate of 21 per cent as unusually high for a species in which breeding is deferred to the age of 3, 4 or 5. The even higher rate of 24 per cent seems to be normal for south-west Germany, and recently it must have been still higher, as the population is decreasing steadily in spite of the fact that south-west German birds begin to breed at a younger age and have a higher rate of reproduction than other populations with stable or increasing numbers. It would be desirable to have comparable results from other areas east of the *Zugscheide*, where numbers are increasing.

# Reconnaissance de schémas reactogènes liés à l'information contenue dans le chant territorial du rouge-gorge (*Erithacus rubecula*)

J.-C.BREMOND

Laboratoire de Physiologie Acoustique, 78 Jouy-en-Josas, France

## INTRODUCTION

Les premières recherches portant sur les signaux acoustiques ont permis de mettre en évidence l'existence de dialectes locaux. Plus récemment les progrès réalisés dans le domaine de l'électro-acoustique ont rendu possible une analyse objective de ces signaux. Il est apparu que la plupart d'entre eux étaient susceptibles de varier autour d'un schéma général, moins complexe que le signal naturel, et qui seul demeurait commun à tous les individus. L'existence de formes dialectales, ou tout au moins de variations individuelles, semble donc plus répandue qu'on ne l'avait tout d'abord supposé. Il y a lieu d'opposer le grand nombre des résultats analytiques mettant ce phénomène en évidence à la rareté des travaux expérimentaux susceptibles de faire apparaître les conséquences comportementales de telles variations. Ces études, de date récente, nous montrent que les fluctuations du signal peuvent atteindre une ampleur suffisante pour éloigner les diverses populations qui en sont affectées. Par contre, il n'a jamais été apporté de preuve expérimentale d'une séparation totale dont le signal acoustique serait à lui seul responsable. Bien au contraire, il apparaît qu'il reste intelligible pour l'ensemble de l'espèce. Tout au plus observe-t-on une variation du taux des réactions positives qu'il induit. Telle est la conclusion qui ressort des études menées par Thielcke (1963) sur les dialectes des pouillots véloces (*Phylloscopus collybita*) peuplant l'Espagne, le sud de la France et l'Allemagne. Dilger (1956), Stein (1956) expérimentant avec une grive du genre *Hylocichla* parviennent à une conclusion similaire. Les appeaux utilisés pour la chasse ne sont le plus souvent qu'une imitation imparfaite des signaux naturels dont ils possèdent les propriétés réactogènes.

Sans vouloir affirmer qu'un signal peut subir indifféremment toutes les altérations possibles, on peut reconnaître que certaines d'entre elles n'affectent pas ou très peu son pouvoir réactogène. Il est donc permis de supposer que

217

# J.-C.Brémond

l'individu récepteur n'intègre pas la totalité des informations qui lui sont transmises, mais seulement certaines d'entre elles, contenues dans un schéma dont il reconnaît la forme. Les recherches expérimentales que nous avons entreprises furent orientées vers l'isolement de ces schémas. Elles portaient plus spécialement sur le chant de défense territoriale du rouge-gorge (*Erithacus rubecula*). Le présent exposé ne traitera que de deux des informations véhiculées par le signal: sa sémantique territoriale et sa spécificité. Les paramètres responsables de ces deux propriétés seront analysés expérimentalement.

## MATERIEL, METHODES

Les rouge-gorges soumis à l'expérience furent toujours des individus sauvages, en liberté dans la nature, au sein de leurs territoires respectifs. Afin d'éviter l'apparition de l'habituation chaque oiseau ne fut, le plus souvent, soumis qu'à une seule série d'expériences (3 essais consécutifs en moyenne). Nous avons pris soin de ne pas utiliser des oiseaux ayant des territoires contigus. Le magnétophone employé pour la diffusion des signaux était un NAGRA du type III B relié à un haut-parleur au travers d'un amplificateur transistorisé d'une puissance de 12 Watts. Le niveau sonore de l'émission atteignait 80 à 100 dB (mesurés en crête) à un mètre, dans l'axe du haut-parleur.

Le comportement de défense territoriale du rouge-gorge peut être induit en totalité par la seule signalisation acoustique, ainsi que Lack (1943) l'a montré. Lors de l'expérimentation il fut donc possible de remplacer l'intrus par un haut-parleur diffusant le signal faisant l'objet de la recherche. La méthode expérimentale consista à modifier successivement et si possible indépendamment tous les paramètres physiques du signal naturel. Ainsi altéré, il induisit chez l'individu récepteur des comportements qui furent comparés à ceux induits par le chant naturel, pris comme témoin. Il fut possible d'en déduire la valeur réactogène des paramètres modifiés. Lors de l'interprétation des comportements de l'individu récepteur il a surtout été tenu compte des taxies vers le haut-parleur et des parades d'intimidation vis à vis de ce dernier. Les réponses acoustiques furent considérées comme étant d'une importance moindre, car elles peuvent être déclenchées par des facteurs nombreux, dont certains échappent au contrôle de l'expérimentateur. L'analyse statistique des comportements induits permet de reconnaître le schéma fondamental intégré par le récepteur. Il repose sur l'ensemble des paramètres physiques qui ne peuvent pas être altérés sans que s'observe une diminution du pouvoir réactogène du signal.

# Le chant territorial du rouge-gorge

## ANALYSE PHYSIQUE DES SIGNAUX

La caractéristique essentielle du chant de rouge-gorge est sa grande variabilité (Brémond, 1962). Un répertoire de notes très étendu permet à l'espèce de construire environ 1200 motifs dont les combinaisons donnent naissance à des chants très diversifiés (Figure 1). Ces derniers sont émis consécutivement et leur suite forme une séquence. Ils sont séparés par des silences qui représentent de 50% à 80% du

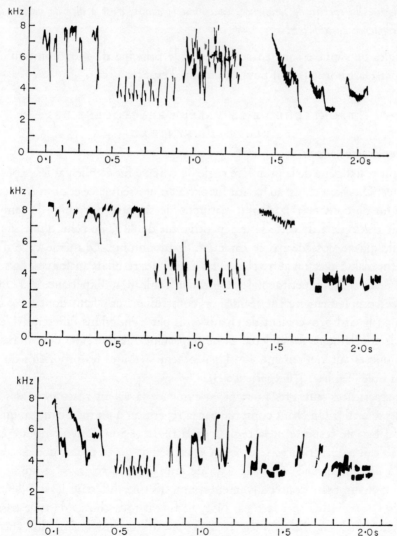

FIGURE 1. Trois chants consécutifs extraits d'une séquence. (Analyse des fréquences exprimées en KHz en fonction du temps exprimé en secondes.)

# J.-C.Brémond

temps total. Malgré la flexibilité de ce signal il est possible d'y reconnaître un certain nombre de règles. Nous envisagerons celles relatives à l'organisation syntaxique, c'est à dire à la répartition temporelle de ses éléments constitutifs.

REGLE N° 1 : *Dans une séquence, tous les chants consécutifs sont différents les uns des autres.*

REGLE N° 2 : *Dans chaque chant tous les motifs sont différents les uns des autres.*

REGLE N° 3 : *Les motifs successifs sont alternativement compris dans la moitié supérieure ou inférieure du spectre de fréquences contenant le chant, c'est à dire de part et d'autre d'une fréquence de 4 KHz.*

Ces règles de syntaxe sont en accord avec le principe de monotonie minimale établi par Hartshorne (1956) pour beaucoup d'espèces.

## RECHERCHE DE LA VALEUR REACTOGENE DES REGLES DE SYNTAXE

### Résultats expérimentaux

La valeur réactogène de la première règle de syntaxe fut établie par les expériences suivantes : Un chant choisi au hasard fut extrait d'une séquence et diffusé répétitivement afin de conserver la densité naturelle de signaux par unité de temps. Le pouvoir réactogène de cette série répétitive fut de 88% de celui d'une séquence naturelle qui ne possède pas ce caractère de monotonie. Le même type d'expérience fut réalisé avec un autre chant et a donné des résultats analogues. La somme de ces deux séries expérimentales figure au Tableau 1, Expérience A. Une expérience complémentaire fut réalisée en construisant un chant dont les 5 motifs choisis au hasard provenaient de chants émis par 5 individus différents. L'assemblage de ces éléments fut effectué en ne respectant que les règles de syntaxe N° 2 et 3 énoncées antérieurement. Le signal obtenu a toutes les propriétés du chant normal isolé (Tableau 1, Expérience B).

Les expériences suivantes mettent en évidence la valeur réactogène des règles de syntaxe 2 et 3. Un chant composé par la répétition d'un même motif, qu'il soit haut ou bas, ne respecte ni la règle 2 ni la règle 3. Son pouvoir réactogène est nul (Tableau 1, Expériences C et D). On en déduit qu'au moins une de ces deux règles a une importance capitale. Afin de satisfaire à la règle N° 2 un chant fut construit en disposant consécutivement six motifs tous différents les uns des autres. Afin de ne pas satisfaire à la régle N° 3 ils furent tous choisis de type bas. Une expérience analogue fut réalisée avec des motifs exclusivement de type haut. Dans les deux cas le pouvoir réactogène d'un tel signal fut notablement inférieur à celui du chant normal non modifié, pris pour témoin (Tableau 1, Expérience

# Le chant territorial du rouge-gorge

TABLEAU I Valeur réactogène des chants modifiés expérimentalement

| Désignation de l'expérience | Signal expérimenté | Qualité de la réponse | | | | Somme des réponses (+) et (±) exprimée en % | Témoin | | Nombre d'épreuves | Nombre d'oiseaux |
|---|---|---|---|---|---|---|---|---|---|---|
| | | Bonne (+) | Moyenne (±) | Faible (−) | Nulle (o) | | Un chant isolé | Séquence | | |
| A | Chant isolé | 21 | 10 | 3 | 1 | 88 | — | 100% | 35 | 19 |
| B | Echange des motifs | 10 | 7 | 2 | — | 89 | 88% | — | 19 | 14 |
| C | Motifs identiques (type bas) | — | — | 1 | 12 | 0 | 88% | — | 13 | 12 |
| D | Motifs identiques (type haut) | — | — | 2 | 10 | 0 | 88% | — | 12 | 9 |
| E | Motifs différents (type bas exclusivement) | 7 | 9 | 10 | 5 | 52 | 88% | — | 31 | 24 |
| F | Motifs différents (type haut exclusivement) | 9 | 10 | 9 | 6 | 56 | 88% | — | 34 | 19 |
| G | Motifs différents extraits de E et F (types bas et hauts) | 19 | 9 | 3 | — | 90 | 88% | — | 31 | 22 |
| H | Signaux synthétiques (règle 3 exclusivement) | 6 | 14 | 26 | 22 | 29 | 88% | — | 68 | 49 |
| I | Signal synthétique (règles 3 et 2) | 10 | 9 | 6 | 2 | 70 | 88% | — | 27 | 21 |
| J | Inversion des fréquences | 8 | 6 | 3 | — | 82 | — | 100% | 17 | 9 |

E et F). Parmi les motifs utilisés antérieurement, six furent tirés au sort, trois de type haut et trois de type bas. Ils furent assemblés consécutivement et alternativement afin de respecter les règles de syntaxe N° 2 et 3. Le pouvoir réactogène d'un tel signal est équivalent à celui d'un chant naturel isolé (Tableau 1, Expérience G).

*Discussion*

Les deux séries expérimentales A montrent qu'un chant isolé contient presque toute l'information, puisqu'il a, à 12% près, une valeur réactogène normale. La règle N° 1 ne contribue donc que faiblement à induire des comportements de défense territoriale. Cette série expérimentale ne porte que sur deux chants. Ceux-ci, bien que choisis au hasard, auraient pu avoir un pouvoir réactogène exceptionellement élevé. En fait cette objection paraît peu fondée, car il fut obtenu des résultats analogues au cours des séries expérimentales B et G qui elles aussi, ne différaient du chant normal que par le non respect de la règle N° 1. En s'appuyant sur les résultats de ces séries expérimentales portant sur quatre chants différents ayant donné lieu à 85 expériences réalisées avec 55 individus, il est permis de penser que tous les chants sont équivalents. Cette équivalence peut être étendue aux motifs, puisqu'à l'intérieur de chaque type ils peuvent être choisis au hasard, ce que prouve leur interchangeabilité (Expériences B et G). Il est possible que contrairement à ce qui eut lieu lors de l'expérimentation l'émetteur ne puise pas au hasard dans son répertoire de motifs lorsqu'il construit son chant. Si un choix de sa part existe effectivement, ce que nous ignorons, l'expérimentation a montré que ce choix n'influe pas sur les propriétés réactogènes du signal.

La valeur réactogène de la seule règle de syntaxe N° 3 n'a pas pu être expérimentée, car il aurait fallu pouvoir construire un chant composé par l'alternance de motifs dont les notes constitutives auraient eu des formes identiques, mais contenues dans des bandes de fréquences différentes. De tels éléments n'ont pas été trouvés lors de l'analyse des chants naturels. Nous verrons ultérieurement que cette difficulté fut surmontée lors de la réalisation de signaux d'origine entièrement synthétique. Quoi qu'il en soit, l'introduction de la règle N° 3 accroît considérablement le pouvoir réactogène du signal.

RECHERCHE DES STRUCTURES RESPONSABLES DE LA SEMANTIQUE ET DE LA SPECIFICITE DU SIGNAL DE DEFENSE TERRITORIALE

*Position du problème*

Le chant de l'émetteur véhicule plusieurs informations dont un certain nombre sont intégrées par le récepteur et induisent le comportement de défense territoriale.

# Le chant territorial du rouge-gorge

Parmi toutes ces informations, nous avons limité notre étude à deux d'entre elles qui sont la sémantique territoriale et la spécificité. Il est bien évident que seuls les signaux possédant cette sémantique peuvent induire des comportements territoriaux. Dans les conditions naturelles le rouge-gorge ne livre pas de luttes interspécifiques. Le signal a donc des caractéristiques de formes qui sont originales et lui confèrent sa spécificité. Nous nous proposerons donc de rechercher quelles sont les structures qui sont reconnues par le récepteur comme vecteurs de ces deux types d'information. Au cours des séries expérimentales antérieurement décrites nous avons vu qu'un chant composé de motifs identiques n'avait pas de valeur réactogène (Expériences C et D). Cette dernière n'apparaît que dans les séries expérimentales E et F. On peut donc affirmer qu'à ce stade de reconstruction, le signal possède déjà une sémantique territoriale. Le faible pourcentage de réponses positives obtenues laisse supposer que seuls quelques individus récepteurs peuvent intégrer la valeur territoriale d'un tel message qui, de par sa syntaxe, est très différent du chant naturel.

*Résultats expérimentaux*

Nous avons construit un signal à partir de sons issus d'un audio-oscillateur (modulateur de fréquences). La règle de syntaxe N° 3 était intégralement respectée, car les motifs furent alternativement situés dans la partie haute ou basse du spectre. Par contre, la règle N° 2 ne fut que très sommairement représentée, puisque tous les motifs synthétisés présentaient entre eux de grandes analogies morphologiques (Figure 2). Dans le chant naturel les différences de formes entre les motifs sont considérables (Figure 1). De plus les notes ne furent pas une imitation exacte de celles du rouge-gorge. Leur forme générale était intermédiaire entre celle du rouge-gorge, du troglodyte (*Troglodytes troglodytes*) et du rossignol (*Luscinia megarhynchos*) (Figure 3). Les trois espèces ont des écologies et des éthologies territoriales analogues et ne se livrent pas de combats territoriaux interspécifiques. Chacun de ces quatre signaux synthétiques induisent dans quelques cas des réactions de défense chez le rouge-gorge (Tableau 1, Expérience H). Bien que des expériences systématiques n'aient pas été réalisées, il a été remarqué que parfois le rossignol et surtout le troglodyte attaquaient le haut-parleur diffusant ces signaux. Il a également été possible d'observer que ces chants artificiels induisaient chez le merle (*Turdus merula*) des comportements de fuite accompagnés de l'émission du cri d'alarme représenté par Figure 3(d) et dont la structure n'est pas sans offrir quelques similitudes avec les signaux diffusés.

# J.-C.Brémond

Afin de satisfaire totalement à la règle de syntaxe N° 2, les quatre chants synthétiques expérimentés ci dessus furent assemblés de la manière suivante: Deux motifs furent extraits de chacun d'entre eux au hasard, mais en ne retenant que 2 motifs de type haut et 2 motifs de type bas. Ils furent disposés consécutivement et alternativement afin de satisfaire également à la règle de syntaxe N° 3. Ce nouveau

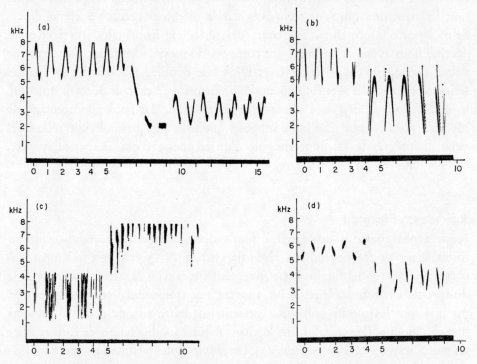

FIGURE 2. Quatre chants synthétiques obtenus à partir d'un générateur électro-acoustique. Seuls les deux premiers motifs ont été représentés.

signal a un pouvoir réactogène très accru par rapport aux précédents (Tableau 1, Expérience I). De plus il a acquis une valeur spécifique pour le rouge-gorge.

Dans les signaux synthétiques précédents les notes différaient notablement de celles des chants naturels. Les notes naturelles peuvent donc subir des modifications. Afin de confirmer ce résultat, l'expérience suivante fut réalisée: Une séquence naturelle de chant a été modifiée en permutant les fréquences de part et d'autre de la fréquence 4 KHz, représentée par une ligne pointillée sur la Figure 4. Les fréquences ascendantes sont devenues descendantes et inversement. Les notes résultantes ne sont pas très différentes de ce qu'elles étaient avant la transformation, mais leur contenu fréquentiel a été bouleversé ce qui entraîne la destruction de tous les rapports harmoniques contenus dans le signal naturel. La syntaxe n'est pas altérée, car il a été prouvé par ailleurs (Brémond, non publié) qu'un chant débute ou se termine indifféremment par un motif de type haut ou bas. Un tel signal a un pouvoir réactogène qui n'est pas très éloigné de celui du chant naturel (Tableau I, Expérience J).

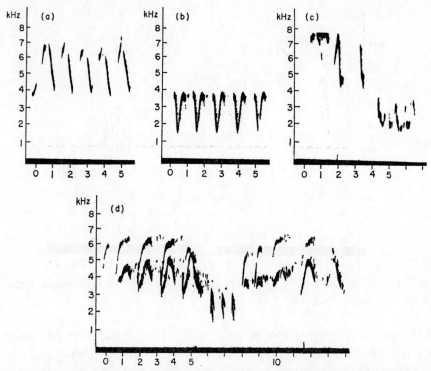

FIGURE 3. Motifs extraits de chants émis par le troglodyte (a), le rossignol (b), le rouge-gorge (c). Remarquer leur analogie avec les signaux synthétiques représentés par Figure 2. Signal d'alarme du merle (d).

DISCUSSION

Un signal monotone composé de motifs identiques situés dans une même bande de fréquences n'induit aucun comportement dans les conditions expérimentales décrites antérieurement. Il peut donc être considéré comme dépourvu de sémantique, y compris celle relative au territoire. Par contre, cette propriété apparaît dès que la suite des motifs cesse d'être monotone. Cette diversité peut résulter des règles de syntaxe N° 2 ou 3. Si la règle N° 2 est appliquée, tous les motifs ont des formes différentes, mais ils sont situés dans la même bande de fréquences (Expériences E et F). Si la règle N° 3 est appliquée, les motifs ont des formes semblables, mais sont alternativement situés dans deux bandes de fréquences. Le facteur réactogène résultant de la sémantique territoriale du signal est donc lié à cette diversité, quelque soit le procédé mis en jeu pour l'obtenir. La forme exacte des notes (donc des motifs) est un caractère secondaire qui ne peut à lui

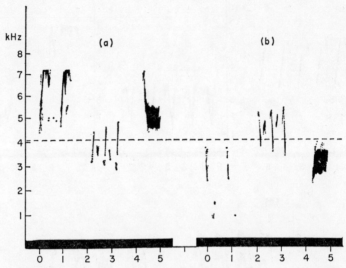

FIGURE 4. Chant de rouge-gorge (seules quelques notes ont été représentées). Signal naturel (a), signal inversé (b).

seul induire de réaction (Expériences C et D). Cette conclusion est confirmée par le fait que des notes très altérées, comme le furent celles des signaux synthétiques H ou du chant naturel inversé J, peuvent constituer un signal ayant une sémantique territoriale. Ce raisonnement ne doit toutefois pas être poussé à l'extrême, car dans la forme de la note il existe des caractéristiques dont l'altération réduit considérablement le pouvoir réactogène du signal. Il a été montré expérimentalement (Brémond, 1965) que ce phénomène se produisait lors de la transposition des fréquences hors de leurs domaines naturels.

La spécificité, comme la sémantique, peut être attribuée à la règle de syntaxe N° 2, puisque les signaux C et D qui ne respectent que cette règle sont spécifiques. Par contre, les signaux tels que H satisfaisant à la seule règle 3 sont dépourvus de cette propriété, mais ils l'acquièrent dès que l'on introduit la règle 2.

Il est donc possible de conclure que la sémantique et la spécificité sont deux informations distinctes qui, l'une et l'autre, sont transmises par des structures résultant de la diversité interne du signal. La sémantique est liée aux règles de syntaxe N° 2 et 3. La spécificité dépend essentiellement de la règle N° 2. La règle N° 1 ne semble pas indispensable à la transmission de ces informations.

### CONCLUSION GENERALE

Malgré leur diversité, tous les chants consécutifs composant une séquence véhiculent le même message territorial. Cette suite possède donc un taux élevé de redondance. Une remarque analogue relative aux motifs peut être faite pour chaque chant. En effet, on démontre en analyse combinatoire qu'avec n motifs différents répartis en deux classes il existe $2^n$ possibilités de construction. C'est ainsi que par exemple les chants constitués par 6 motifs sont au nombre de 64. Parmi toutes ces structures, deux seulement satisfont aux règles de syntaxe N° 2 et 3. Cette restriction a pour conséquence l'apparition d'un taux élevé de redondance. La théorie de l'information indique que l'intelligibilité d'un message croît en même temps que la redondance. Le signal théorique idéal ayant une intelligibilité maxima devrait donc être composé par la répétition du même motif. Or, nous avons démontré qu'une telle construction était sans valeur pour le récepteur, car dépourvue de sémantique. Elle n'est pas utilisée par l'émetteur. Bien au contraire, ce dernier donne à ses chants une diversité maxima ce qui semble opposé à ce que laissait prévoir la théorie. En fait la contradiction n'est qu'apparente, puisque tous les motifs d'un même type (haute ou basse fréquence) sont interchangeables sans que le sémantique du signal en soit modifiée. Les facteurs véhiculant l'information sémantique sont donc affectés d'un taux élevé de redondance, tant au niveau de la séquence qu'au sein de chaque chant. Ce phénomène a pour conséquence un accroissement de la probabilité de bonne réception de ce type d'information. Il est possible de voir là le résultat d'une sélection qui a favorisé la transmission de cette sémantique qui paraît être particulièrement importante pour le rouge-gorge, dont le comportement territorial est très développé.

Lorsqu'une structure physique contribue à donner au signal ses propriétés sémantiques, on en conclut qu'elle est le support de cette information. Si cette même structure se retrouve chez une autre espèce, peut-on par analogie supposer qu'elle transmet le même type d'information? Il semble que cela soit possible dans quelques cas particuliers étudiés par Marler (1957). Cet auteur a effectué l'analyse physique des signaux d'alarme, d'appel au vol chez différentes espèces et a montré que pour chaque type de comportement les signaux avaient en commun une structure physique particulière. Ce type de résultat ne peut, cependant, pas être étendu à tous les signaux. Nous avons vu que l'arrangement temporel des motifs selon la seule règle syntaxique N° 3 avait une sémantique territoriale pour le rouge-gorge, alors que pour le merle une telle construction induisait un comportement d'alarme. Les similitudes des signaux étudiés par Marler résultent d'une convergence de formes imposée par des lois acoustiques. Ce phénomène ne se rencontre pas toujours, et le plus souvent seule l'expérimentation permet d'établir de telles relations.

Le récepteur n'intègre pas la totalité des éléments contenus dans le signal. Dans les chants territoriaux de diverses espèces l'expérimentation a permis de montrer que ce ne sont pas toujours les mêmes paramètres qui véhiculent les informations nécessaires à l'induction des comportements territoriaux. Chez le rouge-gorge, nous avons vu que les schémas les plus importants étaient de nature syntaxique. Il a été montré par ailleurs (Brémond, 1965) que quelques uns des paramètres, relatifs aux fréquences acoustiques, ne devaient pas être altérés. Falls (1963) a montré que chez l'oiseau des fours (*Seiurus aurocapillus*) l'un des paramètres les plus importants était de nature temporelle, tandis que chez le moineau à gorge blanche (*Zonotrichia albicollis*) ces éléments étaient relatifs aux fréquences acoustiques et aux caractéristiques temporelles.

Chaque information n'est pas liée à un seul paramètre physique, mais à une combinaison de plusieurs d'entre eux aboutissant à un schéma dont la forme est reconnue par le récepteur.

Plus un signal est dégradé, plus diminue le taux des réactions comparables à celles déclenchées par le signal non altéré. Seul le taux est affecté, la nature du comportement induit n'est pas modifiée. Les comportements attendus n'apparaissent pas ou sont plus on moins incomplets.

Les mécanismes de la signalisation acoustique ne paraissent donc pas être très différents de ceux mis en évidence par Tinbergen lors de l'étude de la signalisation optique.

### RESUME

La caractéristique essentielle du chant du rouge-gorge (*Erithacus rubecula*) est sa grande variabilité. Il fut néanmoins possible de dégager trois règles de syntaxe régissant la succession temporelle des divers types de motifs.

REGLE N° 1: Dans une séquence tous les chants consécutifs sont différents les uns des autres.

REGLE N° 2: Dans chaque chant tous les motifs sont différents les uns des autres.

# Le chant territorial du rouge-gorge

REGLE N° 3 : Les motifs successifs sont alternativement compris dans la moitié supérieure ou inférieure du spectre de fréquences contenant le chant, c'est à dire de part et d'autre d'une fréquence de 4 KHz.

Deux des informations contenues dans le chant ont pu être rattachées à ces dispositions syntaxiques. La sémantique est supportée par les règles 2 et 3. La spécificité du signal est liée à la règle N° 2. La règle N° 1 ne semble contribuer que pour une faible part au pouvoir réactogène du signal naturel.

La sémantique et la spécificité sont deux informations distinctes. Elles apparaissent successivement lorsque sont introduits progressivement les paramètres du chant naturel dans un signal obtenu à partir de générateurs électro-acoustiques.

Chaque information est véhiculée par un groupe de paramètres physiques qui définissent un schéma dont le récepteur effectue la reconnaissance. Ce dernier n'intègre pas la totalité des caractéristiques du signal. En plus de ceux déjà cités et se rapportant à la syntaxe il a été donné un autre exemple de ce phénomène. Il était relatif à la forme des notes.

### BIBLIOGRAPHIE

BREMOND J.-C. (1962) Paramètres physiques du chant de défense territoriale du rouge-gorge (*Erithacus rubecula*). *C.R. Acad. Sci.* **254**, 2072–2074.

BREMOND J.-C. (1965) Valeur réactogène des fréquences acoustiques dans le signal de défense territoriale du rouge-gorge (*Erithacus rubecula*). *C.R. Acad. Sci.* **260**, 2910–2913.

DILGER W.C. (1956) Hostile behavior and reproductive isolating mechanisms in the avian genera *Catharus* and *Hylocichla*. *Auk* **73**, 313–353.

FALLS J.B. (1963) Properties of bird song eliciting responses from territorial males. *Proc. XIIIth Intern. Ornithol. Congr.* 259–271.

HARTSHORNE C. (1956) The monotony threshold in singing birds. *Auk* **73**, 176–192.

LACK D. (1943) *The Life of the Robin*. London.

MARLER P. (1957) Specific distinctiveness in the communication signals of birds. *Behaviour* **11**, 13–39.

STEIN R.S. (1956) A comparative study of advertising song in the *Hylocichla* thrushes. *Auk* **73**, 503–512.

THIELCKE G. & LINSENMAIR K.E. (1963) Zur geographischen Variation des Gesanges des Zilpzalps, *Phylloscopus collybita*, in Mittel- und Südwesteuropa mit einem Vergleich des Gesanges des Fitis, *Phylloscopus trochilus*. *J. Orn.* **104**, 372–402.

# Comparative study of song development in sparrows

P.MARLER

Rockefeller University and the
New York Zoological Society

Considered as a pattern of natural behavior the song of the Chaffinch *Fringilla coelebs* represents a most unusual phenomenon in behavioral development. Broadly interpreted, learning plays some role in the development of any piece of behavior. Learning commonly affects the orientation with which a piece of behavior is given, or the stimulus situation in which it occurs. However, it is rare to find an example of the complete reorganization of the internal pattern of a set of natural actions as a result of experience, such as we can observe in the development of song in the Chaffinch.

In 1950 Poulsen reported to this conference on the abnormal development of song in Chaffinches raised in isolation (Poulsen, 1951). Subsequently Thorpe (1955, 1958, 1961) conducted the necessary careful experiments to confirm that the development of normal singing behavior in the Chaffinch is indeed dependent on exposure of the young male to the sounds of older males. Deprived of the opportunity to hear such sounds the young male develops a song which is abnormal in the sense that it has a pattern which is never represented in the population of birds from which the male was taken. The normal pattern of singing behavior is thus transmitted by tradition from generation to generation. The work of Lanyon (1960), Thielcke (1961) and others reveals a similar process in certain other songbirds. This unusual phenomenon has interest from many viewpoints. Apart from man the transmission of vocal traditions is not known to occur in any animal groups other than birds (Marler, 1965). Anthropologists and linguists find themselves concerned with the parallels with the development of human behavior and particularly, of course, human language.

If the phenomenon is indeed so rare in the animal kingdom it becomes an issue of special interest to try to discern the ecological correlates of this distinctive behavior. What is so unusual about the circumstances of the Chaffinch and similar birds that leads them to this particular pattern of development? One way to get at this question would be to look at a group of closely related species, some of which display the transmission of vocal behavior by tradition while others have the

R

apparently more common method of direct genetic transmission. I believe that we have found one such group of suitable birds, and I propose first to describe the results we have obtained on the development of their vocalizations, and then to put forward some thoughts about what the conditions favoring transmission by tradition might be.

My colleagues and I at Berkeley have been studying song development in three groups of species: first the Song Sparrow *Melospiza melodia* studied by Dr James Mulligan; secondly the White-crowned Sparrow *Zonotrichia leucophrys*; and thirdly several species of the genus *Junco*, which Miss Tamura and I have worked with in Berkeley. Dickerman (1961) and Paynter (1964) have pointed out the close relationship between the members of these three so-called genera, *Melospiza*, *Zonotrichia* and *Junco*, and would seek to place at least the first two within a single genus. The occurrence of intergeneric hybrids leaves no doubt that they are closely related. Within this small group of species there seem to be several very different modes for the development of song. Consider first the White-crowned Sparrow.

We have found song development in this species to resemble that in the Chaffinch rather closely (Marler & Tamura, 1962, 1964). There are strongly marked dialects in the natural song (Figure 1). If young birds are taken from the nest and raised in either individual or group isolation, they develop song patterns which lack the characteristics of the local dialect, and are also sufficiently abnormal to fall outside the class of natural patterns for the species, or at least the subspecies with which we worked, *nuttalli* (Figure 2, A1 and 2). If instead birds are brought into the laboratory a few weeks after the time of fledging, and then kept in sound-proof chambers, their song develops normally and they display the characteristics of the local dialect from which they came (Figure 2, C1).

Experiments show that if nestlings are brought in and then given recordings of a local dialect of White-crowned Sparrow song to listen to for a period of 3 weeks during the first few weeks of life, then they subsequently develop a normal pattern of singing, with the dialect properties of the model to which they were exposed. A bird can be taught the dialect of an area different from that where it was born. Thus the details of singing behavior are learned in much the same way as in the male Chaffinch, although in the White-crowned Sparrow the period at which this learning takes place is concentrated much earlier in life, probably from about 10 to 100 days or so. Training before 10 days of age fails to result in imitation (Figure 2, B). If fledglings are brought in after about 3 months of age, attempts at retraining them to a new dialect fail (Figure 2, C2–4).

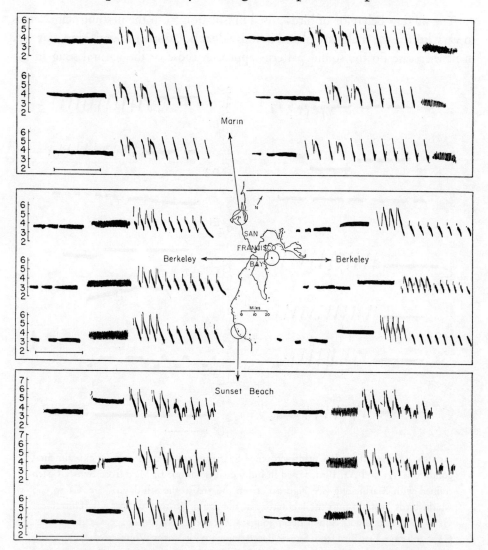

FIGURE I. The songs of eighteen male White-crowned Sparrows at three localities in the San Francisco Bay area. The sound spectrograms show close conformity among the six birds from each area in the detailed structure of syllables in the second part of the song and consistent differences between localities. The introductory whistles and vibrati show more individual variation. Each adult male has a single song type which varies only slightly. The vertical scale is marked in kilocycles per second. The time marker indicates half a second.

# P. Marler

The singing behavior of birds raised in isolation from the nestling stage seems to vary little if the males are placed in individual isolation or are raised in a group. In neither case do the sound patterns approach those of the natural song in the

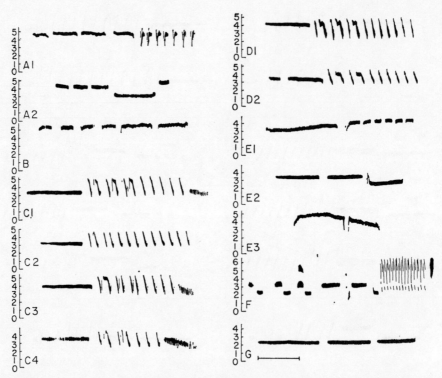

FIGURE 2. Songs of twelve White-crowned Sparrows raised under various experimental conditions. A1 and A2, Birds raised in individual isolation. B, Male from Sunset Beach trained with Marin song (see Figure 1) from the 3rd to the 8th day of age. C1 to C4, Marin birds brought into the laboratory at the age of 30 to 100 days. C1, Untrained. C2 to C4, Trained with Sunset Beach songs; C2 at about 100 days of age, C3 at 200 days, C4 at 300 days. D1, Bird from Sunset Beach trained with Marin White-crowned Sparrow song and a Harris's Sparrow song (see G) from the age of 35 to 56 days. D2, Marin bird trained with Marin White-crowned Sparrow song and a Song Sparrow song (see F) from the age of 6 to 28 days. E1 to E3, Two birds from Sunset Beach and one from Berkeley trained with Song Sparrow song from the age of 7 to 28 days. F, A Song Sparrow training song for D2 and E1 to E3. G, A Harris's Sparrow training song for D1.

details of their structure. They do, however, have some natural properties, including particularly the presence of the sustained thin whistles which characterize members of the genus *Zonotrichia*. An ornithologist would probably identify these isolated songs as coming from a member of the genus, but would be puzzled as to the species. As in the Chaffinch, the learning process has some interesting properties. Thorpe found it hard to teach the male Chaffinch to copy songs of other species. Similarly three male White-crowned Sparrows raised in isolation and exposed at the critical period to recordings of Song Sparrow song failed to show any influence of the training in their subsequent song development (Figure 2, E1–3). Two birds given a choice of copying either a White-crowned Sparrow song or that of another species, a Song Sparrow in one case, a Harris's Sparrow *Z. querula* in the other, each ignored the alien species and made a close copy of the song of their own (Figure 2, D1 and 2). There is thus a clear predisposition to learn only songs with certain properties. It remains to specify exactly what these properties are.

So much for the White-crowned Sparrow; what of the Song Sparrow? At the last International Ornithological Congress Mulligan (1963) described the extraordinary complexity of its song. Unlike the White-crowned Sparrow in which each adult male sings virtually the same song the whole of his life, the adult male Song Sparrow has a repertoire averaging sixteen different song types, comprising many different phrases and syllables. Mulligan (1966) finds that the Song Sparrow is much less dependent than the White-crowned Sparrow upon the opportunity to hear adult birds, for normal song development to take place. In fact, normal development occurred in birds which were fostered from the egg by a pair of canaries, out of earshot of other Song Sparrows. Song patterns developed by these birds were indistinguishable in detail from those found in the population from which the eggs were taken. This is not to say that a male Song Sparrow is incapable of mimicry. He can certainly copy the songs of adult birds in the neighborhood. In fact, about one song in ten in the repertoire of an individual resembles that of a neighbor, apparently as a result of imitation. Mulligan confirmed this by training experiments. Thus copying occurs regularly in the development of song in this species. Nevertheless, exposure to adult song is not a prerequisite for the development of normal song patterns. Here then is a mode of development which contrasts with that in the White-crowned Sparrow, rather surprisingly generating a more complex pattern of singing behavior in Song Sparrows than in White-crowns.

So far then we have two extremes, the White-crowned Sparrow strictly dependent on early exposure to adult song for normal development to occur, the Song Sparrow not dependent upon such an experience for normal development. The two species of junco that we have studied, the Arizona Junco *Junco*

# P.Marler

*phaeonotus* and the Oregon Junco *J. oreganus*, seem to fall somewhere between these two extremes. I shall first describe the results with the Arizona Junco. We selected this species for study because of the complexity of its song patterns. A field study was first made in Durango, northern Mexico (Marler & Isaac, 1961). We found no

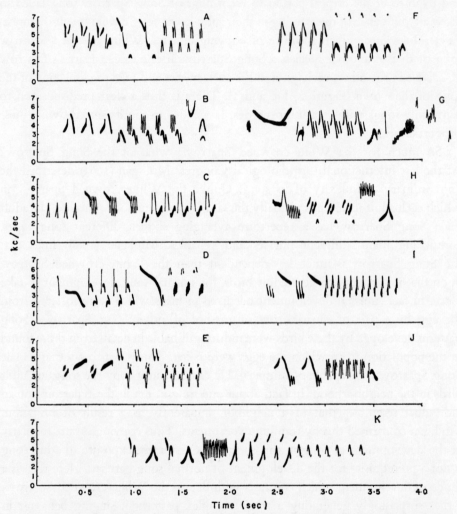

FIGURE 3. Songs of eleven male Arizona Juncos recorded near El Salto, Durango, in Mexico, selected to show the range of patterns encountered. A–E: These songs represent the most common condition (based on such characteristics as overall duration, number of syllable types per song, number of trills per song, etc.). F–K: These songs represent extremes as follows: F—few syllable types; G—many syllable types; H—few trill syllables; I—many trill syllables; J—a short song; K—a long song.

236

# Comparative study of song development in sparrows

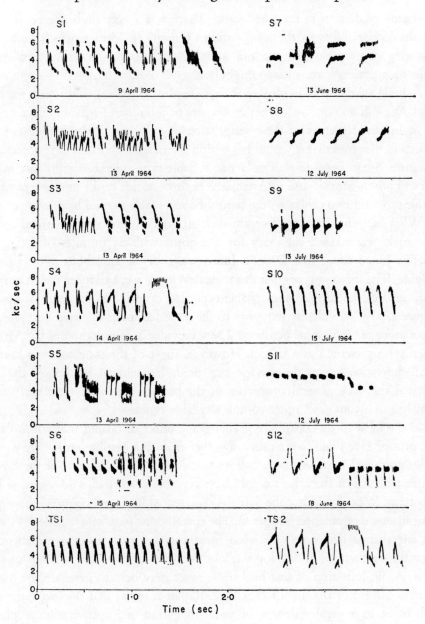

FIGURE 4. Songs of two male Arizona Juncos raised in individual isolation from the nestling stage, one with training by playback of normal Oregon and Arizona Junco song (TS1 and 2), the other without training. The trained bird (S1–6) and the untrained bird (S7–12) each produced six song types. The details of training are given in the text.

suggestion of dialects in the usual sense. There was a very high degree of intra-population variability in the song patterns (Figure 3). Most juncos have a song consisting of a simple trill, and our initial hypothesis was that the complexities of the song of the Arizona Junco might be a result of learning.

A male raised in individual isolation (Figure 4, S7–12) developed six song types. We still do not know whether the size of this repertoire is abnormal or not. Surveying the structure of these song patterns, only one of them appears to be normal in the sense that it would fall within the range of possibilities encountered in nature. Songs consisting of only one syllable type are exceedingly rare in this species both in Mexico and in Arizona. Yet three of this bird's songs were of this simple type and two others would hardly be acceptable as wild birds' songs.

What happens if we try to train such an isolated bird with recorded songs? One male was trained each day for 2 months with 23 minutes of song, half Arizona Junco song, half Oregon Junco song, beginning about 3 weeks after fledging. The six song types that this male developed were all more or less normal, with none of the simple, one-syllable type that occurred in the untrained isolate (Figure 4, S1–6). Evidently exposure to the recorded songs diverted development into a more or less normal pathway. There is evidence of imitation of the Arizona Junco song presented as a model. However, most of the song patterns bear no detailed relationship to the models presented. It is almost as though the bird imitated the very general properties of the pattern, but was stimulated not to copy but to invent new, more complex syllable types.

In the light of this possibility, what is the effect of raising males in isolation as a group? Five males were raised together from the nestling stage. They eventually produced between them twenty-one song types. Only one of these was a simple trill. All of the others would be acceptable as normal wild songs, at least in pattern. We can tabulate the patterns represented here, and compare them with those in a wild population (Figure 5). The correspondence is remarkable. Evidently the interchange that occurs between members of such a group is sufficient for normal song patterns to develop without the need for exposure to songs of adult birds. Again imitation of one bird by another may help to generate the overall patterns but is not the main factor here. Rather it seems that the birds stimulate each other to a greater degree of vocal invention or improvization, a phenomenon not encountered in either White-crowns or Song Sparrows, so far as we can tell.

By comparison with the Arizona Junco the song of the Oregon Junco is simple. In the great majority of cases a song consists of identical repetitions of the same syllable—a single trill (Figure 6). Only very rarely do we encounter in nature a song that includes two syllable types. The effect of raising Oregon Juncos in isolation differs from that with Arizona Juncos in an interesting way. We have seen that in the Arizona Junco individual isolates tend to have a larger proportion of simpler songs than wild birds. With Oregon Juncos the reverse is true. Seven males were raised in individual isolation from an early nestling age. As adults they produced altogether 28 song types. Only eight of these consisted of

| One-trill songs | | | | Two-trill songs | | | | Three-trill songs | | | |
|---|---|---|---|---|---|---|---|---|---|---|---|
| W | | EI | (E2) | W | | EI | (E2) | W | | EI | (E2) |
| 4 | aBc | I | | 13 | AB | 9 | 8 | 5 | ABC | 7 | 4 |
| 3 | Ab | I | I | 12 | ABc | 3 | 0 | 2 | AbCD | 2 | 0 |
| | Abc | I | | 9 | AbC | 6 | 4 | 2 | ABCd | | |
| | A | I | I | 7 | AbCd | 2 | I | I | ABcD | | |
| | | | | 4 | aBC | 3 | 2 | I | AbCDe | | |
| | | | | 2 | aBcD | | | I | ABcDe | I | 0 |
| | | | | I | aBCd | | | | ABCdE | I | 0 |
| Totals 7 | | 4 | (2) | 48 | | 23 | (15) | 12 | | 11 | (4) |

FIGURE 5. A tabulation of the characteristics of songs of wild and experimental Arizona Juncos. A sequence of repeated syllables is designated as a trill and represented by a capital letter. An unrepeated sequence is designated as a phrase and represented by a lower-case letter. The letters run in alphabetical sequence from the start of the song. Thus song A in Figure 3 would be represented as ABC, song B as ABc, and so on. Columns headed W include sixty-five song patterns from wild birds in Mexico. Columns headed E represent songs of five males raised in acoustical isolation as a group. Those in brackets (E2) are the final song patterns of these birds. Those in EI also include song patterns that occurred during development but were subsequently dropped.

a single syllable type, the typical wild pattern. Thus about 75 per cent of them had two or more syllable types, a condition which is, as I have said, rare in nature. Each bird produced at least one song pattern that was perfectly acceptable as a wild song type, and several that were abnormal.

In 1958 and 1959 we did a similar series of studies with group isolates (Marler, Kreith & Tamura, 1962). Two groups of males, one of three, one of five birds, were raised in isolation as groups (Figures 7 and 8). Again there was a rather higher incidence of multi-partite songs than occurs in nature, but the frequency of normal songs was greater than in individual isolates, with twenty one-part songs and seven two-part songs. This suggests that the interchanges between the members of a group suffice at least partly to bring the course of development back to a normal pathway.

We have yet to do the crucial experiment here, namely to train individual

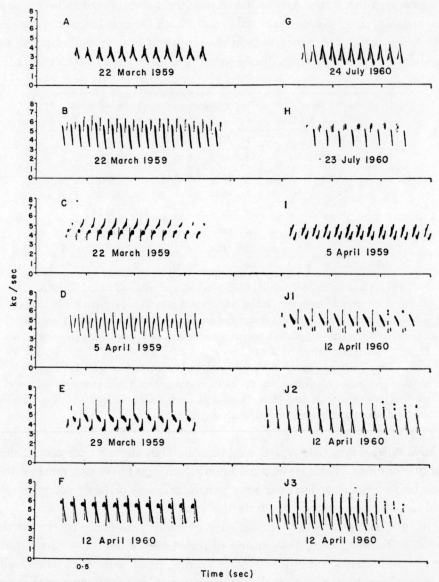

FIGURE 6. Twelve songs of wild Oregon Juncos. J1–3 are from a single bird. The others are from different individuals in the same population. Note the variation in syllabic structure.

240

## Comparative study of song development in sparrows

isolates with normal junco song. We do know that birds captured in the wild and brought into individual isolation at about three months of age develop normal one-part songs. Presumably exposure to one-part songs serves to virtually eliminate multi-partite songs from the repertoire. If we are right, this would seem to be a case where exposure to environmental sounds is necessary, not to generate a more complex pattern than would otherwise occur, but rather to restrict development to a simpler pattern than would otherwise be the case.

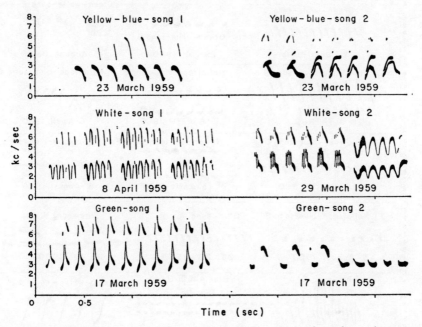

FIGURE 7. Songs of three male Oregon Juncos raised as a group from the nestling stage.

There is good evidence that Oregon Juncos are capable of precise imitation. But the great variability in the structure of syllables in group isolates and in the songs of wild birds seems to preclude precise imitation as a dominant element in syllable development. It seems as though they acquire the overall song pattern by imitation but not the detailed structure of the syllables. We did try raising four male Oregon Juncos in individual isolation trained to songs of Arizona Juncos. Again we found a high proportion of multi-partite songs developing, apparently even further encouraged by exposure to the multi-partite songs of the model. Again the syllabic diversity did not seem to be the result of imitation in the usual sense. As in the Arizona Junco it seems necessary to propose a process like invention or improvisation to explain development of syllabic structure in the Oregon Junco, even though they may imitate the general patterns of songs that they hear.

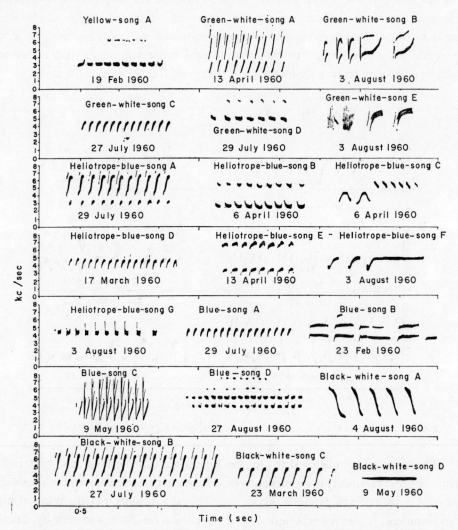

FIGURE 8. Songs of five male Oregon Juncos raised as a group from the nestling stage.

This, then, is the situation as far as we know it in these three groups of species. A Song Sparrow seems to be able to develop quite normal song patterns when raised in isolation from members of its own species. At the other extreme the male White-crowned Sparrow requires exposure to the song of adults for normal development to occur. The juncos are in an intermediate condition, developing some abnormal song properties when raised in isolation, and requiring exposure to sounds of siblings or adults for completely normal development. The exposure is needed, at least in part, not to permit imitation but to generate a higher degree of improvisation or invention, thus bringing forth the development of normal song patterns.

What sense can we make of these very divergent developmental pathways in such a closely related group of birds? I am frankly puzzled by this question. All are territorial, but the White-crowned Sparrow and the juncos undergo local migrations whereas the Song Sparrow in this area is resident the year round. One might argue that the very sedentary life of Song Sparrows in the San Francisco Bay area should have repercussions on the method of song development. They occupy their territories all the year, in circumstances that should be ideal for the occurrence of traditional inheritance, and yet this does not occur. Conversely the White-crowned Sparrows in California are at least in some degree migrant, moving in small flocks away from their breeding area during the winter. They also mingle freely with populations of other subspecies that come through during the winter on migration. The situation might seem to favor the control of variation in song patterns by genetic influences, and yet this is the most striking case of traditional inheritance in the group.

The particular timing of the sensitive period in the White-crowned Sparrow may be explicable in this way. Song learning is probably completed before migrants from the north come in, thus ensuring that the properties of song in the several subspecies shall not mingle. If the choice of territory or a mate is also controlled in part by the properties of the song, then this would serve to maintain separation between the subspecies. But this still does not explain why a traditional type of inheritance should be favored in place of genetic control. Could it be that a learned song is more readily susceptible to change in the face of natural selection? It should be possible to change the song patterns of a population more quickly if variations in their structure are controlled by learning rather than genetic inheritance. Perhaps this ability has permitted White-crowned Sparrows to invade many different areas more readily and more quickly than would be the case if modification of the song had to wait upon genetic change? Presumably the invasion of new avifaunas will favor change in the structure of the song, for example, if species specificity is to be maintained, or if habitat differences call forth changes in the social system. On the other hand, few species have undergone as much racial diversification as the Song Sparrow, and yet its song is not dependent on the

# P.Marler

traditional type of developmental control. Perhaps those more intimate with the ecology of these species may be able to suggest how this puzzle can be solved.

## ACKNOWLEDGEMENTS

This paper is the outcome of joint research with Mrs Marcia Kreith and Miss Miwako Tamura with generous help from Dr Mark Konishi, Dr James Mulligan, Dr Fernando Nottebohm and others. The work was supported by grants from the National Science Foundation.

## REFERENCES

DICKERMAN R.W. (1961) Hybrids among the fringillid genera *Junco-Zonotrichia* and *Melospiza*. *Auk* **78**, 627–632.

KONISHI M. (1964) Song variation in a population of Oregon Juncos. *Condor*, **66**, 423–436.

LANYON W.E. (1960) The ontogeny of vocalization in birds. In *Animal Sounds and Communication*. Ed. W.E.Lanyon and W.N.Tavolga. Publ. No. 7. AIBS Washington, D.C.

MARLER P. (1965) Inheritance and learning in the development of animal vocalizations. In *Acoustic Behavior of Animals*. Ed. R.C.Busnel. Elsevier, Amsterdam.

MARLER P. & ISAAC D. (1961) Song variation in a population of Mexican Juncos. *Wilson Bull.* **73**, 193–206.

MARLER P., KREITH, M. & TAMURA, M. (1962) Song development in hand-raised Oregon Juncos. *Auk* **79**, 12–30.

MARLER P. & TAMURA M. (1962) Song dialects in three populations of White-crowned Sparrows. *Condor* **64**, 368–377.

MARLER P. & TAMURA M. (1964) Culturally transmitted patterns of vocal behavior in sparrows. *Science* **146**, 1483–1486.

MULLIGAN J.A. (1963) A description of Song Sparrow song based on instrumental analysis. *Proc. XIII Intern. Ornithol. Congr.* pp. 272–284.

MULLIGAN J.A. (1966) Singing behavior and its development in the Song Sparrow, *Melospiza melodia*. *Univ. Calif. Publ. Zool.* **81**, 1–76.

NICE M.M. (1943) Studies in the life history of the Song Sparrow. II. The behavior of the Song Sparrow and other Passerines. *Trans. Linn. Soc. N.Y.* **6**, 1–329.

PAYNTER R.A. (1964) Generic limits of *Zonotrichia*. *Condor* **66**, 277–281.

POULSEN H. (1951) Inheritance and learning in the song of the Chaffinch (*Fringilla coelebs* L.). *Behaviour* **3**, 216–228.

THIELCKE G. (1961) Ergebnisse der Vogelstimmen Analyse. *J. Ornithol.* **102**, 285–300.

THORPE W.H. (1955) The analysis of bird song with special reference to the song of the Chaffinch (*Fringilla coelebs*). *Proc. XI. Intern. Ornithol. Congr.* pp. 209–217.

THORPE W.H. (1958) The learning of song patterns by birds, with especial reference to the song of the Chaffinch *Fringilla coelebs*. *Ibis* **100**, 535–570.

THORPE W.H. (1961) *Bird Song. The Biology of Vocal Communication and Expression in Birds.* Cambridge Univ. Press, Cambridge.

# Vocal imitation and antiphonal song and its implications

W.H.THORPE

Cambridge University Sub-Department of Animal Behaviour,
High Street, Madingley, Cambridge

The fact that parrots and the 'Indian Hill Mynah' (*Gracula*) are able to mimic the human voice has long been known—the former since well before the time of Aristotle, and the latter since the early sixteenth century. As the scientific study of bird behaviour has developed, and as new methods of recording and analysis of bird sounds have become available, so the evidence for vocal mimicry of various types has steadily become more extensive and more reliable—though results obtained with these new methods also suggest that many earlier records of vocal imitation are now suspect or unacceptable. Now, there is one very general comment which seems worth making at this stage. This is to point out the astounding difference between the birds and the mammals in this respect. There are few abilities which separate man more clearly from other members of the animal kingdom than his powers of imitation. If we consider vocal imitation alone, the difference between man and the other mammals is even more striking. Even with the chimpanzee a capacity for vocal imitation seems to be almost non-existent, and no satisfactory scientific evidence seems yet to have been presented on behalf of claims made for exact powers of vocal imitation amongst porpoises (Andrew, 1962; Lilly, 1962). This remarkable difference between man and the rest of the mammals is considered by Konorski (1963) to be explicable on certain differences between the brain structure of man and the apes. Whether this is so is still in dispute, but at least we are not at present in any position to make a useful comparison, either between birds and mammals in this respect, or even between the imitative and the non-imitative birds. The investigation of the neurology of the birds' central nervous system has not nearly reached the stage at which useful comparisons can be made; indeed, the only birds on which modern neurological investigations have been extensively carried out are members of the *Columbidae*, and all the evidence as yet available (Lade & Thorpe, 1964) points to the doves being incapable of vocal imitation. However, an excellent beginning with the investigation of the brain of a song-bird, the Red-winged Blackbird *Agelaius phoeniceus*, has been made by Brown (1965, 1966). But it will probably be many years before anything useful can be said about the neurology of vocal imitation in birds; for quite advanced and detailed studies of centres and connecting tracts of a number of species will be needful before reports of any correlation between structure and performance in this respect could be convincing.

In this matter of vocal imitation it has often in the past been thought useful to divide imitative species into two classes: (i) those species which imitate con-specifics only and (ii) those which imitate other species or sounds of non-avian origin. This feeling has been expressed in the fairly widespread usage whereby members of the first group are regarded as displaying '*imitation*', and that of the second group '*vocal mimicry*'. We now know that this division is of little funda-mental or physiological importance, and that the classes are not mutually exclusive; though it does have the merit of drawing attention to points of biological interest which need further study.

The minimum basic assumptions necessary to account for the phenomena we have observed during the course of many years' study of the song of the Chaf-finch *Fringilla coelebs* (Thorpe, 1965) appear to be as follows: (1) there must be some predilection for hearing a certain type of sound pattern; (2) there must be a predilection and a mechanism for achieving vocal control of the sounds the bird itself is capable of uttering; (3) there must be a tendency to experiment with the vocal organs—to play with them, so to speak—until a sound is produced very similar to, or identical with, the sound to which the bird has been listening. Making these assumptions the unrewarded learning of unfamiliar song-patterns produced by other Chaffinches becomes at least partially comprehensible. Our knowledge of this point has been noticeably advanced by the current work of my colleague, Dr Joan Stevenson; and I have her permission to quote her recent results (in press, 1966). The amorphous rambling sub-song of the Chaffinch only develops into the normal song of the species after the bird has had sufficient exposure to adult song. This suggests that the development of full-song from the sub-song is only possible if notes which resemble the adult song have reinforcing properties. If so, then hearing these notes, either from himself or from another source, should be rewarding to a young bird whose song is developing out of the sub-song. This has been tested in an operant conditioning situation in a sound-proof chamber in which a young bird can play the recording of an adult song by hopping on to an 'active' perch, but not by hopping on to an 'inactive' one. The reinforcing effect of hearing the song is said to be shown if the bird perches relatively more on the 'active' perch, as compared with the 'non-active' perch, when the 'active' perch plays the song than when it does not. By this technique it was found that adult song was a reinforcer for autumn-caught testosterone-injected males, and that a rush of white noise of a volume and duration similar to the adult song was not a reinforcer. Thus, adult song does have a reinforcing effect, which is fairly specific to the song. However, the adult song was not a reinforcer for testosterone-injected males hand-reared in isolation from adult song. Since it has previously been shown that hearing adult song in the early months of life does improve later song development, it seems clear that this difference between autumn-caught and hand-reared birds is due to previous song experience rather than to previous experience of other kinds.

At this point it is worthy of note that young Chaffinches will quite readily incorporate in their sub-song notes heard from a number of other species. This is reasonably well established in the case of six different species comprised in the genera *Parus, Regulus, Prunella, Chloris* and *Serinus* (Thorpe, 1955). The most significant point, however, is that in no case, either with our experimental birds or in searching the literature, have I been able to find an example of a Chaffinch including notes of an alien species in its full-song. Thus, although we had a hand-reared Chaffinch which picked up a complex phrase of about fifteen notes from a canary and included these virtually unchanged in its sub-song, it dropped them completely when it produced its full-song. This suggests that it is important in the Chaffinch that the full-song be not contaminated with the sounds of alien species even though this is allowable in the sub-song. This is consonant with the view based on many different observations that in those species where the full-song has an important function as a territorial signal the sub-song is without communicatory value.

The work of Dr Stevenson, just mentioned, shows that there are features in the normal song of the Chaffinch which have in themselves sufficient stimulus value to serve as 'reinforcers' or 'rewards' for flight and perching behaviour in a sound-proof chamber, independent of any previous association with reinforcement of the classical type. In other words, under the conditions of the experiment, Chaffinches will work in order to hear the playback of a song of their own species but not white noise of similar duration and intensity. It is also worth recalling that 'talking birds' such as the 'Indian Hill Mynah' *Gracula religiosa* and the Budgerigar *Melopsittacus undulatus* can be taught 'to talk for a food reward'. This is to say, as the psychologists are wont to put it, 'reinforcement control' or 'stimulus control' of vocal responses has been demonstrated. (Reference to various species as follows: Ginsburg, 1960, 1963; Grosslight, Harrison & Weiser, 1962; Lane, 1961. But compare the contradictory results of Foss, 1964.)

We are now achieving much new knowledge as to the physiological mecha-

S                    247

nisms involved in the learning and development of song in a number of species. These include the domestic fowl (Konishi, 1963) where it was found that birds could develop and also maintain the normal repertoire and the normal form of their vocal signals without any auditory feedback. Two species of *Junco, J. oreganus* and *J. phaeonotus*, where some aspects of the song develop normally without auditory feedback while some other aspects are abnormal (Konishi, 1964), and the American Robin *Turdus migratorius*, Black-headed Grossbeak *Pheucticus melanocephalus* and White-crowned Sparrow *Zonotrichia leucophrys nuttalli*, where results very generally were similar to those with juncos, may be cited (Konishi, 1965 a, b). These and other aspects of such studies on the Chaffinch, including his own work, are dealt with by Dr Nottebohm (p. 265), so the matter need not be followed any further here.

In my earlier series of experiments I attempted to teach Chaffinches 'artificial' songs. The conclusion emerged that the Chaffinch will imitate only sounds of a tonal quality approximately similar to its own utterances. Thus it was found to be impossible to teach inexperienced Chaffinches, even though hand-reared and isolated, new songs by means of playback on a tape recorder if those songs were strikingly abnormal in tonal quality. If, however, the abnormal songs used as models were constructed of notes from Chaffinch songs, or of notes from a species that the sound-spectrograph showed to have sounds of a similar frequency-amplitude distribution, the experiments were successful and some quite abnormal songs could be learned, e.g. an experimental Chaffinch song with the end in the middle— the structure thus being a - c - b, instead of a - b - c—or the song of a continental Tree Pipit *Anthus t. trivialis*.

What can be the selective advantage of this tendency to imitate songs of members of its own species? First, the song in the Chaffinch is a territorial proclamation, a warning to rival males, and a signal system conveying information identifying the singer (both as a species and as an individual) to potential mates as well. Hinde (1958) has shown that when songs of different types are played back to a Chaffinch, those song types it uses most frequently are the most effective in evoking singing irrespective of whether they resemble normal song or not. Thus when a Chaffinch is singing against other Chaffinches in neighbouring territories it will (if these experimental results hold good under natural conditions) tend to reply with that song in its repertoire which most nearly resembles the song of its rival. Thus it seems plausible to assume that the ability of a Chaffinch to reply to a neighbouring male defending a near-by territory with the kind of song that male is itself singing may be recognized by the rival as a more effective, a more threatening, territorial defence mechanism than if the song it replied with were independent of the song it had just heard. In other words, the Chaffinch song must be maintained as characteristic of the species. That is, the overall pattern must be such that another Chaffinch (and *ipso facto* a field ornithologist) can recognize the signal at once as being that of a Chaffinch. In the normal Chaffinch song there is sufficient complexity to allow for considerable variation by the individual without overstepping the bounds of the specific Chaffinch pattern. So you can have variations which will specify particular individuals; and these variations can be learnt, and are learnt, while the birds are still in their first year, and in this way local dialects can be passed on from one generation to another. Thus the ability to imitate the fine details of song is important in that it enables the song to be not merely a specific signature tune but an individual signature tune as well. And this supposition gives a reasonable explanation of the fact that a Chaffinch, in the wild, never contaminates its full-song by notes copied from other species. But it is, of course, widely known that different species of birds vary very greatly in their song-learning ability, as Marler (1966) has clearly shown. Thus amongst European finches we find that many are very good at learning alien songs when hand-reared under experimental conditions; the Bullfinch *Pyrrhula pyrrhula* and the Greenfinch *Chloris chloris* at once come to mind. But there is little evidence that it is important for such birds to restrict their imitations of other species to their sub-song. In fact, the indications are that species such as these, which are highly imitative, have songs which are much less important as territorial proclamations. It seems probable that these songs are more concerned with co-ordinating the breeding cycle and adjusting the behaviour of the mated pair and conceivably also with individual recognition. If this is so, then there is at least a plausible reason why such songs could remain flexible without endangering the process of territory establishment and the breeding cycle that follows from it. As Marler (1960) suggests, if the song is concerned in maintaining a pair bond that lasts for a number of seasons, individual recognition may be important and variation will be encouraged. Similarly, physiological synchronization might be better effected by variation than by stereotypy. Such finches as these, then, are members of both our classes: that is they imitate their own species and they can, under experimental conditions, imitate alien species also.

As all ornithologists know, there are other species which readily extend their imitative powers* to the sounds produced by other bird species, often not in

* There are two extremely interesting and important recent developments in this field which must be briefly mentioned here. Nicolai (1964), studying the brood parasitism of widow-birds

any way related to themselves. A few temperate-region Passerines, e.g. Blyth's Reed Warbler *Acrocephalus dumetorum* and the Mocking Bird *Mimus polyglottus*, habitually do this under natural conditions; and when we extend our survey to the tropics we can find many more examples of such mimics.

Most such species restrict their powers of imitation to sounds which in timbre, timing and pitch are within the normal range of the voices of song-birds. With the parrots and mynahs, on the other hand, the vocal apparatus has such extraordinary flexibility, and such wide range, that it is difficult to instance any sound audible to the human ear which would appear to be intrinsically impossible for such species to imitate. The ability, in other words, seems to have gone far in advance of any conceivable biological utility. If, however, it were possible to show that the imitative powers of these birds are sometimes employed for recognizing and maintaining contact, by means of very subtle vocal inflections, with other members of the species or, particularly, with the mate—then, at any rate in social species such as mynahs, the powers of mimicry would be easier to understand. It is not at present possible to show this; the problem of the origin of vocal mimicry is, as yet, by no means solved. However, the use of the voice as a social bond, particularly in tropical and sub-tropical species, may (Thorpe & North, 1965) provide a clue indicating another possible way in which high powers of vocal imitation could have been evolved in species not strongly territorial.

In the tropics, although there are many species of birds the song of which is doubtless just as territorial in function as is usual in the temperate regions, the ornithologist is also struck by the number of examples where song appears much less aggressive in intent and where its function is apparently as a social signal, for maintaining pair and family bonds and as part of the sexual display, rather than a

---

of various genera, has shown that race and species formation has occurred parallel to that of their hosts and that the behaviour patterns of the Viduinae are adapted to the special circumstances of their brood parasitism, and that this has involved close adaptation of their songs. Studies of ten species of Viduinae and five species of Ploceidae have shown that the songs of the Viduinae are composed of two groups of elements; in each case one is weaver-like, while the other encompasses the entire vocal repertoire of the particular species of Estrildinae concerned. Thus the songs of the Viduinae reveal the identity of the host species which they parasitize. Although the role of imitative learning in this remarkable story has not been investigated, one must assume, I think, that the basis of this astonishing adaptation is now largely 'instinctive' whatever part learning may have played in its original development or its fine adjustment. Similarly, Tretzel (1965) has shown that in the Crested Lark *Galerida cristata*, the population of the species in a certain area of Germany has incorporated into its song the characteristic whistles by which the shepherds of the area control their dogs.

territorial one. Moreover, it is perhaps significant that most of the outstanding vocal imitators are found among tropical or sub-tropical species. We suggested that the extreme developments of imitative ability occur where the main function of the song is to provide for social recognition and cohesion rather than for territorial defence (Thorpe & North, 1965). This seems to apply specially in the tropics.

In 1903 Waite described how two captive Australian Magpies *Gymnorhina tibicen* learned to sing a fifteen-note melody, played to them on the flute, as an antiphonal duet. When the younger bird died, the survivor resumed the performance of the whole, which it had never been heard to produce during the years when it had a companion. A rather similar case of the antiphonal division of a learned melody between a pet Canary *Serinus c. canarius* and a captive Bullfinch *Pyrrhula pyrrhula* was described in the same year by the famous musician Sir George Henschel (1903). Gwinner & Kneutgen (1962) described how, with both Ravens *Corvus corax* and Shama *Copsychus malabaricus*, the males and females each had sounds or song elements which were principally, if not exclusively, their own private utterances and were not normally used by their mates. However, when the partners were absent, the remaining bird would use the sounds normally reserved for his partner, with the result that the said partner would return as quickly as possible as if called by name. Gwinner and Kneutgen find the method to be particularly effective if it is the male who is absent, since, they suggest, there is nothing more stimulating to a mated male than to hear its own repertoire repeated in its own territory. Thus, the vocalizations of these species appear to be used for securing the return of the desired partner—a conclusion relevant to the work on operant control of vocalization mentioned above.

The study of the antiphonal singing of certain tropical birds (*Laniarius, Cossypha, Cisticola* and *Trachyphonus*), on which I have now been engaged for some years, is particularly relevant to these problems. This is especially true of the antiphonal performances of the tropical Boubou Shrike *Laniarius aethiopicus*. In this species each pair in the wild may have a considerable number of alternative duet patterns. Consequently, while many of the simpler patterns may be very widespread in a given population, some are likely to be peculiar to individual pairs. If this is correct, then the mate is that bird which can answer with the right pattern of notes in the right time. Figure 1, 2 and 3 show typical examples of duets of this species.

From our field and laboratory observations it appears that (a) either sex can start and the other finish, (b) either bird can sing the whole pattern alone if the partner is absent, (c) when the partner returns the two birds can either duplicate in perfect time or (more usually) sing antiphonally again. Thus it appears that in the course of developing its elaborate duets each individual of the pair has, in fact,

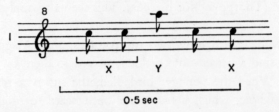

FIGURE 1. Antiphonal song of *Laniarius aethiopicus sublacteus*, recorded at Vipingo, Kilifi, Kenya; December 1954. (From Thorpe & North, 1965.) In this and the next two figures, middle 'C' is at approximately Scientific Pitch (i.e. 256 cycles/sec.). 'X' & 'Y' indicate the contributions of the two different birds, though 'X' is not necessarily the ♂.

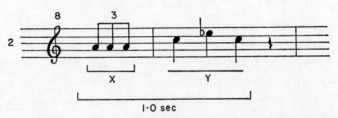

FIGURE 2. Antiphonal song of *Laniarius aethiopicus major*, recorded at Dundori, Nakuru, Kenya; March 17, 1964. (From Thorpe & North, 1965.)

FIGURE 3. Antiphonal song of *Laniarius aethiopicus major*, recorded at Meadow Point, Lake Nakuru, Kenya; March 17, 1964. (From Thorpe & North, 1965.)

learned the contribution of the other member and its relation to the whole—which means that it must possess considerable powers of imitation. Thus the imitative powers of *L. aethiopicus* (Thorpe & North, 1965) enable each bird to learn the normal contribution of its mate as well as its own, and subsequently, as it seems, to use this appropriately for maintaining contact with a partner and

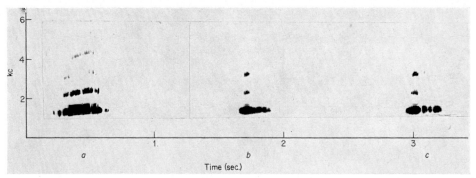

FIGURE 4. (*a*) Sound spectrogram of three mature single notes of Boubou Shrike 'W' *Laniarius aethiopicus* in tropical aviary at Madingley, Cambridge; *a*, 28 July 1965; *b* and *c* 4 August 1965. (In this and the following figures vertical scale shows frequency in kilocycles per second and horizontal scale shows time in seconds.)

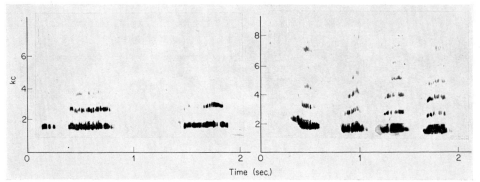

(*b*) (left) Sound spectrogram of the single notes, still somewhat immature, of Boubou Shrike 'M' *L. aethiopicus* in tropical aviary at Madingley, Cambridge, 30 July 1965. (In these as in the other figures comparisons should be made solely on the basis of the lowest marks on the graph. The upper marks, which indicate harmonics, vary greatly with the intensity of the recording and are not comparable from one figure to the next.)

(*c*) (right) Series of four successive juvenile notes produced by Boubou Shrike 'M' *L. aethiopicus* when learning to duet with shrike 'W' in tropical aviary at Madingley, Cambridge, 4 August 1965.

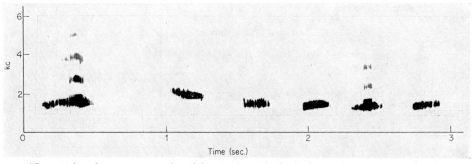

(*d*) Complete duet pattern produced by Boubou Shrike 'W' *L. aethiopicus* alone after the loss of shrike 'M'. It is seen to consist of its own introductory note followed by a series of five somewhat juvenile-type notes imitative of the four note series formerly contributed by shrike 'M' (tropical aviary at Madingley, Cambridge, 12 August 1965.) (All from Thorpe & North, 1966.)

FIGURE 4

recalling him or her when absent. Field observations suggest at times that one bird is calling its partner back 'by name'.

Since this work was published we have obtained remarkable experimental evidence of this in our tropical aviaries at Madingley (Thorpe & North, 1966). In the summer of 1965 I had two hand-reared Boubou Shrikes in captivity. The first bird (a male), ringed 'White', had been hand-reared in the spring of 1964 at Sotik in Kenya, and was sent to us in July 1964. During the following 12 months it had not developed its vocalizations very notably, although the two single notes that it was in the habit of producing were fully mature in tonal quality (see Figure 4a). On December 10, 1964, another bird ringed 'Mauve', a female, also reared in the same way and the same place, was received from Kenya. The bird, being somewhat delicate, was kept for the greater part of the time in a separate cage indoors in the laboratory at room temperature. During the period, its voice developed somewhat and it was in the habit of producing a series of four notes, still rather juvenile, and quavering in pitch (see Figure 4c). On July 8, 1965, this bird was transferred to the aviary in which 'White' was established, and in the course of the subsequent month, 'White' and 'Mauve' together had developed a simple antiphonal song—usually commenced by one or two simple notes from 'White', followed immediately by the juvenile four-note performance of 'Mauve'. During the period these birds were constantly recorded and 'White' was never heard to give anything but its normal two notes. On August 10, 1965, 'Mauve' died suddenly from an obscure infection. Immediately, 'White' started to behave in a very agitated manner, searching continually around the aviary as if looking for its lost companion, all the while uttering the full duet pattern, namely its own single pure note and the four, or more often five, quavering notes characteristic of its now dead companion (Figure 4d). The bird continued to behave in this remarkable way for some days but its production of the combined duet pattern gradually became less frequent and was not heard much after August 20. On August 24 it was given a new female. There was no noticeable antiphonal singing for over 6 months, but it redeveloped in new forms in the spring of 1966 and by the end of June, when the birds commenced breeding, was highly co-ordinated and quite 'normal'; though the duets were not as elaborate as those often heard in the wild.

It seems then that this result constitutes an unexpectedly dramatic confirmation of the view that one of the major functions of the imitative ability of such birds is to establish and strengthen the social bonding. It also suggests that the remarkable social antiphonal singing of L. aethiopicus, which sometimes extends to trio singing as well as duetting (Thorpe & North, 1965), is also in the nature of a mutual display which serves to maintain cohesion and ensure recognition. Thus the results obtained by Gwinner & Kneutgen and ourselves provide a remarkable explanation and extension of the strange observations of Waite, Henschel and others which are to be found scattered through the literature over more than 60 years.

No discussion of imitation or mimicry in birds would, of course, be complete without some reference to those supreme performers the parrots and the 'mynahs'. As I have made clear above, the so-called 'Indian Hill Mynah' (*Gracula religiosa* and its races) is both the most outstanding exponent of this type of mimicry and is also the best studied; so in what little space remains I shall confine myself to this species. *G. religiosa* is remarkable not merely for the precision and accuracy of its imitation of human voices but also for the fact that, in spite of one or two vague statements to the contrary, there is still no convincing evidence that the bird ever imitates other bird species in the wild. As far as is yet known it is only in captivity that it will attend to and reproduce the voices of humans and the sounds made by mammals and by other birds, and sounds of inanimate origin. I had originally intended in this paper to give a much greater proportion of the time to discussing the vocal apparatus of birds and the way in which it is able to give forth sounds of such a completely 'unbird-like' nature. Unfortunately, our work in this field has not yet got far enough to warrant more than a brief allusion to some new results. But these results, such as they are, seem to me to be sufficiently promising to deserve mention.

The most challenging problem concerning the vocalization of mynahs, and particularly their ability to imitate the human voice, lies in their powers of producing human vowels—the most important constituents of human speech. Some 7 years ago (Thorpe, 1959) I showed by means of sound-spectrographic analysis that, contrary to previous expectation, the mynah's imitations of human voices contain formants or resonances closely similar to those produced by man. These formants in ourselves are the result of resonances in the three or four main cavities of our own vocal apparatus, namely our mouth, nose and throat, which act in co-ordination on the overtones produced by the vocal cords and, by suppressing some, give apparent reinforcement to others that we recognize as the vocal resonance. And it is the position and relationships of the three main formants which determine the characteristic sound of vowels and which define, more than any other feature, the quality—indeed the very existence—of human speech. The problem then is—how can the mynah and other talking birds produce these sounds when their vocal apparatus apparently lacks the necessary cavities to give the resonant frequencies essential to vowel production? We still cannot answer that question. But further study with the sound-spectrograph, in connection with which I am much indebted to my colleague Mr Richard White, has shown that the resemblances between human and mynah 'speech' are even closer and more exact than we had previously thought. Figures 5 and 6 show the sound-spectrograms

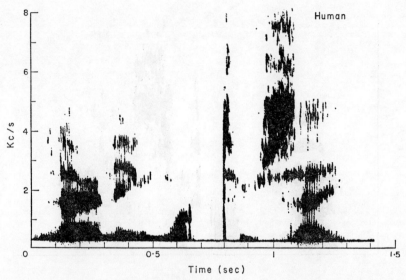

FIGURE 5. Sound spectrogram of the sentence, *'Learning what to say'*, spoken by the human voice. Scales as in Fig. 4, above.

of a human being and a mynah uttering the phrase 'Learning what to say'. Looking first at the human vocal performance, the shifting bars or formants which determine the vowel sounds will be easily seen. Comparing the mynah's performance with that of man one observes that, though the picture is not quite so clear, nevertheless essentially the same bars and hubs can be detected shifting about in essentially the same way. We now have a precise method of measuring the differences in vowel structure between different samples of human speech and when we apply this technique for comparing human with mynah speech we find quite dramatic evidence of similarity (Figure 7). In this figure the three lowest and most important formants, $F_1$, $F_2$ and $F_3$, are plotted aginst the corresponding frequencies for British English. The most important is $F_2$, and is known as the 'hub'. The data from the mynah were obtained from some of our own birds—

including the one whose utterance is shown in Figure 6. The formant frequency for British English was measured at University College, London, on twenty-five male speakers. In these diagrams the frequencies of the formants of the mynah spectrograms are plotted against the corresponding frequencies of the human spectrograms. Thus we see that for formant 1, the fit is, all things considered, astoundingly

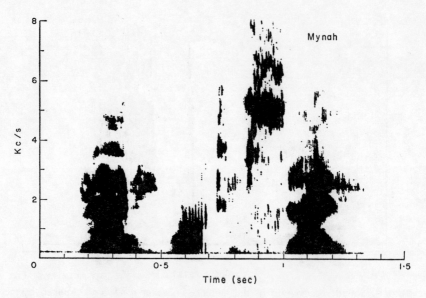

FIGURE 6. Sound spectrogram of the sentence, *'Learning what to say'*, spoken by an 'Indian Hill Mynah' *Gracula religiosa intermedia*. Scales as in Fig. 4, above.

good. With formant 2, 'the hub', the range of which is between 600 and 2000 cycles, the fit is not quite so good. With the third formant, similarity is again not so good as that of formant 1. (For each plot, the Spearman correlation coefficient is shown, small 'r'.) So in a sense the mystery deepens! I doubt whether there is a laryngologist or phonetician anywhere in the world who would have supposed it possible that a vocal apparatus basically so different from that of man as is the syrinx of birds should be able to produce an imitation of this degree of exactitude.

In conclusion, I want to discuss an even more fundamental problem which current developments in linguistics are bringing to the fore. Earlier in this paper I was discussing, both in regard to Chaffinches and mynahs, the evidence for

# Vocal imitation and antiphonal song

reinforcement and reinforcement-control of vocalization. In so far as results of such work apply, they strengthen the view that the acquisition by birds of much of the elaborate detail of song, and particularly the acquisition of mimetic resemblances with an older or territorially established associate, might be explained on what can be called a 'behaviourist' or Skinnerian type of theory. According to Skinner (1957) the human child learns to speak the language of his social group by

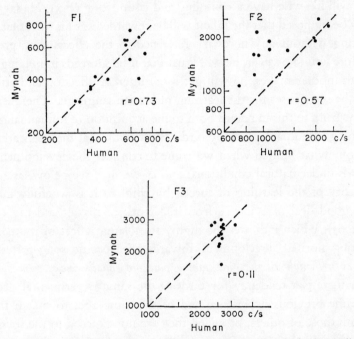

FIGURE 7. Diagrams comparing vowel production and control in the 'Indian Hill Mynah' *Gracula religiosa intermedia* with that of man. 'F1' 'F2' & 'F3' indicate the first three vocal formants. 'r' = the Spearman correlation coefficient. (For further explanation see text.)

being rewarded at every stage, in a piecemeal fashion, by the material and social rewards, by the interest and attention which he secures when he succeeds in imitating a word or phrase correctly. This is, so to speak, an 'atomic' theory of language acquisition; for it supposes that language is acquired by the building up as a result of reinforcement according to the classical Pavlovian theory, of a syntax out of a series of randomly imitated sounds. That there might be some truth in this in regard to the birds is indicated by the work I have already described, and a similar explanation was applied by Mowrer (1950). If Mowrer is right about the psychology of talking birds, it appears very similar to his view of the human infant's first steps in learning to talk. Birds and babies, according to this hypothesis, both make their first efforts at reproducing words or other sounds because these sounds seem good to them—they are, in fact, self-stimulatory. Mothers often talk or croon to their children when attending to them, and so the sound of the mother's voice has often become associated with comfort-giving measures. So it is to be expected that when the child, alone and uncomfortable, hears its own voice, this will likewise have a consoling and comforting effect. He says: 'In this way it may be supposed that the infant will be rewarded for his own first babbling and jabbering without any necessary reference to the effects they produce on others. Before long, however, he will learn that if he succeeds in making the kind of sound his mother makes, he will get more interest, affection and attention in return; so the stage is set for the learning of human language.' There is, without doubt, some truth in this in regard both to the acquisition of human language and to the learning of human speech by birds. But I think that the application of this theory is somewhat limited when we come to consider the development of song in wild birds under natural conditions; and as we shall see below, as a comprehensive theory of the learning of speech by children it is woefully inadequate. There is a good deal of evidence from the work of myself and my colleagues (Thorpe, 1965), which indicates the highly stimulating effect of mutual practice in promoting normal development towards the specific song-pattern in the Chaffinch *even though all the birds taking part are equally inexperienced*. But it is found that there is a tendency for birds of the same experimental group, that is of the same previous experience and of the same age, to match their song endings with those of others, provided they are not exposed to the song of birds other than those in the group. There is little doubt that this is the way in which local song dialects are built up and perpetuated. The important point to emphasize here is that, as a result of this, social stimulation in social animals, even though it is apparently of a very inferior and inexperienced kind, may be very important in achieving uniformity. There are, it seems, some very elementary aspects of the specific song pattern which are so well coded genetically that the Chaffinch can produce them without any help at all from any other individual. Over and above this, imitation is perpetuating *minor* differences in fine song structure, and so perpetuating local dialects from generation to generation. But in addition to this there are other important details of *species-characteristic* song pattern which, while absent in the complete isolate (i.e. true auditory 'Kaspar Hausers'), nevertheless appear as a result of singing in company with other Chaffinches of the same age-group, *even though these are equally inexperienced*. This singing experience is sufficient, so to speak, to realize the song elements—to bring them to the surface. Thus it seems that although the innate tendency to produce a few of the absolutely basic features of the song is strong enough to force them out into the bird's performance, even in complete experimental isolation, there are other parts of the inborn pattern which, although genetically coded in the same way, need the trigger-like stimulus of competitive singing to enable them to emerge into the actuality of performance. Such relatively weak inherited tendencies, albeit strong enough ultimately to find their way out through experience, seem the necessary explanation of the fact that even long-isolated populations of Chaffinches, such as those introduced to South Africa and New Zealand last century, while showing the same tendency to form local dialects, have nevertheless failed, even in the 60–80 years of their separation (and over a century in the case of New Zealand), to drift far away from the specific norm of Europe. Their songs are instantly recognizable as those of Chaffinches and are no more divergent than the songs of some of the Chaffinch populations of Western Europe are from one another. If song development in the individual was taking place merely according to behaviourist or Skinnerian principles, it is quite inconceivable that the song of these populations of Chaffinches in the Antipodes would be recognizable as such after the lapse of time.

Here, however, modern linguistic theory enters again. The Skinnerian view of the acquisition of verbal behaviour by the human infant is now under very strong, one might almost say devastating, attack from linguistic theorists (see Chomsky, 1959, 1967; Lenneberg, 1960). The argument of these writers, greatly simplified, is that the Skinnerian hypothesis is utterly inadequate to account for normal language acquisition in human beings. No anthropologist has ever described a speech community where children have not mastered the essential structure of their mother-tongue by the age of 4. This seems to point conclusively to the view that man has the organic equipment to learn any language and that no one language calls for the presence of peculiar innate skill. No child is born to learn French rather than Chinese. Nor does it seem likely that a child who fails to learn the language of his native land, because it is (to an alien adult) too 'difficult', could learn a 'simpler' foreign language without trouble. It is true that both parrots and babies are imitative and that some sounds in the utterances of both may be random. But parrot language is not baby language. These linguistic theories point out that there are aspects in which all human languages are formally alike and that the child must have an innate ability somehow to select out of the great

259

variety of sounds he hears when listening to adult speech those features or relationships that are in some sense 'essential' for speech while being uninterested in the
imitation of sound features that are accidental.* In short, there are some absolutely
general, logical and grammatical rules which lie at the basis of all human language
and which the child has an innate mental equipment to respond to, understand
and use. This innate equipment is referred to by Chomsky under the heading
'Deep structures' (Chomsky, in press 1967).

I suggest that there is something extraordinarily similar between the genetic
tendencies for song in a bird such as the Chaffinch, which are too weak to emerge
by themselves, but which can be brought out by social stimulation; and, on the
other hand, the 'deep structures' for language which modern language theorists
find it necessary to postulate in the human species. This conclusion merely high-
lights another problem: birds exceed all other animals save man himself in their
powers to develop and use vocalizations for communication. How is it, then,
that mammals gave rise to a being with true language and not the birds? Between
the evolution of the apes as we know them and the first men, two immense steps
in mentality and the production of the associated neurological structures were
achieved. The first was the power of vocal imitation; the second was the 'deep
structures' underlying human language. Birds have the first and something
strongly resembling the second; apes, it seems, have neither! This, with our
present knowledge and outlook, is a mystery indeed; and the study of bird song

---

* A striking example of the kind of evidence for this new approach to language, with particular
regard to pronunciation, is given by Lenneberg's own experience. He had to learn to speak Portuguese, in addition to his native German, at the age of 12. Within a couple of years his pronunciation in the second language was so close to standard Portuguese that native speakers frequently
disbelieved his German origin. He was completely bilingual throughout this time. At the age of
22 he had to switch languages once more, this time to English, and in contrast to the previous
learning situation, he has since spoken this new language almost to the complete exclusion of
both German and Portuguese. The result is interesting. His ability to speak English has completely
displaced his facility in Portuguese and even the availability of his German vocabulary seems to
have suffered in the course of the years. Yet his pronunciation of English is marked by a gross
and virtually insuperable foreign accent, while his German continues to sound like that of a native
and his Portuguese, as evidenced in the pronunciation of isolated words, continues to have the
phonological characteristics of perfect Portuguese. Yet he has heard and spoken more English
during his life than either German or Portuguese. The conclusion is that childhood and early
adolescence are physiologically more propitious for the acquisition of phonemic structures than
adult age. Most people can, if strongly motivated, learn the grammar, syntax and vocabulary of
a new language well into middle age if not later; few indeed retain the imitative powers to acquire
a perfect accent after childhood is past.

serves to focus attention on some of the most crucial problems concerning the origin of human speech and the nature of imitation.

## SUMMARY

1. The main function of the song of many birds is to serve as a signal which is sufficiently stereotyped to provide a recognition mark *characteristic of the species* and yet capable of sufficient *individual* variation to differentiate one individual bird from another. The paper discusses the mechanisms by which the bird develops its song so as to ensure that these requirements are met.

2. It is now known that in the Chaffinch *Fringilla coelebs* the full-song pattern (including the fine variations within the specific pattern which are characteristic of individuals and local populations) is achieved by action and interaction of three processes.

(a) There are some very elementary aspects of the specific song pattern which are so well coded genetically that a Chaffinch can produce them without any help at all from any other individual.

(b) Over and above this a highly developed imitative ability is concerned with perpetuating other differences in song structure, including many fine details which are characteristic of isolated groups and populations. It has recently been shown that there are features in the normal song of the Chaffinch which have in themselves sufficient stimulus value to serve as reinforcers for motor activity in an operant conditioning situation. This discovery will doubtless help to explain a considerable part of the process of developing song by imitation.

(c) There are some features of the species-characteristic song pattern which, so it seems, can be realized as a result of singing in company with other Chaffinches of the same age-group, even though these are equally inexperienced. It appears that these features, although they must be genetically coded, need the trigger-like stimulus of competitive singing to enable them to emerge into the actuality of performance. Thus this singing experience with inexperienced associates is sufficient to realize certain of these coded song elements, which would otherwise not appear; and, so to speak, to bring them to the surface.

3. The imitative ability of the 'Indian Hill Mynah' *Gracula religiosa intermedia* is considered. When hand-reared in isolation from other members of its species this bird can produce practically any sound to which it is exposed. New evidence for the precision of its imitation of human vowels is presented.

4. The antiphonal singing of African shrikes (e.g. *Laniarius aethiopicus*) is discussed as an example of use of the imitative ability for the purpose of establish-

# W.H.Thorpe

ing and strengthening social bonding. It is suggested that such types of social bonding could well account for the development of imitative powers in birds where the territorial function of song may be reduced or absent.

5. The resemblance between the type of song coding mentioned under 2(c) above and the so-called 'deep structures' which are now postulated by many linguistic theorists in connection with the production of human language is stressed. It is pointed out that to acquire a vocal language two prime abilities are required in the human species. The first of these is the capacity for vocal imitation and the second is the 'deep structure' type of mental and neural organization. Between the evolution of the apes as we know them and the first men, these two abilities must have been acquired, since apes, it seems, have neither. Birds on the other hand have the first and something strongly resembling the second. How is it, then, that mammals were capable of giving rise to a being with true language and not the birds?

## REFERENCES

ANDREW R.J. (1962) Evolution of intelligence and vocal mimicking. *Science* **137**, 585-589.

BROWN J.L. (1965) Vocalization evoked from the optic lobe of a songbird. *Science* **149**, 1002-1003.

BROWN J.L. (1965) Loss of vocalization caused by lesions in the *Nucleus mesencephalicus lateralis* of the Redwinged Blackbird. *Amer. Zool.* **5**, 328.

BROWN J.L. (1966) Some neural substrates of vocalization in the Redwinged Blackbird. (In press.)

BROWN J.L. (1966) *Brain Atlas of the Redwinged Blackbird.* (In press.)

CHOMSKY N. (1959) Review of *Verbal Behaviour. Language* **35**, 26-58.

CHOMSKY N. (1967) (See also Fodor & Katz, 1965) The general properties of language. In *Brain Mechanisms Underlying Speech and Language.* Ed. F.L.Darley. New York (in press).

FODOR J.A. & KATZ J.J. (Eds.)(1965) *The Structure of Language: Readings in the Philosophy of Language.* Englewood Cliffs, N.J.

FOSS B.M. (1964) Mimicry in mynahs (*Gracula religiosa*): A test of Mowrer's theory. *Brit. J. Psychol.* **55**, 85-88.

GINSBURG N. (1960) Conditioned vocalization in the Budgerigar. *J. Comp. Physiol. Psychol.* **53**, 183-186.

GINSBURG N. (1963) Conditioned talking in the mynah bird. *J. Comp. Physiol. Psychol.* **56**, 1061-1063.

GROSSLIGHT J.H., HARRISON P.C. & WEISER C.M. (1962) Reinforcement control of vocal responses in the mynah bird (*Gracula religiosa*). *Psychol. Rec.* **12**, 193-201.

GWINNER E. & KNEUTGEN J. (1962) Über die biologische Bedeuting der 'zweckdienlichen' Anwendung erlernter Laute bei Vögeln. *Zeit. f. Tierpsychol.* **19**, 692-696.

HENSCHEL G. (1903) Bullfinch and Canary. *Nature*, **67**, 609-10.

HINDE R.A. (1958) Alternative motor patterns in Chaffinch song. *Anim. Behav.* **6**, 211-218.

# Vocal imitation and antiphonal song

KONISHI M. (1963) Role of auditory feedback in the vocal behaviour of the domestic fowl. *Zeit. f. Tierpsychol.* **20**, 349–367.

KONISHI M. (1964) Effects of deafening on song development in two species of juncos. *Condor* **66**, 85–102.

KONISHI M. (1965a) Effects of deafening on song development in American Robins and Black-headed Grossbeaks. *Zeit. f. Tierpsychol.* **22**, 584–599.

KONISHI M. (1965b) The role of auditory feedback in the control of vocalization in the White-crowned Sparrow. *Zeit. f. Tierpsychol.* **22**, 770–783.

KONORSKI J. (1963) Analiza patofiziologiczna Róznych Rudzajoiv Zaburzen Mowy I Próba ich Klasyfikacji. *Rozprawy Wydziatre Nauk Medycznych (Warsaw)* R.6 **2**, 11–32.

LADE B.I. & THORPE W.H. (1964) Dove songs as innately coded patterns of specific behaviour. *Nature*, **202**, 366.

LANE H. (1961) Operant control of vocalizing in the chicken. *J. Exp. Anim. Behav.* **4**, 171–177.

LENNEBERG E.H. (1960) Language, evolution, and purposive behavior. Chapter in *Culture in History*. Ed. S.Diamond. New York. (See also Fodor & Katz, 1965.)

LILLY J.C. (1962) Vocal behavior of the Bottle-nosed Dolphin. *Proc. Amer. Phil. Soc.* **106**, 520–529.

MARLER P. (1960) Bird songs and mate selection. In *Animal Sounds and Communication*. Ed. W.E.Lanyon and W.N.Tavolga. Washington, D.C.

MOWRER O.H. (1950) The psychology of talking birds: A contribution to language and personality theory. *Learning Theory and Personality Dynamics*, chap. 24. New York.

NICOLAI J. (1964) Der Brutparasitismus der Viduinae als ethologisches Problem. *Zeit. f. Tierpsychol.* **21**, 129–204.

SKINNER B.F. (1957) *Verbal Behaviour*. New York and London.

STEVENSON J.G. (1967) The reinforcing properties of song. *Anim. Behav.* (in press).

THORPE W.H. (1955) Comments on *The Bird Fancyer's Delight*: Together with notes on imitation in the sub-song of the Chaffinch. *Ibis* **97**, 247–251.

THORPE W.H. (1959) Talking birds and the mode of action of the vocal apparatus of birds. *Proc. Zool. Soc. Lond.* **132**, 441–455.

THORPE W.H. (1965) The ontogeny of behaviour. *Ideas in Modern Biology*, chap. 17, pp. 485–518. Ed. J.A.Moore. New York.

THORPE W.H. & NORTH M.E.W. (1965) Origin and significance of the power of vocal imitation: With special reference to the antiphonal singing of birds. *Nature*, **208**, 219–222.

THORPE W.H. & NORTH M.E.W. (1966) Vocal imitation in the tropical Boubou Shrike, *Laniarius aethiopicus major*, as a means of establishing and maintaining social bonds. *Ibis* **108**, 432–435.

TRETZEL E. (1965) Imitation und Variation von Schäferpfiffen durch Haubenlerchen (*Galerida c. cristata* L.). *Zeit. f. Tierpsychol.* **22**, 784–809.

WAITE E.R. (1903) Sympathetic song in birds. *Nature* **68**, 322.

# The role of sensory feedback in the development of avian vocalizations

FERNANDO NOTTEBOHM

Rockefeller University, New York

The rather abundant work which has been done on the song of the Chaffinch *Fringilla coelebs* up to the present time and which has been reviewed in the preceding paper by Professor Thorpe has shown beyond doubt that we are dealing here with the acquisition of a very complex motor skill. It is clear that for it to be achieved the bird has to be exposed to the song of the species. It should be noted, though, that present knowledge does not allow us to say in which way the bird's genetic endowment makes possible the end-product as we observe it in the song of adult males. The ontogeny of the learning process in its sensory and motor particulars remains obscure.

My experiments were designed as an attempt to gain some understanding of the physiological correlates of this learning process. However, before I present my results I shall briefly review what is known about the song of the Chaffinch and its ontogeny

## The Song of Normal Adult Male Chaffinches

Normally only male Chaffinches sing in nature. The song of normal wild Chaffinches can be characterized in the following manner (Figure 1): (1) Its length is about 2–2.5 seconds. (2) It consists of two or three trill-like phrases and ends with a more complex and dissimilar set of notes which have been called a 'flourish'. (3) Each phrase of the song is composed of more or less identical syllables. Each phrase is a distinct structural unit, different from the phrase preceding it and from the one following it. (4) There is a progressive, usually step-wise descent in the average frequency of the fundamental from the beginning to the end of the song. In addition, the flourish may also include the highest frequencies in the song. (5) The overall sound envelope of the fundamental frequencies lies between 2 and 6 kc. (6) The pitch characteristic of the song is determined by the fundamental frequencies since harmonics are virtually absent.

An adult male Chaffinch will have from two to six song themes in its repertoire. The rendering of a song theme each time it occurs shows extremely little variability. The various song themes are not rendered in a random order. Rather, a sequence of songs of one theme is followed by a sequence of songs of another theme and so on. The temporal separation between songs is of the order of 20 seconds.

### The Ontogeny of Song in First-year Male Chaffinches

The incidence of full song in a first-year bird is preceded by many other vocalizations which make their first appearance at earlier stages in the bird's life. As a

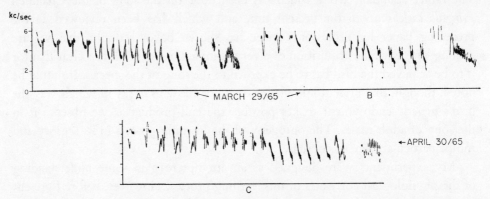

FIGURE I. Normal adult male Chaffinch $RW^2/RW^2$. A, B and C are its three full-song themes.

nestling the bird will produce food begging calls. Later on as the bird fledges and becomes independent, those same calls may by gradual transition become the elements of incipient subsong. Some of the call notes which will develop into the calls of the adult are also making their first appearance at this time. By the end of its first summer and beginning of the fall a first-year bird has had a variable amount of auditory-motor experience performing several calls and subsong. The final extent of this experience will be determined by how early or late the bird was born in the season.

With the onset of shorter days and cold weather the subsong of first-year Chaffinches ceases. Not until mid-February or so in the following spring will subsong be heard again.

As subsong reappears it will first be of a simple kind mainly composed of loose notes rendered at a soft volume. This will gradually lead into a more complex and rambling type of subsong. A time is reached when without a change in amplitude, interspersed within the subsong, stretches of singing occur which by virtue of their tonality and general structure are reminiscent of the full song of adults. They are usually preceded and followed by short silent intervals. These subsong sequences identified as having some of the full song characteristics gradually become more recurrent, louder, more stereotyped and less closely associated with subsong. We may consider them as constituting the first emergence of 'plastic' full song (Figure 2).

'Plastic' full song shows already all the characteristics of normal full song, but in an imperfect fashion. The structure of the syllables, phrases and flourish of a particular theme shows still considerable variability. Two or three more weeks will elapse before the structure of song conforms to all the characteristics of adult full song. Once the full song themes have 'crystallized' into their final structure, the latter will remain unchanged for the rest of that season and in future years.

### The Song of Males Reared in Auditory Isolation

It has been known for some time that Chaffinches have to learn their song. However, the crucial evidence for this point was not presented until 1951 by Poulsen, and 1954 by Thorpe, who obtained similar results. Since Thorpe accompanied his publication with sound spectrographic analysis of his data I shall be referring mainly to his results in this respect.

Thorpe hand-reared in auditory isolation male Chaffinches which were collected from their nests when they were only a few days old. Birds thus treated developed a very simple type of song. Such a song has usually no phrase structure, no terminal flourish and the notes composing it are of the simpler kind found in normal song. However, it does have a syllabic structure and its tonality and length compare favourably with normal song (Figure 3).

It should be noted that this kind of experimental approach does not allow to discriminate between the strictly motor and the sensory elements participating in the development of song in the naïve males. We may ask the question: Are those birds relying on a sensory template to develop their 'isolate' songs, or is the motor pattern of their song developed through a maturational process, without the need for them to listen to their own vocalizations and accumulate some sort of auditory-motor experience?

### The Song of Deaf Male Chaffinches

Male Chaffinches were deafened after they had had varying amounts of auditory-motor experience. Chronic deafness was achieved by removal of the cochlea.

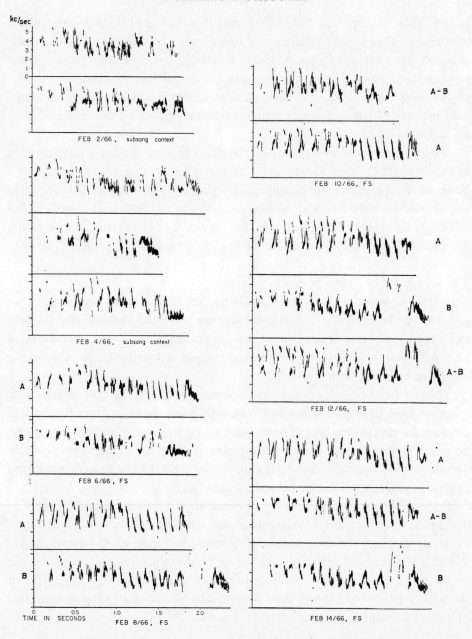

FIGURE 2. Development of full song in first-year male RBW/RBW. This figure shows the development of themes A and B, and the incidence of 'intermediate' (A–B) themes. The last pre-deafening recording of this bird, on February 16, 1966, is shown in Figure 5.

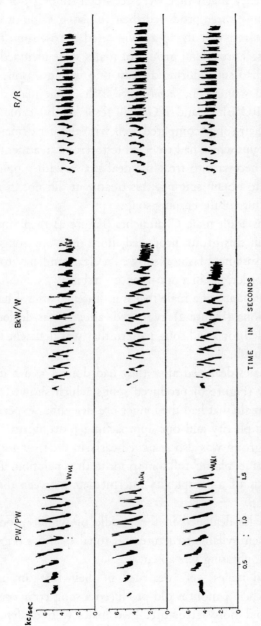

FIGURE 3. Three consecutive songs by each of three different intact hand-reared males. The birds' identifications refer to Thorpe (1958). Reproduction by kindness of W.H.Thorpe.

# Fernando Nottebohm

Out of a total of twenty males that were recorded singing full song after they had been deafened, only three produced their full song without the aid of hormone treatment. The rest had to be administered testosterone in the form of injections or implants. Three main groups of males were included in my experiment: *adults*, which had sung during at least one whole season; *first-year* birds caught in the fall and winter; and *hand-reared* males. One male in each of these three groups (Y/R; RG/BkY; and P.GW$^2$/- respectively) came into full song of its own accord. Their songs compared well with the performance of the birds in their respective groups which had received testoterone treatment. This indicates that although it was necessary to treat the deaf males with supplementary doses of testosterone so as to obtain singing, this treatment did not in itself introduce changes into the structure of the ensuing song.

When one deafens adult male Chaffinches (Figure 4) their song remains undistorted. All males in this group produced more than one song theme. Those males that sang in a sustained fashion showed a clear tendency to produce their songs in a sequential order, i.e. in a non-random fashion.

The singing performance of a male that was deafened after it had produced 12 days of 'plastic' full song (Figure 2) 'regressed' after it was deafened (Figure 5). This male finally settled for a full song pattern that was deficient in the structure of its phrases and flourish.

Two first-year males deafened after they had done 1 and 2 days of 'plastic' full song respectively (Figure 6) produced songs which showed some phrasing but no flourish. The male that had the longer pre-deafening experience produced a song of greater complexity and one approaching more normal song. A third bird included in this group was also deafened early in the spring and presumably had also engaged in some 'plastic' full song prior to the operation. The structure of its song (Figure 6) was of a complexity intermediate between that of the other two birds in this group.

Four first-year males deafened in the middle of winter produced songs of great simplicity in their syllabic structure and tonal qualities (Figure 7). Except for one male (PW/O), phrasing was absent.

Three hand-reared males were deafened in their first summer (Figure 8). The male deafened when 4 months old produced a song composed of 'syllables' of a very indefinite and 'noisy' structure. Two males were deafened at an age of 3 months. One of these birds produced a song which was virtually a continuous screech from beginning to end. Sometimes this song included an element very reminiscent of the subsong 'chirrup' (Figure 8). The other bird which was deafened

270

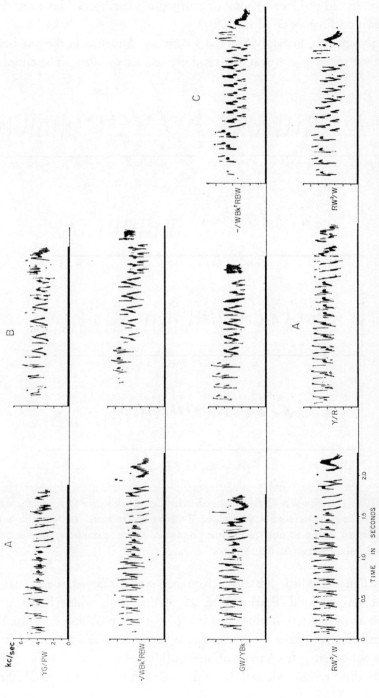

FIGURE 4. The song of deaf adult males. Theme 'A' is shared by five males, theme 'B' by three and theme 'C' by two males. These birds were deafened in the winter of 1964–65 and recorded in the spring and summer of 1965.

# Fernando Nottebohm

when 3 months old produced a song of a structure intermediate between that of the other two deaf hand-reared birds.

Strikingly enough, not only was the song very abnormal in the hand-reared birds, but their subsong also was of a similarly 'scratchy' nature. These birds had

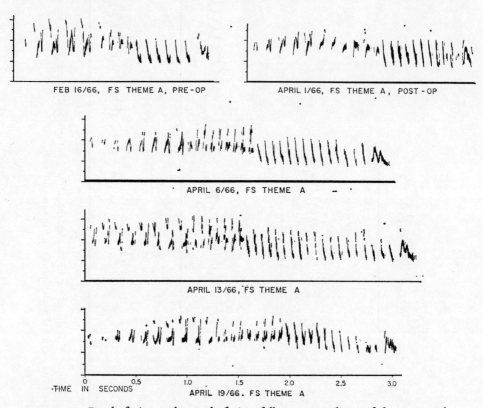

FEB 16/66, FS THEME A, PRE-OP

APRIL 1/66, FS THEME A, POST-OP

APRIL 6/66, FS THEME A

APRIL 13/66, FS THEME A

APRIL 19/66. FS THEME A

TIME IN SECONDS

FIGURE 5. Pre-deafening and post-deafening full-song recordings of first-year male RBW/RBW. This bird was deafened immediately after the February 16 recording was made. The date of each recording is indicated in this figure. On March 11, 1966, this bird was implanted with a 10 mg testosterone propionate pellet; a similar supplementary dose was administered on March 28, 1966.

presumably done very little subsong before they were deafened, if any, and then only of the simpler kind. Furthermore, all of their calls which I managed to record were abnormal too. In this category fell the owl-mobbing calls ('huit' and 'chink'), and the courtship 'chirrup'. These same vocalizations in adult deaf males were not different from those of intact adult males.

What do these results indicate? They show that as first-year male Chaffinches

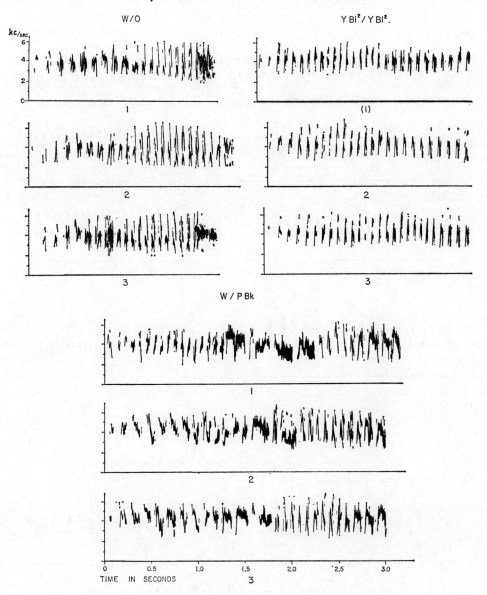

FIGURE 6. Full song of three first-year males deafened in early spring 1965. Recordings were done in May and June 1965. Except for song number (1) of YBl²/YBl², all songs are consecutive. W/PBk was deafened after it had produced 'plastic' full song for 2 days; YBl²/YBl² was deafened after it had produced 'plastic' full song for only 1 day. W/O was deafened early in the spring, on March 6, 1965, and presumably had engaged in some 'plastic' full song before it was deafened.

273

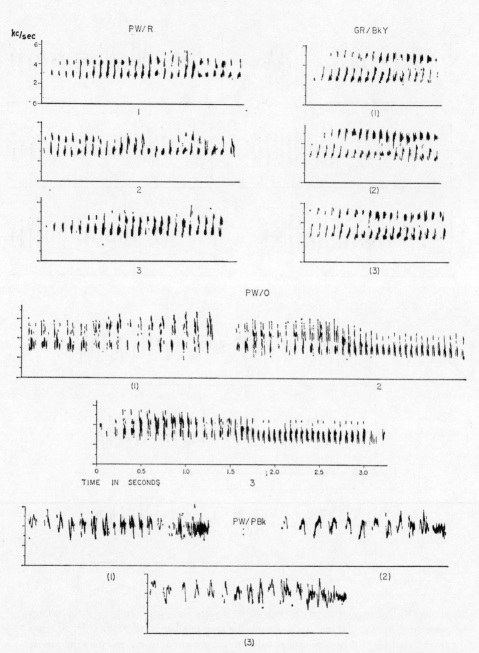

FIGURE 7. Full song of four first-year males deafened in midwinter 1964–65. Songs are consecutive unless their number is bracketed. Recordings were done in May–July 1965.

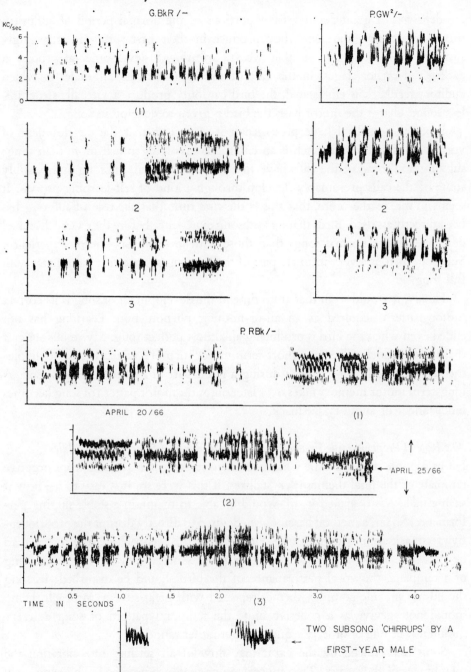

FIGURE 8. Songs of three first-year hand-reared deaf male Chaffinches. Songs are consecutive unless their corresponding numbers are bracketed. The three males included in this group were deafened in their first summer, 1965: P.GW²/- at 4 months of age; G.BkR/- and P.RBk/- at 3 months of age. The recordings presented here were done in the following spring, 1966.

are deprived of greater and greater portions of the normal period of auditory-motor experience, the song they produce in their first spring is accordingly simpler. This, then, suggests that we are arresting a developmental process at earlier and earlier stages. In the case of the hand-reared deaf males in which auditory feedback is eliminated, the bird can only produce a virtually structure-less song. That is the motor basis the bird is given to develop its song.

From the results I have presented it is also clear that the development of vocalizations in the Chaffinch is an enterprise involving much more than song: subsong and some of the calls have to be learned as well. Subsong and possibly some of the calls presumably develop through a kind of self-learning process. It seems to me, furthermore, that this is the first time that the role of subsong has been directly assessed. Birds that had subsong experience before they were deafened developed more normal songs than those with less auditory-motor experience. Subsong, then, is a very intimate part of the learning process that culminates with full song.

Finally, it would seem that at no time in the development of song is its correct motor pattern acquired as an all-or-nothing phenomenon. Learning has not ended even when the bird is producing an almost perfect song. My results suggest that the Chaffinch relies on a short-term motor memory which has to be supplemented with auditory feedback during a good part of its first singing season. A long-term motor memory takes over later on, as the motor pattern of song becomes independent of auditory feedback.

## The Role of Proprioceptive Feedback in the Maintenance of Song in Adult Males

Let us suppose that as a male Chaffinch learns its song it acquires a proprioceptive template of the final themes it crystallizes. If this were so, it is easy to see how if such a male was deafened it still would be able to maintain a stable singing performance. So far, a method has not been devised to directly disrupt the proprioceptive feedback accompanying song. However, if this feedback is so distorted as to be rendered unusable for the matching process demanded by the functioning of a template, the vocal performance of the bird should be disturbed: its song should not include complex themes repeated with great stereotypy; each theme should not survive as a cohesive unit; the temporal pattern of song delivery should not be one of orderly sequences, but rather random.

Song is produced by the expiratory flow of air setting into vibration the membranes of the syrinx. Two motor components are involved. The expiratory musculature exerts its force on the air sacs, acting as a system of bellows; the musculature of the syrinx controls the tension on its membranes and the bore of the air passage at that level. The syrinx acts as a valve, and thus determines the impedance against which the expiratory musculature is working. Motor denervation of the syrinx will then presumably result in a peripheral disrupture of the motor mechanism producing sounds, and therefore also in a drastic alteration of whatever proprioceptive feedback it might normally emit. This was the method used in the following experiment.

Two adult males were used. One of them (Figure 9) was deafened as an adult.

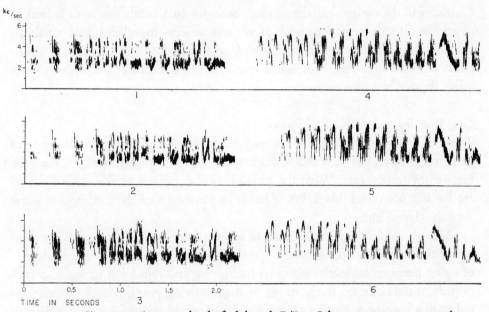

FIGURE 9. Six consecutive songs by deaf adult male R/P on July 25, 1965: songs 1, 2 and 3, theme 'A'; songs 4, 5 and 6, theme 'B'. This bird was deafened on December 16, 1964, and the roots of its hypoglossus nerves were bilaterally severed on February 22, 1965.

Subsequently the motor innervation to its syrinx was severed by sectioning the roots of the hypoglossus nerves. A few months later this bird came into full song, after going through subsong. It had two full-song themes which, despite the structural abnormalities which inevitably resulted from defective peripheral motor control, were surprisingly normal in many of their aspects: they were of normal complexity, showed clear-cut phrases, and were very stereotyped on successive repetitions. Furthermore, they were rendered in a perfectly normal sequential order.

# Fernando Nottebohm

The second male used in this study had its syrinx denervated on one side, but otherwise was intact. It was recorded 5 days later. This male also produced two song themes. Those themes also showed clear phrasing, stereotypy on successive repetitions and normal orderly programming. The structure of the individual notes and the overall tonality of the song were markedly abnormal.

I interpret those results as indicating that the adult male Chaffinch is not particularly disturbed when forced to accept a very novel sensory feedback. Once full song is acquired on a long-term basis, it no longer depends on peripheral feedback for its control. Both its structure and programming are laid down centrally. If the entirety of the singing behavior in Chaffinches were indeed to depend on strictly central control, as my results seem to indicate, this would be the only available example of such a phenomenon for an entirely learned motor pattern. Naturally, this does not mean that environmental influences cannot affect the performance of song.

## Song Learning and the 'Critical Period'

The fact that many passerines can only learn their song at a particular time in their lives, which has been called the 'critical period' for song learning, has been known for some years. What the physiological correlates of this critical period are has not been established, but it has been assumed that the timing is in some way age-dependent.

A single experiment was planned to test this hypothesis. A male was castrated in its first winter. As a result of this operation the bird was not under the influence of rising testosterone levels during its first spring and following summer; consequently, it did not sing. In the spring of the following year this bird was implanted with a testosterone pellet. After it had performed 'plastic' song for 2 days, it was subjected to a song-tutoring programme several hours a day for 12 days. Figure 10 shows the tutor song and the results obtained.

The results show a clear effect of one of the tutor themes on the two song themes developed by the 2-year-old Chaffinch. This evidence, restricted as it is to the single bird that was subjected to this operational procedure, strongly suggests that the ability to develop song for the first time is not age-dependent.

### ACKNOWLEDGEMENTS

The work presented here was done at the University of California, at Berkeley, and at the Sub-department of Animal Behaviour at Cambridge. I am extremely grateful to Professor Marler for the stimulation, advice and help which he

# Sensory feedback and avian vocalizations

gave me during the course of this research. I am grateful to Professor Thorpe for making my stay at Madingley possible.

## SUMMARY

The effects of deafening on the development and maintenance of vocalizations were studied in male Chaffinches *Fringilla coelebs* which had varying amounts of pre-deafening auditory-motor experience. Males deafened as adults retained

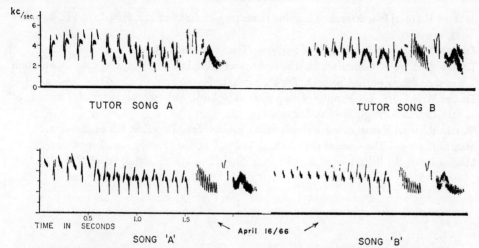

FIGURE 10. Response to tutoring by adult male castrate Chaffinch GW$^2$/Bl under hormone treatment. Tutor themes *A* and *B* are shown at the top of the figure; GW$^2$/Bl's themes 'A' and 'B' after they had crystallized are shown at the bottom. Tutoring started on March 8, 1966, and was discontinued on March 20, 1966. The final version of the two song themes developed by GW$^2$/Bl was recorded on April 16, 1966.

their normal song. Males deafened as juveniles produced a virtually unstructured sound, which was much more rudimentary than the song of hand-reared auditory isolates. The motor substrate of song unimproved by auditory-motor development is thus shown to be a virtual *tabula rasa*. The development of vocalizations affects not only song, but also subsong and several calls. Subsong in first-year males serves as a functional stage in the development of full song.

Learning of the motor pattern of song proceeds by two stages. The first one establishes the correct pattern of song, but so as to be maintained, the latter still has to rely on auditory feedback. The second stage is reached when the motor pattern persists unchanged after the elimination of auditory feedback.

The maintenance of the structure of song and the temporal programming of its delivery in adult birds is not dependent on auditory or proprioceptive feedback. It survives in spite of distorted peripheral feedback.

The learning of song in nature is restricted to a 'critical period'. The nature of this 'critical period' is explored. It is shown that in the Chaffinch it is not an age-dependent phenomenon. It comes to an end the first time male Chaffinches develop their full song under the influence of high hormonal levels.

## REFERENCES

POULSEN H. (1951) Inheritance and learning in the song of the Chaffinch, *Fringilla coelebs*. *Behaviour* **3**, 216–228.

THORPE W.H. (1954) The analysis of bird song. *Proc. Roy. Instn.* **35**, No. 161.

THORPE W.H. (1955) Comments on 'The bird fancier's delight': Together with notes on imitation in the subsong of the Chaffinch. *Ibis* **97**, 247–251.

THORPE W.H. (1958) The learning of song patterns by birds, with especial reference to the song of the Chaffinch *Fringilla coelebs*. *Ibis* **100**, 535–570.

MARLER P. (1952) Variation in the song of the Chaffinch *Fringilla coelebs*. *Ibis* **94**, 458–472.

MARLER P. (1956a) The voice of the Chaffinch and its function as a language. *Ibis* **98**, 231–261.

MARLER P. (1956b) Behaviour of the Chaffinch, *Fringilla coelebs*. *Behaviour*, Suppl. V.

# Radar in orientation research

FRANK BELLROSE

Illinois Natural History Survey,
Havana, Illinois, U.S.A.

One of our primary objectives when we began to study bird migration by radar surveillance in 1960 was to evaluate various environmental cues birds ostensibly use in navigation. We reported on our 1960 findings 4 years ago at the 13th International Ornithological Congress (Bellrose & Graber, 1963). Since that time, continued radar surveillance of bird migration has resulted in much more information on this problem.

Although we have used radar for diurnal surveillance of bird passage, most of our investigation has been with nocturnal migrants, for in our region of study most migration occurs at night. Consequently this paper is concerned only with an evaluation of environmental cues in relation to nocturnal migration. The environmental cues we have considered as possible navigational references employed by nocturnal migrants are: (1) stars and moon, (2) wind, and (3) landscape. As we stated at the last Congress (Bellrose & Graber, 1963, pp. 362–363): 'By defining the navigational attributes of migrants, it is anticipated that the role of topographic and celestial cues can be more precisely determined. Also, assessment of the navigational ability of birds in the absence of landscapes and celestial cues might be expected to confirm or refute the necessity for birds to rely solely upon these guideposts.' This approach to the problem applies as well today as it did 4 years ago.

We are still in the process of analyzing volumes of data from our own radar surveillance programme and from a cooperative project with WSR-57 radar stations of the U.S. Weather Bureau. Therefore, the findings presented here as well as the conclusions reached may be modified as additional information becomes available.

Furthermore, it is impossible to present in this limited report all the data available on each topic. We have tried to select either typical examples or extreme differences. As it is, tens of thousands of items have been tabulated and analyzed for the findings in this report.

# Frank Bellrose

## MATERIALS AND METHODS

In 1960, we utilized radar data largely from our Champaign, Illinois, station. Data analyzed for 1962, 1963 and 1964 are from our station at Havana, Illinois. Both radars are aircraft type of similar power, wave and pulse lengths, beam characteristics and scope displays. Detailed descriptions of the aircraft-type (APS-31 and APS-42A) radar we used for bird detection have been reported previously (Graber & Hassler, 1962; Bellrose & Graber, 1963; Bellrose, 1964).

In this analysis we have also made limited use of data obtained from WSR-57 radar operated by the U.S. Weather Bureau. This radar commonly recorded bird targets out to 20 nautical miles whereas our APS radar sometimes recorded bird targets up to 4 nautical miles; however, few bird targets were recorded beyond 3 nautical miles.

Bird target data for each hour of each night obtained from radar surveillance were tabulated by altitudinal strata of two thicknesses (500 and 716 feet). Direction of flight was determined to the nearest 5°, and was tabulated by 10° intervals. Samples of the ground speeds of migrants were taken throughout the study.

Sky cover and wind are the only weather factors considered in this paper. Information on the degree of sky cover in the Havana region was obtained from hourly observations made at the Peoria, Illinois, weather station, 35–45 miles north-north-east of the two radar sites used, and at the Springfield, Illinois, station, about an equal distance to the south-south-east. In addition to these official records, we recorded the sky conditions and surface wind at the radar sites. A sky was classed as overcast when observations at the radar sites (Springfield and Peoria) indicated the probability of a solid cloud cover over the entire region throughout the night. This classification included a few nights in which a slight break in the solid overcast was indicated for a brief interval at either Peoria or Springfield, but never during the same night at both stations. The altitude of the cloud base was continuously measured by ceileometers at both the Peoria and Springfield stations. Overcast nights created by clouds laden with concentrations of water droplets are not considered, because echoes from water in these clouds completely obscured the radar scope.

Winds aloft were recorded four times daily (0600, 1200, 1800, 2400 hours) by radiosonde at the Peoria station, the only station in Illinois recording winds by this method. Because the temporal pattern of migration characteristics shows most birds aloft at or near 2400 hours, this recording was the most suitable for comparing the speed and direction of winds aloft with the speed and direction taken by migrating birds. Since the speed and direction of migrating birds were compared with the speed and direction of wind at similar altitudes, wind graphs were drawn and interpolations made for altitudes not recorded by radiosonde. Winds aloft usually change slowly in speed and direction with altitude and time.

FINDINGS

*Sky Cover*

We have compared the number of bird targets for nights with visible astral cues with the number of targets for nights when astral cues were lacking because of cloud cover. The comparison was further broken down into categories of favorable and adverse winds. A favorable wind was a following wind blowing within 45° on either side of the flight path; an adverse wind was an opposing wind within the same limits.

*Magnitude of migration.* Figure 1(a) shows that when winds were favorable in the springs of 1962 and 1963, the number of bird targets per night for nights with clear skies was similar to that for nights with overcast skies. With adverse winds, the volume of migration was considerably lower on nights with overcast skies than on nights with clear skies.

The situation was somewhat different in the falls of 1962 and 1963 (Figure 1(b)). The volume of small-bird migration was reduced under overcast skies, especially in 1962. In that season, the decrease in numbers of migrants was proportionally greatest on overcast nights with unfavorable wind, but in the fall of 1963 the number migrating on overcast nights with adverse winds was slightly larger than the number migrating with clear skies and adverse winds.

We draw the following conclusions from this comparison of sky condition and wind in relation to magnitude of spring and fall migration: (1) Large numbers of small birds migrate without astral cues. (2) Astral cues, however, are of some benefit in migration, as indicated by the larger number of migrants under clear than under overcast skies. (3) Apparently, when birds are under reduced motivation to migrate, as in the fall, they are more prone to wait for clear skies than in the spring, when motivation is greater. (4) Wind direction is more important than sky cover in determining the magnitude of migration.

*Temporal pattern.* We considered that, even though the number of bird targets was usually only slightly reduced by overcast skies, birds might not migrate as far under these overcast conditions as they would under a clear sky. A comparison of the temporal pattern of migration on clear nights with the pattern on overcast nights is believed to provide comparative information on distances flown.

283

# Frank Bellrose

The broader the pattern near its peak, the longer the period of flight, and, consequently, the greater the distance covered. Figure 2(a) shows the temporal pattern of small-bird migration on clear and on overcast nights during the spring of 1963. On overcast nights birds descended earlier, after peak numbers were reached at 2230 hours, than on clear nights. In the spring of 1962, birds remained aloft slightly longer on overcast nights than on clear nights (Figure 2(b)).

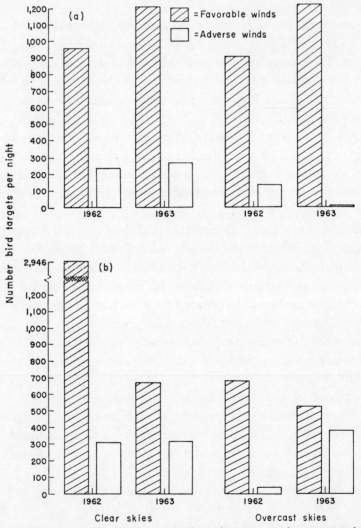

FIGURE 1. The number of bird targets per night at the Havana radar station under clear and under overcast skies, as affected by favorable and adverse winds, (a) during the springs of 1962 and 1963, (b) during the falls of 1962 and 1963.

# Radar in orientation research

In the fall of both 1962 and 1963 (Figure 3 (a) and (b)), departures of migrants under overcast skies were much delayed in comparison with departures under clear skies. Yet the birds migrating under overcast skies delayed their descent in early morning to the extent that they remained aloft as long as migrants under clear skies.

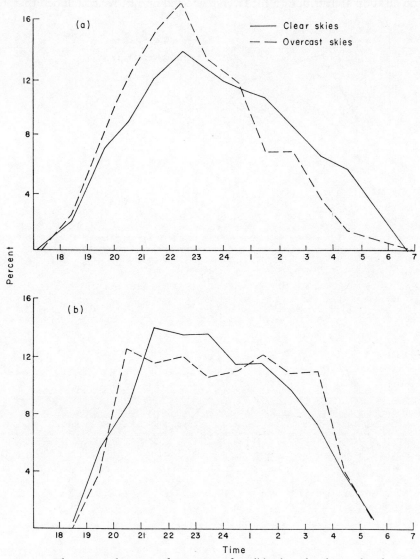

FIGURE 2. The temporal pattern of migration of small birds under clear and under overcast skies during (a) the spring of 1963 and (b) the spring of 1962.

# Frank Bellrose

We conclude that although overcast skies alter the temporal pattern of migration to some extent, birds are aloft as long on overcast nights as they are on clear nights. Consequently, distances migrated under both conditions of sky cover are similar.

*Altitude.* In our previous study (Bellrose & Graber, 1963, p. 380), after studying data on altitudinal distribution for twelve selected nights, we concluded that 'birds

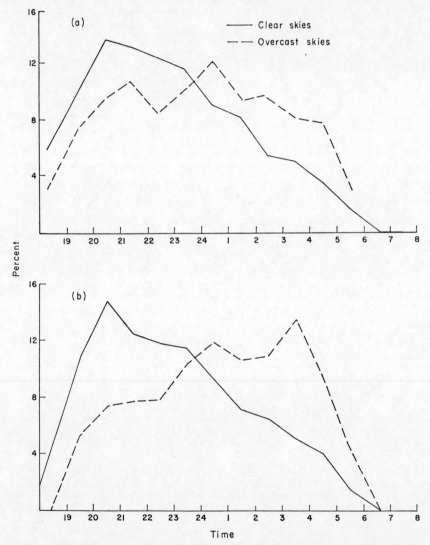

FIGURE 3. The temporal pattern of migration of small birds under clear and under overcast skies during (a) the fall of 1962 and (b) the fall of 1963.

286

were prone to migrate at higher altitudes when skies were overcast than when they were clear'.

Since then we have appraised the altitudinal distribution of bird targets on radar for four seasons at Havana. There were only slight differences between altitudinal distributions of migrants under clear and overcast skies in the spring and fall of 1962 (Figure 4). However, both during the spring and fall of 1963, a greater proportion of migrants occurred at altitudes lower than 4299 feet under overcast skies than under clear skies (Figure 5).

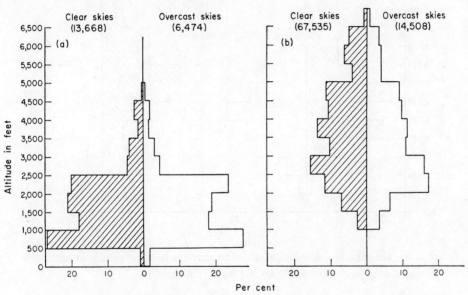

FIGURE 4. The altitudinal distribution of bird targets on radar under clear and under overcast skies during (a) the spring of 1962 and (b) the fall of 1962.

A comparison of cloud-base heights with altitudes of migrating birds discloses that most birds migrate below the clouds when skies are overcast. When cloud bases are lower than altitudes usually used by migrating birds, as at times in the fall of 1963, migrants fly lower than usual. Occasionally, low layers of clouds also have low tops, and, under these conditions, migrants fly above the clouds (Bellrose & Graber, 1963, pp. 379-380).

Nisbet (1963, p. 66) recorded only one instance of birds above clouds at Cape Cod, Massachusetts. He concluded: 'All this evidence suggests that birds normally remain below clouds at medium and high levels and do not climb through them'.

# Frank Bellrose

In England, Eastwood & Rider (1965, p. 411) reported that under overcast skies birds migrated at altitudes which averaged higher than under clear skies. They tracked migrants within cloud layers and above them. On the night of November 29, 1962, they found that about 35 per cent of the migrants were flying within the cloud layer.

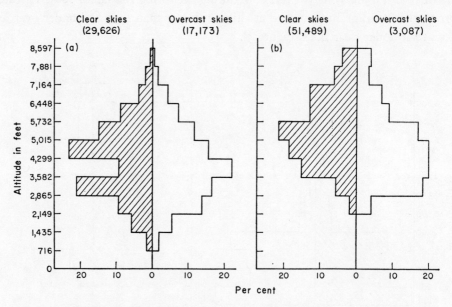

FIGURE 5. The altitudinal distribution of bird targets on radar under clear and under overcast skies during (a) the spring of 1963 and (b) the fall of 1963.

We believe our evidence on cloud cover and altitude still supports our earlier conclusion (Bellrose & Graber, 1963, p. 389): 'Birds migrating under overcast skies attempt to fly above the clouds unless they are too high. When they are not able to surmount the cloud deck, the migrants continue in flight, sometimes in the clouds but usually immediately below.'

## Flight Dispersion

Since we do not know the specific goal of each bird tracked, it is difficult to compare the reliability of flight directions between clear and overcast skies. Nevertheless, the dispersion in flight directions can be measured by calculating standard deviations, and by comparisons made in the spread of flight directions under these two sky conditions.

# Radar in orientation research

Standard deviations in the flight directions of migrating birds on thirty-two overcast nights have been obtained during the spring and fall of 1960, 1962, 1963 and 1964 in Illinois, and for twenty-one adjacent nights during these same years when the sky was entirely or largely visible.

Tables 1 and 2 show standard deviations of mean flight directions between overcast and clear nights by altitudinal strata for late spring 1962 and 1963, and early fall 1962 and 1963. The standard deviation implies that about two-thirds

TABLE I

Comparison of standard deviation of mean flight directions between overcast and clear skies, late spring 1962 and 1963

| Altitude in feet | Overcast | | Clear | | Difference in S.D.; overcast–clear |
|---|---|---|---|---|---|
| | Number of targets | S.D. | Number of targets | S.D. | |
| 0–499 | 89 | +20° | 28 | ±20° | 0° |
| 500–999 | 1950 | ±20° | 744 | ±17° | +6° |
| 1000–1499 | 1833 | ±20° | 1302 | ±25° | −10° |
| 1500–1999 | 972 | ±28° | 639 | ±25° | +6° |
| 2000–2499 | 3316 | ±24° | 1919 | ±27° | −6° |
| 2500–2999 | 2825 | ±25° | 2621 | ±23° | +4° |
| 3000–3499 | 265 | ±30° | 448 | ±24° | +12° |
| 3500–3999 | 2723 | ±28° | 1536 | ±23° | +10° |
| 4000–4499 | 2561 | ±28° | 2255 | ±25° | +6° |
| 4500–4999 | 59 | ±30° | 99 | ±20° | +20° |
| 5000–5499 | 1862 | ±26° | 1133 | ±21° | +10° |
| 5500–5999 | 998 | ±26° | 891 | ±27° | −2° |
| 6000–6499 | 679 | ±20° | 273 | ±26° | −12° |

of the flight tracks occurred within the stated number of degrees on either side of the mean flight directions. Many different mean flight directions are involved but are not given, because we are concerned here solely with comparing the spread in flight directions, not with the flight directions *per se*.

For most altitude strata during both spring and fall there is a slightly greater spread in flight directions under overcast skies than under clear skies (Tables 1 and 2). Most of the instances where the spread in direction was less for overcast skies than for clear skies occurred for higher altitudes where the migrants appeared to be above the clouds.

# Frank Bellrose

Figures 6 and 7 show examples of the dispersion in flight tracks by altitudinal strata on clear and on overcast nights during the spring and fall. Note the slight difference in the spread of flight directions between small birds flying under overcast and flying under clear skies. Contrary to the usual situation, in one of these examples (Figure 6), there is a greater spread under clear skies than under overcast skies.

On the basis of their radar study of bird migration at Truro, Cape Cod, Massachusetts, Drury & Nisbet (1964, p. 98) also stated: 'We conclude that

TABLE 2

Comparison of standard deviation of mean flight directions between overcast and clear skies, early fall 1962 and 1963

| Altitude in feet | Overcast | | Clear | | Difference in S.D.; overcast–clear |
| --- | --- | --- | --- | --- | --- |
| | Number of targets | S.D. | Number of targets | S.D. | |
| 1000–1499 | 240 | ±25° | 29 | ±18° | +14° |
| 1500–1999 | 720 | ±18° | 292 | ±18° | 0° |
| 2000–2499 | 1934 | ±25° | 1461 | ±23° | +4° |
| 2500–2999 | 2197 | ±27° | 1940 | ±26° | +2° |
| 3000–3499 | 1083 | ±25° | 1328 | ±19° | +12° |
| 3500–3999 | 1885 | ±25° | 2898 | ±25° | 0° |
| 4000–4499 | 1537 | ±30° | 2586 | ±24° | +12° |
| 4500–4999 | 785 | ±30° | 815 | ±16° | +28° |
| 5000–5499 | 586 | ±25° | 2104 | ±26° | −2° |
| 5500–5999 | 514 | ±24° | 1166 | ±27° | −6° |
| 6000–6499 | 455 | ±31° | 1801 | ±30° | +2° |

small birds regularly migrate at night under extensive overcast in the South Truro area; there is no evidence that overcast skies *per se* impair their orientation in any way, and so far we have only slight evidence that overcast skies significantly deter birds from starting to migrate.'

However, both we and Drury & Nisbet (1964, pp. 99ff) have observed widely scattered directional movements, under overcast skies, which are attributed to other weather factors. The greatest spread in flight directions that we have so far observed occurred on the nights of May 24 and 27, 1960.

On May 24, thunderstorms with rain occurred between 1800 and 2100 hours (Bellrose & Graber, 1963, p. 378). The rain ceased before midnight, but overcast skies continued for the rest of the night. The standard deviations by altitude were much greater during the first half of the night concomitant with the rain than during the last half of the night without rain (op. cit. p. 374).

On May 27, 1960, ground fog prevailed throughout the night and the cloud

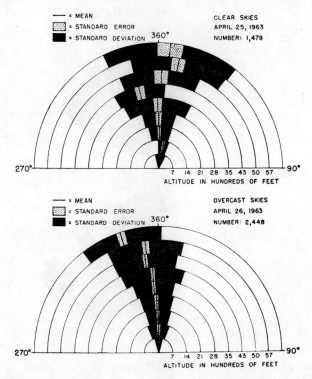

FIGURE 6. The comparative dispersion in flight tracks of birds on radar between clear skies (April 25, 1963) and overcast skies (April 26, 1963). Altitudes were rounded to the nearest 100 feet.

base was extremely low, only 900–1400 feet above the ground. Under these adverse conditions, standard deviations were almost twice as large as on May 28, when partly broken clouds occurred.

In four of the five instances on which Drury & Nisbet (1964, p. 103) observed disorientation, rain appeared on the radar screen, and on three of those five occasions, weather stations reported fog.

Lack (1963, p. 487) concluded 5 years of radar observation in England by stating: 'They [birds] are occasionally disoriented, always with full overcast in the area concerned, but it is not clear whether migrants are always disoriented in full overcast.' Earlier, Lack (1962, p. 144) had reported that on a few occasions migrants flew at random. When this occurred, total cloud cover or rain was recorded at near-by coastal weather stations. Lack associated the disorientation

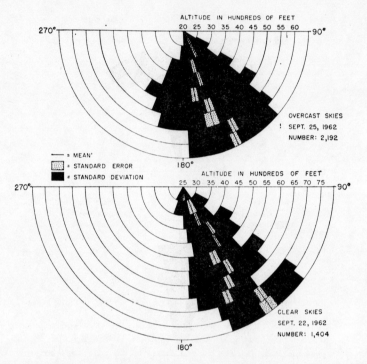

FIGURE 7. The comparative dispersion of flight tracks of birds on radar between clear skies (September 22, 1962) and overcast skies (September 25, 1962).

with loss of the bird's 'sun-compass or star-compass', but we believe that it may have resulted from the rain rather than from the overcast.

We believe that sufficient evidence is available to support the conclusion that birds are able to migrate on a goal-oriented course without the aid of astral cues.

*Wind Vectors*

Winds play a much more important role in migration than has been generally realized. Figures 8 and 9 compare the abundance of migrating small birds when winds were in the various 10° sectors of the compass rose to the frequency in which winds blew toward each of those sectors. It is readily apparent that in the spring of 1962, most birds selected winds blowing toward the north and north-north-east. Very little movement was recorded when winds were blowing toward the east, south-east, south or south-west (Figure 8).

Likewise, during the fall of 1962, small birds strongly selected winds blowing to the south and south-south-east (Figure 9). Migrants were comparatively low in abundance when winds blew toward the north-west, north and north-east.

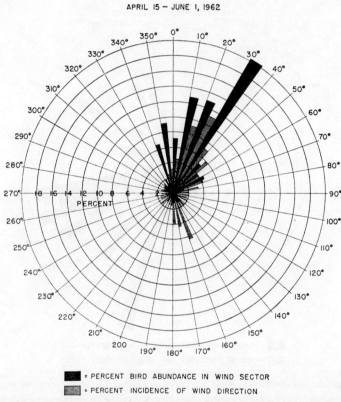

APRIL 15 – JUNE 1, 1962

■ = PERCENT BIRD ABUNDANCE IN WIND SECTOR
▨ = PERCENT INCIDENCE OF WIND DIRECTION

FIGURE 8. The occurrence of wind direction compared to the per cent of small birds migrating when winds were in a particular 10° sector of the compass rose, late spring 1962.

Obviously, migrating birds are able to appraise wind direction, for they select certain wind directions much more frequently than they do others. On occasion they do migrate when winds are adverse or otherwise disadvantageous, but usually such flights take place only after several days of unfavorable weather.

Birds are aware not only of the direction the wind is blowing but are also aware of wind speed. Tables 3 and 4 show the selection of high wind speeds by birds (considered to be largely waterfowl) in early spring 1963 and late fall 1962. It is evident that waterfowl selected strong winds to migrate, especially in spring and to a lesser extent in the fall.

On the other hand, small birds in three out of four seasons (Tables 5–8)

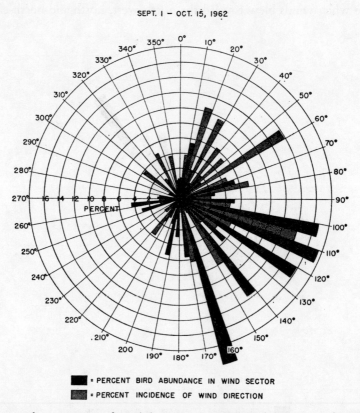

FIGURE 9. The occurrence of wind direction compared to the per cent of small birds migrating when winds were in a particular 10° sector of the compass rose, early fall 1962.

selected winds of low velocity. The exception to this general rule occurred in late spring of 1962, and the dates when this selection of high wind speeds occurred suggest shorebirds and late migrating waterfowl. Weekly waterfowl censuses showed ducks migrating later in 1962 than in other recent springs.

To make the selections they did, waterfowl and small birds showed preferences for wind speeds not only on certain nights but also at certain altitudes. Eastwood & Rider (1965, p. 425) believed that a migrant might select its altitude and air

# Radar in orientation research

TABLE 3

Selection of wind speeds by waterfowl, March 11–April 14, 1963

| Wind speed in knots | Bird targets | | Wind frequency | | Bird index rating |
|---|---|---|---|---|---|
| | Number | Per cent | Number | Per cent | |
| 1–10 | 3,342 | 17.7 | 44 | 25.0 | 0.70 |
| 11–20 | 1,406 | 7.5 | 69 | 39.2 | 0.19 |
| 21–30 | 4,782 | 25.3 | 43 | 24.4 | 1.04 |
| 31+ | 9,340 | 49.5 | 20 | 11.4 | 4.34 |
| Total | 18,870 | 100.0 | 176 | 100.0 | 1.00 |

TABLE 4

Selection of wind speeds by waterfowl, October 16–November 23, 1962

| Wind speed in knots | Bird targets | | Wind frequency | | Bird index rating |
|---|---|---|---|---|---|
| | Number | Per cent | Number | Per cent | |
| 1–10 | 12,533 | 20.8 | 96 | 29.6 | 0.7 |
| 11–20 | 19,363 | 32.1 | 96 | 29.6 | 1.1 |
| 21–30 | 22,702 | 37.7 | 87 | 26.9 | 1.4 |
| 31+ | 5,677 | 9.4 | 45 | 13.9 | 0.7 |
| Total | 60,275 | 100.0 | 324 | 100.0 | 1.0 |

TABLE 5

Selection of wind speed by migrating birds, April 15–June 1, 1962

| Wind speed in knots | Bird targets | | Wind frequency | | Bird index rating |
|---|---|---|---|---|---|
| | Number | Per cent | Number | Per cent | |
| 1–10 | 2,690 | 10.3 | 86 | 21.2 | 0.48 |
| 11–20 | 4,771 | 18.2 | 102 | 25.2 | 0.72 |
| 21–30 | 7,937 | 30.4 | 109 | 26.9 | 1.13 |
| 31+ | 10,740 | 41.1 | 108 | 26.7 | 1.54 |
| Total | 26,138 | 100.0 | 405 | 100.0 | 1.00 |

TABLE 6

Selection of wind speeds by small migrating birds, September 1–October 15, 1962

| Wind speed in knots | Bird targets | | Wind frequency | | Bird index rating |
|---|---|---|---|---|---|
| | Number | Per cent | Number | Per cent | |
| 1–10 | 3,845 | 22.1 | 35 | 14.6 | 1.52 |
| 11–20 | 8,543 | 49.1 | 103 | 42.9 | 1.14 |
| 21–30 | 4,334 | 24.9 | 79 | 32.9 | 0.76 |
| 31+ | 681 | 3.9 | 23 | 9.6 | 0.41 |
| Total | 17,403 | 100.0 | 240 | 100.0 | 1.00 |

TABLE 7

Selection of wind speeds by small migrating birds, April 15–June 1, 1963

| Wind speed in knots | Bird targets | | Wind frequency | | Bird index rating |
|---|---|---|---|---|---|
| | Number | Per cent | Number | Per cent | |
| 1–10 | 7,880 | 39.1 | 57 | 19.6 | 1.99 |
| 11–20 | 7,272 | 36.1 | 89 | 30.7 | 1.18 |
| 21–30 | 2,934 | 14.6 | 95 | 32.8 | 0.44 |
| 31+ | 2,066 | 10.2 | 49 | 16.9 | 0.61 |
| Total | 20,152 | 100.0 | 290 | 100.0 | 1.00 |

TABLE 8

Selection of wind speeds by small migrating birds, September 1–October 15, 1963

| Wind speed in knots | Bird targets | | Wind frequency | | Bird index rating |
|---|---|---|---|---|---|
| | Number | Per cent | Number | Per cent | |
| 1–10 | 18,149 | 58.5 | 215 | 33.2 | 1.76 |
| 11–20 | 7,687 | 24.8 | 259 | 40.0 | 0.62 |
| 21–30 | 4,148 | 13.4 | 131 | 20.2 | 0.66 |
| 31+ | 1,012 | 3.3 | 43 | 6.6 | 0.49 |
| Total | 30,996 | 100.0 | 648 | 100.0 | 1.00 |

speed 'as a result of a servo-type equilibrium between its metabolic processes and the temperature and humidity of the ambient air'.

## Wind Drift

Migrants have a great awareness of their goal in relation to wind direction, for all our evidence indicates that they correct within a few degrees for wind drift.

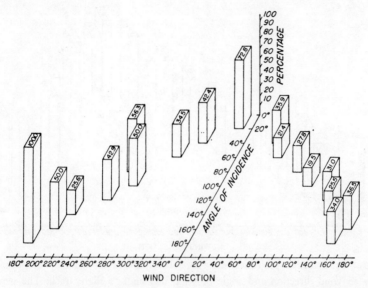

FIGURE 10. Isometric projection showing relationship of abundance of migrating birds between wind direction and angle of wind incidence to flight track. The percentage cubes depict the largest per cent of bird numbers for each 20° shift in wind direction (recorded as the direction toward which it is blowing), late spring 1963.

Four years ago (Bellrose & Graber, 1963, p. 371) we stated: 'It is quite evident that birds correct for wind drift but that the correction is never quite complete.'

Since that time we have analyzed much more data relating to the problem of wind drift. We compared the abundance of migrants for the fall and spring seasons in 1963 by wind direction and angle of incidence of wind to flight track (Figures 10 and 11). These isometric graphs show the peak per cent by angle of incidence and direction of the wind. As the wind moved to the east or west of 340–350° in the spring of 1963, a comparable increase occurred in the angle of incidence. Likewise in the fall of 1963, as the wind moved east or west of 180–190°, there was a comparable change in angle of incidence of wind to flight path.

Hence, as the wind shifted, the birds' flight paths remained much more fixed by their goal than displaced by the wind.

To evaluate further the problem of wind drift, we analyzed the nightly migration direction in relation to the east–west force of the wind by altitudinal strata. Most nights showed no direct relationship between shift in direction of migration with altitude and the east–west force of the wind. Three nights are

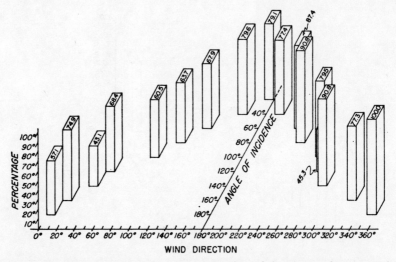

FIGURE 11. Isometric projection showing relationship of abundance of migrating birds between wind direction and angle of wind incidence to flight track. The percentage cubes depict the largest per cent of bird numbers for each 20° shift in wind direction (recorded as the direction toward which it is blowing), early fall 1963.

presented (Figure 12) which illustrate the independence of migration direction from the lateral force of the wind. The two scales, mean migration in degrees and east–west wind force in knots, are roughly comparable.

On April 7, 1962, an overcast night, the mean flight direction gradually shifted within 3800 feet of altitude some 15° to the east. Over the same interval of altitude, the wind force shifted some 23 knots to the east. On the overcast night of April 16, 1962, the mean migration direction varied with altitude over 23° to

FIGURE 12. The effect of the lateral force of the wind upon the mean flight direction of birds, by altitude, (a) under overcast skies, April 7, 1962, (b) under overcast skies, April 16, 1962, (c) under clear skies, September 4, 1962. The slopes of the two lines are on comparable scales.

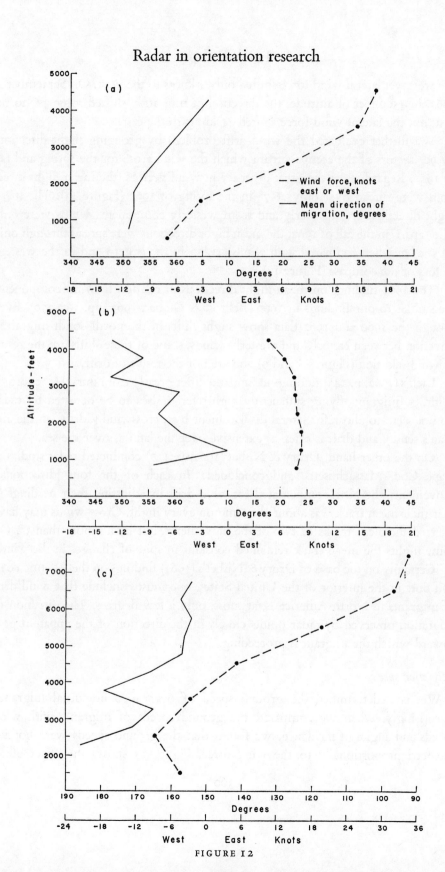

FIGURE 12

the west, yet lateral wind force shifted only 4 knots to the west. On September 4, 1962, in 4500 feet of altitude, the direction of migration shifted some 33° to the east, but the lateral wind force shifted 41 knots to the east.

We further evaluated the wind-drift problem by grouping flight directions by 90° sectors of the compass from which the wind arose for the spring and fall of 1962. Regardless of the great diversity in wind vectors, the mean flight directions were spread over only 26.7° in the spring of 1962 (Figure 13). The mean flight directions from easterly and from westerly components winds were only 23.0° apart. In the fall of 1962, the mean flight directions were spread through only 19.5° even when compared with winds arising in the eastern and in the western sectors of the compass (Figure 14).

The 1962 findings on mean flight directions in relation to wind components are similar to our findings in 1960 (Bellrose & Graber, 1963, pp. 367–370). Even though the 1960 and 1962 data show slight shifts in the north–south migration direction between easterly and westerly winds, some of these shifts are the result of wind selection (Figures 8 and 9) and are not the result of drift.

Lack's (1962, p. 143) findings in England differ greatly from ours. He reported: 'Thirdly, migrants flying sufficiently high over the sea to be detected by radar do not seem to allow for lateral displacement by a crosswind ("drift" in the airman's sense), and drift is often as extensive over the land as over the sea.'

On the other hand, Drury & Nisbet (1964, p. 117) conducted radar studies at Cape Cod, Massachusetts, and concluded: 'In each of the four [directional] movements, the birds compensated for wind-drift by adjusting their headings so that their mean track was about the same on every night. Cross-winds may have affected the mean tracks of two of the movements, but by no more than 3°. On some nights the mean track remained constant in spite of changes in the wind.'

Certainly on the basis of Drury & Nisbet's (1964) findings on the Atlantic coast and ours in the interior of the United States, one must conclude that wind drift of migrants in North America is, at most, only a few degrees. The direction of migration observed by radar points closely in the direction of the apparent goal toward which the migrant is proceeding.

*Migration speed*

We have determined the ground speed of over 4000 nocturnal migrants. Surprisingly, when we compared the ground speeds of migrants with wind speeds and angles of incidence, we found that the ground speeds were not influenced proportionally to the wind force. Figure 15 shows the effect of an

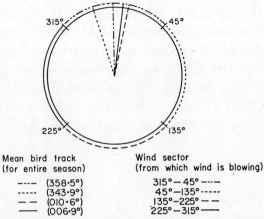

Mean bird track
(for entire season)

---- (358·5°)
----- (343·9°)
— — (010·6°)
—— (006·9°)

Wind sector
(from which wind is blowing)

315°—45° ----
45°—135° -----
135°—225° — —
225°—315° ——

FIGURE 13. Mean flight directions of migrants during periods in which the winds blew from each of the four sectors of the compass rose, Havana station, late spring (April 15–June 1) 1962. Note that the westerly winds resulted in a mean flight direction 3.7° west of the flight direction which occurred with southerly winds.

increasing wind force on the ground speed of 496 migrants on the nights of April 27–28 and 28–29, 1962. The wind force on each migrant was determined on the basis of altitude, the wind speed and the cosine of the angle of incidence between the wind and the flight track. The linear regression shows that small birds averaged 36.3 knots of ground speed without the influence of wind. For each 10-knot increase in favorable wind force, the ground speed of small birds increased only 3.2 knots.

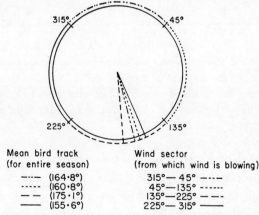

Mean bird track
(for entire season)

---- (164·8°)
----- (160·8°)
— — (175·1°)
—— (155·6°)

Wind sector
(from which wind is blowing)

315°— 45° ----
45°—135° ------
135°—225° — —-
225°— 315° ——

FIGURE 14. Mean flight directions of migrants during periods in which the winds blew from each of the four sectors of the compass rose, Havana station, early fall (September 1–October 15) 1962. Note that the westerly winds resulted in a mean flight direction only 5.2° east of the flight direction which occurred with easterly winds.

# Frank Bellrose

Migration on the nights of October 21–22 and 22–23, 1962, included many waterfowl as well as some passerine birds. The linear regression shows that without wind influence, the ground speed of migrants averaged 35.9 knots (Figure 15). On these two nights, for each 10-knot increase in favorable wind force, the ground speed increased only 3.9 knots. The correlation coefficients ($r = 0.43$ and $r = 0.49$) show an intermediate relationship between an increase in favorable wind force and an increase in ground speed for both series of nights.

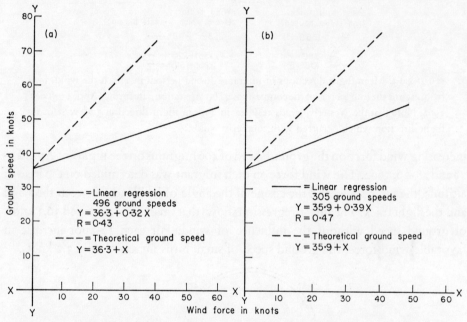

FIGURE 15. Actual and theoretical increase in the ground speed of migrating birds as wind force increased on the nights of (a) April 27 and 28, 1962, (b) October 21 and 22, 1962. The wind force was calculated on the basis of wind speed in knots and the cosine of the angle of incidence between the wind direction and each flight track, by altitude of each.

The low air speed of birds at high winds probably results in a transfer of kinetic energy to potential energy. By shifting altitude up and down birds are capable of increasing the speed of airflow over their wings, thereby acquiring lift. Thus, at high wind speeds, a bird's ground speed may approximate the wind speed and yet receive ample lift from the air itself.

Two factors are apparently responsible for the lack of correlation between the ground speed of migrating birds and wind speed: (1) Birds initiate migration when wind strength is most in keeping with their flight capabilities. (2) Migrants adjust their energy output, within broad limits of flight effort, in relation to the degree of wind assistance or resistance.

It is apparent that migrating birds reduce their own efforts as wind speed increases. An individual bird's reduction in flight speed with wind speed is probably greater than that represented by the regression. As the wind speed increases it obviously attracts strong-winged migrants with great speed capabilities (Tables 3–8). Because fast-flying birds are undoubtedly aloft with the more powerful winds, the reduction in air speed for an individual species would be greater than calculated for all species and individuals.

The daily activity flight speeds associated with natural conditions were obtained by Doppler radar for several species of birds by Schnell (1965). Although he found that wind made differences in a species' ground speed, the variations were not commensurate with wind speeds (see his Figure 4). For example, the mean ground speed of Barn Swallows flying with a 9–11 mph wind was 22.2 mph, while against the same wind the swallows averaged 16.7 mph. Cliff Swallows flying with a 20 mph wind averaged 19.4 mph; flying against the same wind they averaged 12.9 mph. Purple Martins flying with a 9 mph wind averaged 19.2 mph, and 18.8 mph against the same wind. Schnell's findings also suggest that birds alter their own flight efforts depending upon wind speed and angle of incidence.

The reaction of a bird's flight efforts to wind speed demonstrates that birds can quite closely determine the speed of wind. It seems to us that the ability of birds to recognize wind direction and speed and wind drift as precisely as they apparently do, implies their ability to use the wind as a cue in orientation.

*Landscape Features*
Radar observations in the Midwest of the United States show no apparent changes in the nocturnal flight paths of small birds with the courses of large rivers, such as the Mississippi, Ohio and Illinois. Almost all bird paths, intercepting these streams, continue in predetermined directions usually quite different from the courses of the river valleys. At night, even waterfowl do not appear to be influenced in their directions of flight by the Mississippi, Missouri and Illinois rivers, according to a study made by us several years ago (Bellrose, 1964, p. 141).

However, along the Gulf of Mexico, small birds apparently alter their course of flight at night because of landscape features. The outstanding examples have occurred at Galveston, Texas, during the fall migrations of small birds. There, in 1963 and 1964, birds flying south for 10–20 miles over land turned south-westward toward land after passing 5–10 miles out over the gulf.

On certain nights in the spring at Key West, Florida, flight paths shifted from the north-west toward the north-north-west as the birds reached the vicinity of Key West, about midway between Cuba and the Florida peninsula. At Brownsville, Texas, in the spring of 1963, we observed bird tracks on radar film turning westward toward the coast, and, once over land, turning back toward the north.

Aside from these few instances, we have observed no evidence from radar surveillance over much of eastern United States that birds use landscape features *per se* for orientation at night. Lack (1962, pp. 145–146) reported that at night, departing migrants, upon reaching the coastline of England, continued out to sea without a change in their flight paths. With a nearly full moon and an opposed wind, he rarely noted birds following the coast, and then only when the coastline was close to their normal headings.

There is some evidence that when salient topographic features are visible, nocturnal migrants may make slight changes in their flight courses. However, all evidence indicates that landscape features do not form an integral part of nocturnal navigation.

## DISCUSSION

There can be little doubt but that an intensive and extensive migration by most species of birds occurs on some nights without benefit of celestial cues. However, the magnitude of migration is somewhat reduced on overcast nights, especially with adverse winds and in the fall. This observation shows that astral cues are desirable to most if not all migrants, but, more importantly, that birds do migrate in large numbers without such cues.

The fact that birds in the fall are reluctant to initiate migration in the early hours of the night under overcast skies is further evidence that celestial cues are an asset to migrating birds. Once aloft, birds fly about the same distance under overcast skies as under clear skies, suggesting that the absence of astral cues is no barrier to the distance migrated.

It is apparent that when cloud tops are within a few thousand feet of the earth, most migrating birds fly above the clouds. Because they fly higher than usual to surmount the cloud deck, it is obviously advantageous for migrants to do so; one advantage would be the use of astral cues for guidance. However, it is equally obvious that birds unwilling to fly sufficiently high to surmount the cloud deck readily migrate below the overcast without benefit of stars or moon.

# Radar in orientation research

The flight paths of migrants under overcast skies show a slightly broader distribution in directions than those made under clear or broken-cloud skies. Hence, it is apparent that with the aid of astral cues, migrants fly a slightly more accurate course than without them.

We conclude this appraisal of celestial cues thus: the stars and the moon are of slight to moderate value for migrating birds in orientation-navigation, but these cues are not required for a successful flight lasting no longer than a single night. It is conceivable that migrating birds may not be able to navigate successfully for many nights without the benefit of celestial cues.

Radar findings suggest that, at night, migrating birds make only limited use of prominent landscape cues. For birds to use topographic features successfully for navigation there would need to be an almost continuous feedback of cues. Over much of the area flown by migrating birds, salient landscape features are not numerous enough to permit the necessary continuity of cues. Perhaps during one-fifth of the migration period the moon provides enough light to cast landscape details in bold relief. Yet, even then, flight courses appear to be distributed similarly to those on darker nights.

We are convinced that nocturnal migrating birds do not rely on landscape cues nor do they require celestial ones, at least not for limited movements. If birds are able to migrate in an oriented manner without the aid of celestial or landscape cues, what environmental cue remains available to them? We believe this cue to be wind turbulence. The idea that atmospheric turbulence might be useful to a flying bird was first proposed by I.C.T.Nisbet, in a letter to the editors of *British Birds*. Nisbet (1955, p. 557) stated: 'I would like to point out that the anisotropy and asymmetry of the turbulent velocity fluctuations in the atmosphere provide a simple means whereby a flying bird may, in theory at least, determine the approximate direction and strength of the wind without reference to any external objects.'

Woodcock (1942) has shown that Herring Gulls *Larus argentatus* respond to changes in the convective structure of the atmosphere by changing from circular soaring in vertical thermals to straight-line soaring when higher wind velocities produce longitudinal convection cells. This and other flight habits described by Woodcock demonstrate the ability of these birds to detect and utilize winds to conserve energy.

Our radar findings demonstrate that birds have a phenomenal understanding of winds. They select nights and altitudes having favorable directional winds and favorable wind speeds. They counter wind drift to within at least a few degrees, even under overcast skies. Species with different flight capabilities select for winds of different speeds. Waterfowl and shore-birds select winds of high speeds. Small birds select for winds of low velocities.

Ground speeds of migrants are not proportional to wind speed. As wind speed increases, the flight effort of migrants tends to be reduced when winds are favorable and to be accelerated when winds are adverse.

In order to diagnose adequately wind direction, wind speed and wind drift, birds must be able to diagnose the structure of wind turbulence to obtain the cues necessary to accomplish these feats. Wind turbulence depends upon the velocity of the wind, the wind shear, the stability of the atmosphere, the topography and the roughness of the surface. Wind turbulence consists of a succession of gusts and lulls.

Sutton (1955, p. 14) provides a numerical means of measuring turbulence by its gustiness: the root-mean-square value of the ratio of the departures of the instantaneous wind from the mean wind speed, to the mean wind. There is more vertical motion to air turbulence during the day, especially around noon, than at night, because the ascending warm air is replaced by the descending cool air. Consequently, at night, with lessened vertical exchange of eddies, wind turbulence becomes more gust-like in form. Therefore, in so far as turbulent air structure is concerned, it would be advantageous for birds to migrate at night when there is more homogeneity in the gustiness of the air. Perhaps this is one reason for extensive nocturnal migration in temperate zones.

The asymmetry of the gusts is such that the largest and most rapid change occurs in the front (relative to the mean wind) of the gust. Birds appear capable of sensing the sudden acceleration of air at the front of the gust, and, therefore, capable of determining their position in the air relative to the direction of the wind. The magnitude of the gusts provides a basis for migrants to ascertain the speed of the wind.

It seems that in addition to the orientation reference provided by the gust-form of air, birds need another point of reference. The earth itself provides this in the way of lights of cities, towns and farms; in shorelines of oceans, gulfs, lakes, rivers; in mountains, and in ridges and hills; in the darker shadows of woods to fields; and perhaps even in the waves and swells of oceans.

Migrants could detect shifts in wind direction by a slow but steady change in the angle of gusts striking them in relation to reference points on the earth. Winds at altitudes commonly flown by migrating birds change gradually, much less abruptly than surface winds.

# Radar in orientation research

The use of features on the earth at night as reference points is a far cry from the recognition of landscape features at night for orientation purposes. In over 100 hours of night flying, I have found it almost always possible to find a ground reference point, but virtually impossible when the moon is down to identify natural landscape features.

It is significant that when radar has shown random directional movements both we and Drury & Nisbet (1964, p. 103) have observed that disorientation among migrants was associated with rain and/or fog. Certain intensities of rain falling into the gust area would reduce the gust velocity relative to the mean air-flow. In addition, it is conceivable that rain may reduce the sensitivity of primaries and secondaries to the wind structure. Ground fog is an indication that there is little or no wind turbulence and that the air is in an almost complete laminar state. Rain and/or fog may also serve to disorient migrants by obscuring vital reference points on earth.

Drury & Nisbet (1964, p. 105) considered the wind as one of four theories they evaluated concerning the ability of birds to maintain a preferred heading once in flight. On the grounds that they observed bird tracks on radar which showed the same flight course in spite of wind changes, they discarded Vleugel's (1954) proposal that nocturnal migrants establish their orientation at sunset and thereafter maintain a constant angle between their heading and the wind.

We postulate that it is not the wind *per se* which the birds use for guidance in the absence of celestial and/or landscape cues, but rather the turbulence structure of the wind which, combined with ground reference points, provides a continuous feedback of orientation cues even as the wind shifts direction. Curiously, Nisbet (1955, p. 558) stated over 10 years ago: '. . . the structure of the [wind] gusts is such that the birds could determine the wind direction and strength with reasonable accuracy by the "feel of the air" alone'. We do not know why Drury & Nisbet (1964) failed to consider this theory in their evaluation of migration orientation.

We believe that the evidence presented here warrants giving full consideration to the hypothesis that when celestial and/or landscape cues are wanting, migrating birds use the structure of wind turbulence for migration orientation.

### ACKNOWLEDGEMENTS

These findings were obtained as part of a more extensive study supported by the National Science Foundation. I am much indebted to Mrs Lucille Walker, who read most of the 16-mm radar film; to Messrs Lawrence Auten, Steven Wycoff and Ted Bortell for their conscientious help in tabulating and analyzing data; and to Dr Glen C. Sanderson and Mrs Helen Schultz for suggestions on improving the manuscript.

SUMMARY

Radar surveillance of nocturnal bird migration has provided much new information on its physical nature. By relating the magnitude of migration and degree of directional grouping to the availability of certain environmental cues, we have endeavored to evaluate the references that birds ostensibly use in navigation.

Small birds migrate in a goal-oriented direction without the aid of astral cues. When winds were favorable in the spring, the magnitude of migration was comparable between nights with and without astral cues. In the fall, however, more birds migrated when celestial cues were available. Fewer birds migrated when astral cues were wanting and, in addition, winds were unfavorable.

The temporal pattern was similar in the spring under clear and under overcast skies. In the fall, migrants delayed ascending under overcast skies but also delayed descending, thereby remaining aloft a comparable length of time.

For the most part, nocturnal migrants appear to disregard landscape features as navigational aids in migration. Rarely, birds migrating over the Gulf of Mexico altered their flight direction, apparently on the basis of topographic cues, but, inland, large river courses did not alter the courses of flight.

Birds recognize many characteristics of the wind. Generally they select winds which are favorable for their 'goal', but when forced to use unfavorable winds, they correct to a high degree for lateral drift. Migrants appear to select for wind speeds within their flight capabilities: waterfowl for wind speeds above 30 knots and passerine birds for winds below 10 knots.

Migrating birds appear to reduce their flight speed somewhat proportionately to the increase in wind speed. Hence, the ground speed of migrants tends to remain fairly constant even when wind speeds vary greatly.

The ability of birds to determine the direction and strength of wind suggests that the wind can be used as an orientation reference. Winds blowing across terrain develop a gust structure which migrating birds theoretically, at least, should be able to detect.

Therefore, we propose the hypothesis that when astral and landscape cues are not available, migrating birds have recourse to the turbulent structure of wind, probably in conjunction with earth reference points, as a means of orientation in migration.

# Radar in orientation research

### REFERENCES

BELLROSE F.C. (1964) Radar studies of waterfowl migration. *Trans. N. Am. Wildl. and Nat. Resources Conf.* **29**, 128–143.

BELLROSE F.C. & GRABER R.R. (1963) A radar study of the flight direction of nocturnal migrants. *Proc. XIII Intern. Ornithol. Congr.* 362–389.

DRURY W.H., JR. & NISBET I.C.T. (1964) Radar studies of orientation of songbird migrants in south-eastern New England. *Bird-banding* **35** (2), 69–119.

EASTWOOD E. & RIDER G.C. (1965) Some radar measurements of the altitude of bird flight. *Brit. Birds* **58** (10), 393–426.

GRABER R.R. & HASSLER S.S. (1962) The effectiveness of aircraft-type (APS) radar in detecting birds. *Wilson Bull.* **74** (4), 367–380.

LACK D. (1962) Radar evidence on migratory orientation. *Brit. Birds* **55**, 139–158.

LACK D. (1963) Migration across the North Sea studied by radar. Part 5. Movements in August, winter and spring, and conclusion. *Ibis* **105** (4), 461–492.

NISBET I.C.T. (1955) Atmospheric turbulence in bird flight. *Brit. Birds* **48**, 557–559.

NISBET I.C.T. (1963) Measurements with radar of the height of nocturnal migration over Cape Cod, Massachusetts. *Brid-banding* **34** (2), 57–67.

SCHNELL G.D. (1965) Recording the flight-speed of birds by Doppler radar. *The Living Bird* **4**, 79–87.

SUTTON O.G. (1955) *Atmospheric Turbulence*, 2nd ed., 111 pp. Methuen & Co. Ltd.

VLEUGEL D.A. (1954) Waarnemingen over de nachttrek van lijsters (*Turdus*) en hun waarschijnlijke orientering. *Limosa* **27** (1–2), 1–19. (English summary.)

WOODCOCK A.H. (1942) Soaring over the open sea. *Sci. Monthly* **55**, 226–232.

# Analysis of tracks of single homing pigeons

CHARLES WALCOTT AND MARTIN MICHENER

Department of Biology, Tufts University, Medford, Mass. 02155, USA

We have investigated the navigation of single homing pigeons by following them in a light airplane. Our hope was that by studying the tracks made by individual pigeons on their way home we could discover what factors were responsible for a pigeon's ability to navigate.

This same idea lay behind the work of Griffin (1952), Hitchcock (1952, 1955) and Yeagley (1951) who followed flocks of homing pigeons, and behind Hitchcock's (1955) following of single birds; but in all these studies the difficulty of keeping the birds in sight made long and repeated observations very difficult. In addition, the path of a flock of pigeons may well represent some compromise among the paths chosen by each individual in the flock. Following single birds proved almost impossible because they frequently stopped flying and sat in trees or on barn roofs where they could not be seen from the airplane.

The solution to this problem was provided by the transistor, an invention which made possible a radio transmitter small enough to be carried by a pigeon. By following the transmitter with conventional radio-direction-finding techniques from an airplane, one can track a bird easily over long distances. Such radio telemetry has been used by Graber & Cochran (1965) to track migrating thrushes and by Graue (1965) to study the initial orientation of homing pigeons. We have used radio telemetry to follow single pigeons on their homeward trips. This paper presents the results of this tracking and offers some tentative interpretations of what we feel the tracks indicate about our pigeons' navigation.

## MATERIALS AND METHODS

The homing pigeons used in this study were part of a flock kept in the Biological Laboratories at Harvard University. These were old experienced homers which had been extensively released on a training line to the west of home. Other birds were purchased as young from local racers.

For tracking, each pigeon was equipped with a 28-gram, 52-megacycle, crystal-controlled oscillator whose battery pack gave it an operating life of about

3 days. The transmitter was attached to the pigeon with a harness made of five rubber bands. When first installed, the harness was obviously disturbing to the birds, but after a few hours they again behaved normally, and although the homing times of pigeons wearing harnesses remained on the average somewhat longer than the times of those without, this extra time could be accounted for, for the most part, as a longer period of sitting at the start of a flight. To minimize this effect, the pigeons were equipped with dummy transmitters and given their training flights with these. This training reduced the disturbing effects of the harness.

The pigeons were tracked from a Cessna 180 single-engine airplane. Using two dipole antennas, one on each side of the fuselage of the airplane, we found that we could locate the position of a pigeon within $\pm \frac{1}{4}$ mile. We confirmed the accuracy of this estimate by following light-colored pigeons which we could spot visually after the radio system had shown us where to look.

During the initial tracking, we found that the airplane apparently bothered the pigeons. Single birds seemed to do their best to avoid flying under the airplane and frequently altered their flight directions, apparently to escape from the tracking craft. On twenty occasions, when it was possible to see the bird as well as to track it by radio, the bird clearly attempted to avoid the airplane—each time the plane came between the bird and its intended direction of flight, the pigeon would hover until the plane passed, then fly rapidly on. As the airplane continued to circle over the pigeon, it would frequently change direction, and if pursued closely, the bird would alight and wait, sometimes for several hours, or even overnight.

By the middle of the summer of 1964 we discovered a technique that did not bother the birds and allowed us to plot their position every 5–10 minutes with an accuracy of $\pm \frac{1}{4}$ mile. The tracking was done by flying the plane only over areas through which the bird had already passed. In order to determine the bird's position, the plane was flown toward it until the increase in signal strength indicated that the pigeon was near, then the plane was turned and an accurate directional bearing taken during the turn. The airplane then flew away from the pigeon for 5–10 miles, turned, and made another pass. With this technique we could locate the pigeon's position within $\pm \frac{1}{4}$ mile without getting closer to the bird than 1 mile. Instead of constantly trying to keep up with it as we had done before, we kept an average distance of 5 miles from the pigeon. When we employed this technique, the pigeons' tracks became straighter, and the homing times decreased to normal.

# Analysis of tracks of single homing pigeons

In addition, we took the precaution when releasing birds at an airport to allow them to fly out of radio range before the plane took off. There is no chance at all, therefore, that the presence of the plane had any effect upon the direction of the birds' first 5 miles of flight.

If the consistency of the routes chosen by birds under similar circumstances of release is viewed in contrast to the inconsistency of the flight path of the pursuing airplane, one is forced to conclude that the birds are now bothered little, if at all, by the plane; for if the birds were seriously concerned with the plane, their paths should have reflected at least in part the plane's multitude of course changes. Thus, while there is still some question as to whether a pigeon carrying a radio transmitter and being followed by an airplane should be considered 'normal', at least we are able to obtain straight paths from returning pigeons and generally consistent results in experimental series both for the same and for different birds.

## RESULTS

*Training along a Line*

Pigeons were trained to fly from Fitchburg, Mass., to the Cambridge loft, a flight of 35 miles (56 km) ESE. Figure 1 shows five consecutive tracks made by 'Blue' (the color of the pigeon). They are typical of the total of thirty-six we obtained from five pigeons. The striking feature of these tracks is their variability; no two cover the same ground. And since our pigeons are seen to fly at or below tree-top level, each track passes through a different set of landmarks. These first Fitchburg tracks using our old method of tracking showed the effect of the airplane, and therefore additional training releases were made using the new tracking pattern. Different pigeons were flown from Worcester, Mass., 40 miles (64 km) west of Cambridge (Figure 2). Clearly, these later tracks are much more direct than those from Fitchburg. However, even here no two tracks covered exactly the same route. We believe, therefore, that the new tracking method did not disturb the pigeons and that the great diversity in the Fitchburg tracks was mainly a by-product of the tracking technique.

From a detailed examination of the birds' tracks from Fitchburg, Worcester and other control points, we observed that the tracks were no more or less scattered on days with 5-mile visibility than on days with 50-mile visibility, and strong crosswinds did not blow the birds off course. The speed of return was dependent upon the headwind component, but, on taking this into account, a given bird's airspeed was found to vary by only 2 or 3 miles per hour. In fact, the only variable that seemed to affect the pigeon's homing was whether or not the sun's disc was visible. If the sun was obscured and the pigeon was more than 10–15 miles from home, invariably the pigeon would stop flying and sit until

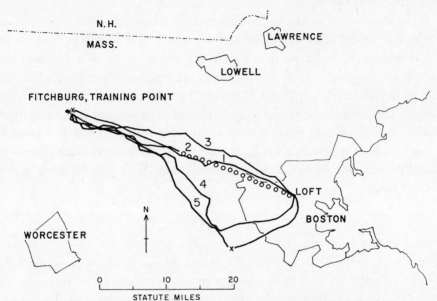

FIGURE I. Five consecutive tracks of Blue from Fitchburg to the loft.

| Track No. | Date | No. of previous releases from this place | Time from release to loft (min.) |
|---|---|---|---|
| I | June 14, 1964 | 15 | 59 |
| 2 | June 18, 1964 | 16 | 60 |
| 3 | June 19, 1964 | 17 | 121 |
| 4 | June 23, 1964 | 18 | 240 |
| 5 | June 25, 1964 | 19 | 71 |

The tracks become progressively more indirect showing the effect of the old tracking technique. The series of circles represents a portion of the return which was not tracked, but, based on the pigeon's return speed, shows its probable track. Crosses show where the bird sat and waited.

the sun reappeared. This finding further strengthened our suspicion that landmarks were not being used by the pigeons as their primary guide, even over this relatively familiar training course.

Our results also show that the birds were almost certainly not using a few distant landmarks (such as a few very tall buildings) to find the loft in northern

# Analysis of tracks of single homing pigeons

metropolitan Boston since the tracks were no different on days with 5-mile or 50-mile visibility. There remains, however, one more alternative: that the pigeons had learned the landscape between Fitchburg and Boston so well that they could choose essentially any path and yet always remain in sight of familiar landmarks.

This possibility was excluded during several flights of these birds from new

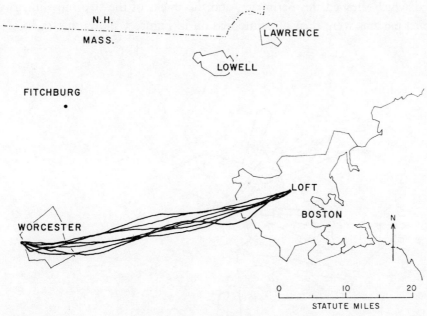

FIGURE 2. The control tracks of several pigeons from Worcester showing the typical straightness of tracks found with the new tracking procedure.

release points, north and south of the training point at Fitchburg. Among twenty releases from non-Fitchburg points during 1964, on three occasions individual pigeons flew across the territory between Fitchburg and Boston without altering their course (a wrong one) in any way. In some of these cases they crossed paths they had flown less than a week earlier! In summary, then, the pigeons do not seem to plot a course by flying from one familiar landmark to the next along their homeward path.

*Landmarks near the Loft*
Landmarks do, however, seem to play an important part in the birds' flight near the home loft. Pigeons approaching the region of the loft frequently corrected

their paths as they approached the loft. It seemed possible that this correction was dependent on landmarks near the loft: the tallest building in Cambridge is located within 200 feet of the loft at Harvard University. Boston is surrounded by hills, and this building is therefore not visible at tree-top level (where our pigeons were observed to fly) beyond a certain irregular perimeter along the tops of these hills and averaging about 5 miles from the building. A map was prepared which showed this perimeter, and the tracks of the two most intensively studied pigeons were then superimposed on it. Figure 3 shows the tracks of one

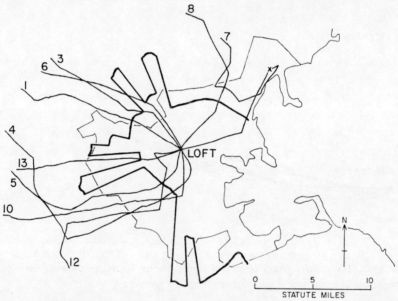

FIGURE 3. The heavy dark line encloses an area from which a high building near the loft can be seen from tree-top level. The final portion of Blue's tracks have been superimposed on this map. See the text for further details.

of these, Blue. Eighteen out of the twenty-four tracks of these two birds make the final turn directly toward the loft within 2 miles after crossing this line. It seems likely, therefore, that the birds were using this building as a signpost to find the loft.

*Releases off the Training Line*
The release of a pigeon trained to fly east from a point either north or south of the east-west training line should show whether the bird is relying on familiar land-

marks or using a learned compass direction, or is truly able to navigate. If it is using landmarks, it should be disoriented at a new release point. If it is flying by a compass direction, it should choose a course parallel to that taken from Fitchburg, but if, on the other hand, it is able to navigate, the pigeon should orient directly to the home loft.

The first of this series of experiments was performed on Blue, which had previously been trained from Fitchburg. Within a week of its last training flight, Blue was released from Worcester, Mass., about 22 miles (35 km) south of Fitchburg. The resulting track (Figure 4) shows that Blue first flew a course parallel to the one it had previously flown from Fitchburg, then after 6 miles on this course turned to the north-east and made a gradually curving track toward home. Blue was next released from Manchester, N.H., 41 miles (66 km) NW of the loft and once again flew for 8 miles in the Fitchburg compass direction. After two additional tracks from Manchester, Blue was released for a second time at Worcester. This time it flew southward as if it had been released from Manchester. Thus the bird showed no sign of recognizing either that the Worcester Airport was familiar from a previous release, or that this place was not the Manchester Airport. Here again the recognition of features at the release point seems to be lacking. But in contrast, the compass direction flown by this pigeon on the first part of this second trip from Worcester was within 10° of that appropriate to a release from Manchester, N.H.

Twenty miles south of the Manchester release point there is a string of cities over which the pigeon passed on each of the three flights: south of Worcester there are no such cities. When released from Worcester, the pigeon flew south for 28 miles (40 km), then turned abruptly north, flew 5 miles (9 km), and landed on a factory in the town of Pascoag. This is the only town in the area with a factory. The pigeon seemed to have been looking for the cities and factories it should have met at about this point had it been released from its familiar release point—Manchester. There are several other examples of reactions to such landmarks during flights on wrong courses. Thus landmarks, while *not* used to direct most of a bird's course, frequently seem to serve as checkpoints along the flight path.

*True Navigation*
What do the pigeons do when they have determined that their compass course is inappropriate? The tracks show that they seem to switch to a 'true navigation', which then takes them to the familiar area around the loft. In the example above,

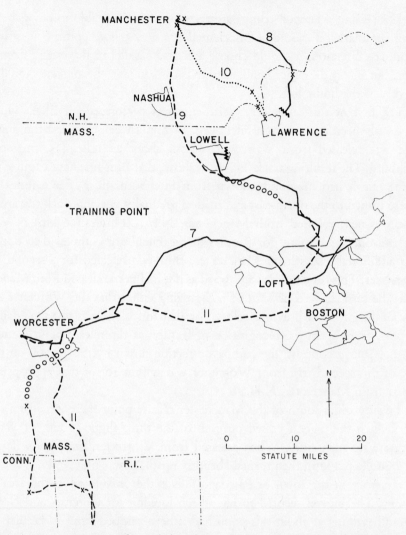

FIGURE 4. Five successive tracks made by Blue on its first releases off the training line. The previous tracks of Blue from the Fitchburg training point are shown in Figure 1.

| Legend | Track No. | Date | From | No. of previous releases from this place |
|---|---|---|---|---|
| ———————— | 7 | July 16, 1964 | Worcester, Mass. | 0 |
| ———————— | 8* | July 17, 1964 | Manchester, N.H. | 0 |
| – – – – – – | 9 | July 20, 1964 | Manchester, N.H. | 1 |
| · · · · · · | 10 | July 27, 1964 | Manchester, N.H. | 2 |
| – – – – – – | 11 | July 30, 1964 | Worcester, Mass. | 1 |

the bird eventually flew back toward the release point, then turned toward the loft, flying a gradually curving course. When the pigeon crossed the hills of southern Boston, it turned directly northward and flew a straight course to the loft.

There are several other examples of flights which were in almost certainly unfamiliar territory but which were directed toward the loft. One of the best was made by Silver on its first release from Windsor Locks, Connecticut, 87 miles (140 km) WSW of the loft. The track stayed within 5 miles of a true straight line from release to loft, an average accuracy of better than ±2°. Since the bird had never been within 40 miles of this place and had not been trained to fly NNE, its navigational ability must be extraordinarily good. Several examples of such navigation are shown in Figure 5, and an explanation is provided in the caption.

The sensory basis for this extremely accurate navigation is unknown, but the results suggest that the sun may play a crucial role in the process. All the pigeons studied during 1964–65 refused to fly at all if the sun was obscured by clouds and if they were more than 10 miles from the loft. In many cases, birds flying straight courses would stop and sit whenever the sun was obscured for more than 5 minutes. The sun, therefore, may be an important reference for pigeons' compass and navigational senses.

## Clock Shifting

The experiments of Schmidt-Koenig (1960) and others show that if a pigeon is placed in a daily light–dark cycle which is altered in phase with respect to the natural day, the bird's initial headings on release are shifted in direction. This finding suggested that resetting pigeons' clocks might give us a way of distinguishing between the use of the sun as a compass and the use of it as a true navigational reference. A shift of a few minutes should greatly disturb a navigational system based on either Matthews's (1955) or Pennycuick's (1960) hypothesis, but several hours' shift should be necessary to upset a simple sun azimuth compass. The argument is as follows: should a bird abandon any attempt to plot its position on earth when removed from the home loft and choose instead to fly immediately in some compass direction that past experience has indicated leads home, an error in its internal clock of 20 minutes would cause an error in its observed flight path

---

\* The portion of this track between Lawrence and Lowell has been omitted since the bird spent so much time exploring these two cities that its track in this region became very complex.

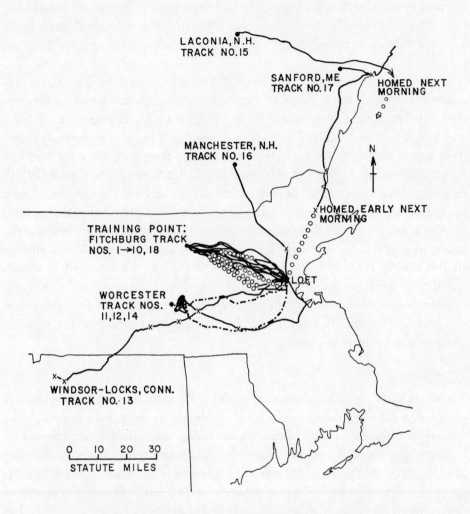

FIGURE 5. All the paths of Silver which were tracked.

| Legend | Track No. | Date | From | No. of previous releases from this place |
|---|---|---|---|---|
| ——————— | 1 | April 18, 1964 | Fitchburg, Mass. | 5 |
| ——————— | 2 | April 19, 1964 | Fitchburg, Mass. | 6 |
| ——————— | 3 | April 21, 1964 | Fitchburg, Mass. | 7 |

# Analysis of tracks of single homing pigeons

| | | | | |
|---|---|---|---|---|
| ——————— | 4 | April 25, 1964 | Fitchburg, Mass. | 8 |
| ——————— | 5 | April 26, 1964 | Fitchburg, Mass. | 9 |
| ——————— | 6 | May 2, 1964 | Fitchburg, Mass. | 12 |
| ——————— | 7 | May 3, 1964 | Fitchburg, Mass. | 13 |
| ——————— | 8 | May 6, 1964 | Fitchburg, Mass. | 15 |
| ——————— | 9 | May 30, 1964 | Fitchburg, Mass. | 25 |
| ——————— | 10 | May 31, 1964 | Fitchburg, Mass. | 26 |
| ——————— | 11* | June 12, 1964 | Worcester, Mass. | 0 |
| · · · · · · · · | 12 | Aug. 5, 1964 | Worcester, Mass. | 2 |
| ——————— | 13 | Aug. 7, 1964 | Windsor Locks, Conn. | 0 |
| - · - - · - | 14 | Aug. 9, 1964 | Worcester, Mass. | 3 |
| ——————— | 15 | Aug. 13, 1964 | Laconia, N.H. | 0 |
| ——————— | 16† | Aug. 18, 1964 | Manchester, N.H. | 0 |
| ——————— | 17 | Sept. 25, 1964 | Sanford, Maine | 0 |
| ——————— | 18 | Oct. 1, 1964 | Fitchburg, Mass. | 42 |

* No. 11 is the first release off the training line. It was followed by another from Worcester, then eleven more on the training line before the next track.

† No. 16 was followed by four releases on the training line before No. 17. All other tracks represent consecutive releases.

x          Shows place where bird sat and waited.

o o o         This part of path not tracked, most probable path taken.

The training directional bias to fly to the east-south-east may be seen recurring in the releases of this bird, which was repeatedly released along the training line from Fitchburg, as the legend footnotes indicate, in between many of the test releases from Worcester, Manchester, Laconia, etc. Track Nos. 11, 12 and 13 from Worcester and Windsor Locks start out to the east-south-east and are then corrected. The bias established by releases from Fitchburg between track No. 11 and No. 12 is finally removed by No. 13, since trip No. 14 from Worcester heads directly homeward. But the next release from Laconia shows a new eastward bias which was undoubtedly set up by the Worcester releases themselves. By track No. 16 from Manchester it appears that the bird is finally 'convinced' that direction-learning is no longer reliable. This track occurred after Silver had sat at the Manchester Airport overnight under a heavy overcast which dramatically withdrew at 6.30 the next morning. The pigeon took off at 6.59 a.m. and homed in 89 minutes over landscape which was probably totally new to it.

The effect of the plane on the pigeon is seen to be diminished in tracks numbered 13 through 18 in which the new following-ellipse method of tracking was employed (see text).

of only 5°. Should the same bird be navigating according to the methods described in the papers of Matthews (1955) and Pennycuick (1960), its course could differ by as much as 180° from the correct homeward course. We have tried some preliminary experiments with birds whose clocks have been shifted by 10, 20 and 120 minutes. Under such circumstances, the few birds we have followed fly a path that approximately bisects the angle between a course that uses the sun as a navigational reference and an erroneous compass course! This occurs only with time-shifted birds and is relatively consistent. It is interesting to note that it would be impossible for a bird to pick a course that would be counter to more of the current theories about bird orientation. In fact, unless we have overlooked something, there is no scheme to date that can easily explain these results. For this reason we wish to be particularly cautious at this point and to emphasize the preliminary nature of these experiments.

The experiments that resulted in these tracks were performed as follows. Pigeons were trained from a specific release point and tracked both from this and other points north and south of it. From these data we derived the measurement of the average compass direction the bird flew on release. Next, the bird was confined to a light-tight box where fluorescent lights were turned on at a predetermined time before or after local sunrise. The same shift was made at sunset so that though artificial and real days were out of phase, their length was the same ± 1 minute. After 4–7 days in this artificial day–night cycle, the pigeon was taken in a covered box to a place from which it had never been released before, released and tracked. After its arrival at the loft, it was again released from the training point and other points to either side of the training line. From this procedure we derived an average compass direction both before and after the shift.

The results of these experiments are summarized in Table 1, and two actual tracks are shown in Figures 6 and 7. The following highly tentative conclusions seem to be warranted by the data:

1. Small time shifts (10 minutes) upset the true navigation but had little effect upon compass orientation.

2. 120-minute shifts alter the sun compass by vastly more than the shift predicted by a simple sun azimuth hypothesis.

3. The direction of flight at no point along the bird's path seems to agree with that predicted by either Pennycuick (1960) or Matthews (1955).

4. The few tracks we have obtained seem quite consistent in their 'errors'. For example, the initial compass error increases with increasing time shift, sug-

## Analysis of tracks of single homing pigeons

gesting that the pigeons are using some consistent technique and not just random guesswork.

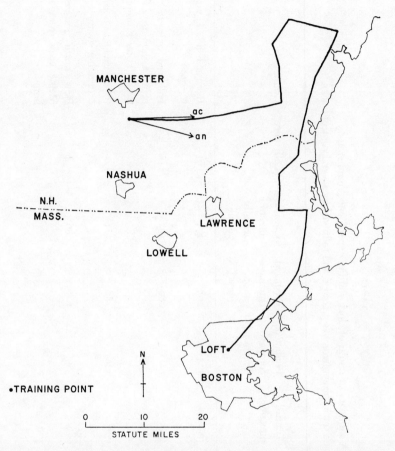

FIGURE 6. Blue Yellow Aluminum's June 26, 1965, track from Manchester after a 10-minute clock shift. The bird was exposed to a day which began 10 minutes before local Boston sunrise. The arrow ac represents the predicted compass direction of flight based on training direction from Worcester with a 10-minute sun azimuth correction. The arrow an represents the direction bird should fly if it were using Pennycuick's (1960) theory.

In short, the nine clock-shifting experiments we have performed do seem to have a relatively consistent, if inexplicable, effect on the pigeons' homing. Further experiments are currently (summer 1966) under way.

TABLE 1

A summary of results of clock-shifting experiments, summer 1965

Note: Each track shown here was preceded and followed by several control tracks

| Bird | Amount of shift, minutes | Release point | Trained direction* | Predicted compass direction† | Predicted true navigation course‡ | Compass direction actually taken§ | Difference‖ | Comments |
|------|------|------|------|------|------|------|------|------|
| 442 | 120 | Gardner, Mass. | 082 | 125 | 295 | 173 | 91 | Returned home via large arc to south |
| YA1 | 120 | Gardner, Mass. | 090 | 132 | 280 | 208 | 118 | Followed only first 10 miles, then transmitter failed. Returned home promptly |
| YA1 | 120 | Manchester, N.H. | 090 | 126 | 280 | 211 | 121 | Flew straight home on encountering river |
| YA1 | 10 | Manchester, N.H. | 090 | 89 | 103 | 086 | 4 | Flew north and encountered Maine coast, turned and flew home |

# Analysis of tracks of single homing pigeons

| | | | | | | | | |
|---|---|---|---|---|---|---|---|---|
| WAl | 10 | Worcester, Mass. | 130 | 132 | 279 | 125 | 5 | Flew 25 miles in compass direction, then sat. Returned 2 days later |
| YAl | 20 | Fitchburg, Mass. | 090 | 094 | 268 | 147 | 57 | After compass for 15 miles, turned in gradual southward arc toward home |
| YAl | 20 | Concord, N.H. | 090 | 083 | 258 | 158 | 68 | Flew compass to coast, then turned and went home |
| WAl | 15 | Concord, N.H. | 128 | 122 | 098 | 210 | 82 | Flew north, spent night and returned on straight course next day |
| 442 | 20 | Attleboro, Mass. | 090 | 095 | 284 | 057 | 33 | Followed gradually curving course toward home |

* The average compass direction flown both before and after shift.
† Compass direction as predicted on basis of sun azimuth change.
‡ True navigation prediction based on Pennycuick (1960).
§ Direction of pigeon's track for the first 10 or more miles.
‖ Difference between trained direction and compass direction flown.

## DISCUSSION

Tentative and incomplete though our data are, it seems possible to come to a few conclusions about our pigeons' navigation. In the first place, it appears that

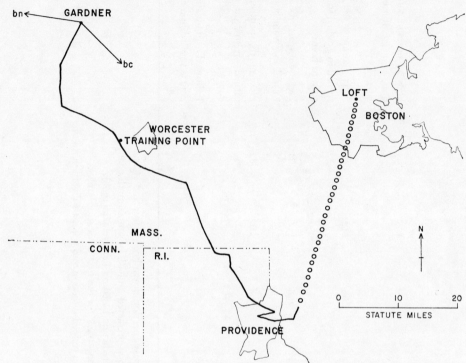

FIGURE 7. Blue Yellow Aluminum's July 31, 1965, track from Gardner with a 2-hour clock shift. The bird was exposed to a sunrise that was 2 hours later than true sunrise. The arrow bc represents the predicted compass course, bn the predicted direction if it were following Pennycuick's (1960) theory.

they use at least three schemes; landmarks, compass orientation and true navigation. Each of these will be discussed in turn.

*Landmarks*

The use of landmarks to find the loft seems to be important as shown by the pigeons' abrupt change in flight direction as the tall building next to the loft becomes visible. On the other hand, there is no evidence to suggest that landmarks at the release point are in any way important; the direction of a bird's departure seems conditioned by the compass directions of previous releases. Landmarks along the route of flight do appear to serve as checkpoints which trigger the transition from compass orientation to true navigation. (This has been shown by Blue's second trip from Worcester, among others.)

*Compass Orientation*

The first thing a pigeon does on being released is to fly in the compass direction that brought it home in the past. This compass orientation is remarkably consistent: comparison of the first 5 miles of a bird's track at an unfamiliar release site with the compass course it last flew shows that the two generally agree within 10°. Our experience with Blue, as well as with other pigeons, shows that as few as three releases are enough to alter the initial direction of flight; but what the pigeon uses for a compass is not known. It seems to depend on the sun, because our birds do not orient when the sun is not visible. But the clock-shifting experiments suggest that it is unlikely that it is a simple sun azimuth compass such as has been described for bees, fish, etc. The effects of time shifts are too large to be explained by sun azimuth error. On the other hand, the fact that clock-shifting has an effect argues against the pigeon's use of a simple magnetic compass.

It has been repeatedly stated by pigeon racers that their birds fly in an overcast, and indeed observation of races in the Boston area supports this statement. Recently we have begun training our pigeons to fly in overcast conditions. So far, in releases of single birds, the returns are extremely slow: our best record is 18 hours to go about 30 miles. Nevertheless, it does appear that pigeons can get home under total overcast, and we are now beginning to track birds under these conditions.

*True Navigation*

There are many examples in our data of birds which have shown accurate orientation toward the home loft from places with which they were almost certainly unfamiliar. Such orientation is remarkably accurate: in all cases sufficient to hit a target 10 miles in diameter; in three cases accurate within 2°. We have never seen navigation if the sun was not visible, and there is a suggestion that 10-minute clock shifts disturb it. All these factors lead us to suspect that at least true navigation depends on the sun. Only further experiments, especially with birds trained to fly in total overcast and at night, will clarify this point.

*Clock Shifts*

The effect of clock shifts must be considered as highly tentative for the following reasons. In the first place, we measured our shift from the time of local sunrise as given in the *Nautical Almanac*. There is no reason, however, to believe that the pigeon uses only the sunrise itself as a reference by which to set its clock. Secondly, pigeons in the light box were unable to see the sun for 4 or 5 days, and one could argue that this effect alone may have been enough to upset their navigation. However, the fact that with 2-hour shifts they returned home promptly seems to contradict this suggestion. In fact, the data suggest that shorter shifts were more disturbing to their navigation than longer (20-minute or 2-hour) shifts.

In spite of what are obviously inadequate controls, the data are interesting because of their consistency. We are now repeating many of these experiments with more rigorous controls and with measurements of the birds' activity rhythm as another means of gauging the amount of clock shift.

## SUMMARY

To summarize our results, it appears that pigeons use at least three ways of finding the home loft: compass orientation at the outset, followed by true navigation and then landmarks near the loft. But the physical basis of both compass orientation and true navigation is thoroughly obscure. The birds' unwillingness to fly without the sun is certainly suggestive, but the homing of pigeons under overcast, and even after sunset, makes us suspect that sun navigation is not the sole basis of their navigation. Exactly what other environmental clues are important to pigeons is unclear. Additional experiments using a variety of training techniques, coupled with the shifting of the birds' clocks, may give us some further clues.

## ACKNOWLEDGEMENTS

We are grateful to Norman Budnitz and Jerome Hunsaker for the many long hours they spent tracking pigeons, and to many representatives of the Federal Aviation Agency who have been so helpful. This research was supported in part by contracts Nonr 1866(46), 1866(12) and 3225(00) between the Office of Naval Research and Harvard University and by NSF grants GB3404, GB4400, and GB5057.

## REFERENCES

GRABER R.R. & COCHRAN W. (1965) Personal communication.

GRABER R.R. (1965) Night flight with a thrush. *Audubon* 67 (6), 368.

GRAUE, LOUIS (1965) Initial orientation in pigeon homing related to magnetic contours. *Am. Zool.* 5, 704.

GRIFFIN D.R. (1952) Airplane observations of homing pigeons. *Bull. Mus. Comp. Zool.* 107, 411.

# Analysis of tracks of single homing pigeons

HITCHCOCK H.B. (1952) Aeroplane observations of homing pigeons. *Proc. Amer. Phil. Soc.* **96**, 270.

HITCHCOCK H.B. (1955) Homing flights and the orientation of pigeons. *Auk* **72**, 355.

MATTHEWS G.V.T. (1955) *Bird Navigation.* Cambridge University Press, Cambridge.

PENNYCUICK C.J. (1960) The physical basis of astro-navigation in birds. *J. Exp. Biol.* **37**, 573.

SCHMIDT-KOENIG K. (1960) Internal clocks and homing. *Symposium on Quantitative Biology* XXV. Cold Spring Harbor, N.Y.

YEAGLEY H.L. (1951) A preliminary study of a physical basis of bird navigation. Part 2. *J. Appl. Phys.* **22**, 746.

# The present status of our knowledge about pigeon homing

HANS G. WALLRAFF

Max-Planck-Institut für Verhaltensphysiologie,
8131 Seewiesen über Starnberg, Germany

There are good reasons to assume that once we know how displaced carrier pigeons can find the way back to their loft we will also know how birds in general can navigate from one place on the earth to another. It seems unlikely that man should have been able to produce such a specialized ability in domestic animals if it were not previously developed in wild animals. In fact, orientation performances equalling those of homing pigeons have been demonstrated in wild birds (for references see Matthews, 1955; Kramer, 1961; Schmidt-Koenig, 1965), suggesting that the mechanisms underlying them are equivalent. However, because carrier pigeons have substantial advantages for experimental research, our knowledge of the homing of pigeons is much more detailed than our knowledge about the homing of any other species.

During the last fifteen years about fifty papers have been published, containing original experimental data on pigeon homing. But the basic question of how pigeons find their way home is still far from being solved. Therefore, this review cannot answer this question but can only attempt to show what we really know about pigeon homing. Emphasis will be laid on the more recent results, and there will be no attempt to deal exhaustively with all the details. After the description of facts, the paper will be concluded with a brief look at the theoretical aspects of pigeon homing.

## THE DIRECTIONS IN WHICH DISPLACED PIGEONS FLY

### Preface: Evidence of Home Orientation

Home orientation in the stricter sense of the word does not only mean that a displaced animal finally arrives at home independently of the method it used. It involves, in addition, a mechanism enabling the animal to 'know' its position in relation to its home area even in an unfamiliar environment. Thus, when dealing

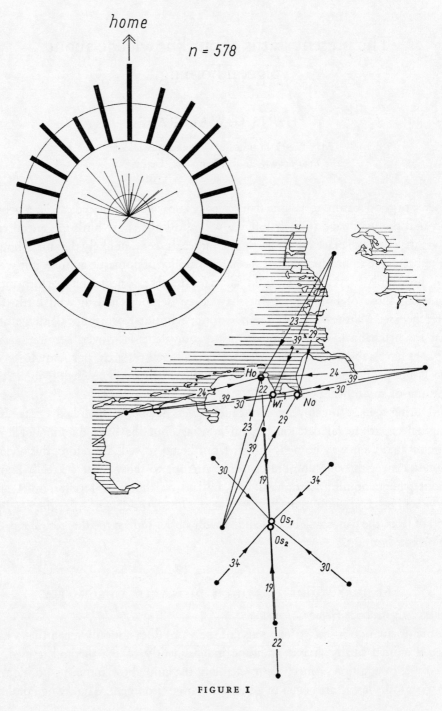

FIGURE I

332

with home orientation of pigeons it should be demonstrated that the phenomenon which is the subject of the investigation really exists. This can only be done by showing that the flight paths of displaced pigeons in unknown country are in some way related to the home loft.

In fact, the departure directions at the release site obviously show a general preference for the home direction (Figure 1). Although the scatter in the summarizing diagram is rather great, the distribution is far from being random ($p \ll 0.0001$) and the mean direction points to the home. The diagram is thought to be conclusive because several precautions have been taken: (1) All pigeons were inexperienced, i.e. they had never been displaced by man before this particular flight. Thus, all birds were of the same standard, not being influenced by earlier experiments. (2) The distance of displacement ranged from 85 to 165 km; it was far beyond the radius of spontaneous flights around the loft which certainly never exceeded 10 km. (3) The numbers of birds released from opposite directions were always equal. In this way, most chance factors working in favour of or against the home direction should have been balanced out. (4) Pigeons of five different home sites were released at twelve different places. Thus, the total is composed of twenty independent samples allowing a statistical test of 'second order' (with the sample means as units; see below) which confirms again that the preference is not caused by the accidental choice of the release sites.

Figure 1 contains the directions at the moment of disappearance from view as seen by an observer following individual pigeons with field glasses. This moment is reached at a distance of about 2 km and at an average time of about 3 minutes after release (Wallraff, 1959b). But a preference for the home direction appears in outline much earlier and can already be demonstrated 20 seconds after release

FIGURE 1. Summary of the vanishing directions of 578 individual pigeons at their first release. Below: The positions of the release sites (black) and of the respective lofts at Hohenkirchen (Ho), Wilhelmshaven (Wi), Nordenham (No), and Osnabrück (Os; two lofts). The respective numbers of birds are indicated. Above: At the periphery, all headings are added together, home direction being uppermost. The outer circle indicates a uniform distribution i.e. $578/24 = 24.1$ birds per sector. In the centre of the diagram the mean vectors of the twenty single stretches as shown on the map are indicated. The radius of the intermediate circle coincides with the greatest possible length of a vector: $\bar{a} = r = 1$. The radius of the innermost circle represents $\bar{a} = 0.29$, i.e. the length of the mean vector of the total which is pointing exactly in the direction of home. (Note: All birds except those of loft $Os_2$ are consanguineous.—In some cases the real numbers in the samples released from opposite directions differ by as many as three birds. If so, the greater sample is reduced by eliminating single birds selected by chance.)

(Wallraff, 1967). Unfortunately, however, it has not been possible so far to extract conclusive information about home orientation before the pigeons were in flight. Many experiments with several kinds of orientation cages did not lead to results of sufficient consistency (Wallraff, unpublished).

Convincing examples of home orientation in pigeons whose home range was extremely restricted are shown below in Figures 2 and 10.

This preface seemed necessary because there is a striking peculiarity in pigeon behaviour which may indeed raise some reasonable doubt as to whether the departure directions are really influenced by the respective position of the birds in relation to the home loft. It is an exceptional event that the mean direction of the headings at a single release point coincides roughly with the home direction. In most cases, the two directions are significantly different from each other, and the deviations can be rather great (see, e.g., Wallraff, 1959b, 1960b, 1967; Schmidt-Koenig, 1963b, 1966). Concerning the material presented in Figure 1, the vectors in the centre of the diagram show that the scatter of the total is caused more by the scatter of the mean directions at different places or to different lofts respectively, than it is caused by the scatter within each release group (compare the lengths of the single vectors with the radius of the innermost circle). It should be emphasized, however, that sixteen out of the twenty mean vectors deviate less than 90 degrees from the home direction. Thus, in our case a deviation from randomness with the expected sign is significant ($p < 0.01$), but with a less balanced selection of release sites it is difficult to prove that apparent home orientation is not a chance result.

From this short survey we can conclude, not only that displaced pigeons must possess some information about the respective home direction, but also that their flight directions are not solely influenced by the geometrical relationship between their position and the home loft. It is shown in the following sections that there are indeed several more factors which exert some influence on the directional choices.

*Directional Tendencies*

In Figure 2 initial headings as well as recovery directions of aviary pigeons are shown. Before the experimental release, these birds were never allowed to leave the aviary in which they lived. It seems quite clear that the recoveries are related to the home locality, but at the same time that they deviate from it. Their mean directions intersect in an area about 40 km south-west of the loft. A conclusion suggested by this would be that the birds tend to fly to an imaginary goal, or in other words that their co-ordinates are distorted. But it is also possible to give

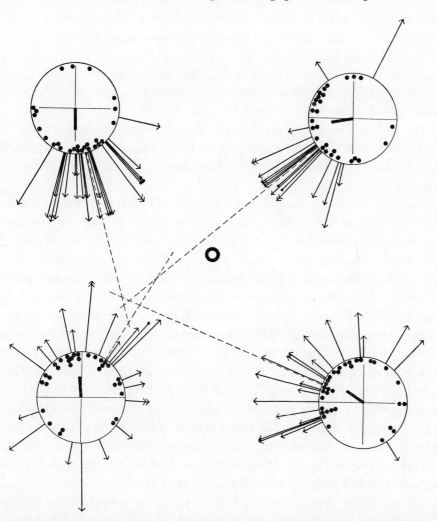

FIGURE 2. Departure headings (dots) and directions of recoveries (arrows) of aviary pigeons released at four points about 90 km distant from their home (centre; $Os_1$ in Figure 1). North is uppermost.—The mean vectors of the headings are indicated by thick lines within the diagrams; the radius of the circle represents $\bar{a} = 1$. The mean directions of the recoveries—calculated irrespectively of the distances covered—are indicated by dotted lines. The distances are classified and represented by the lengths of the arrows: 10–45 km, 45–90 km, and more. Small dots instead of arrow-heads designate recoveries within the town of Osnabrück. (Modified from Wallraff, 1967.)

another interpretation: the homeward tendency of the pigeons may be interfered with by a preference for a certain compass direction, in our case by a preference for west to south-west. The result would be a compromise between these two tendencies. In fact, it is quite probable that this last interpretation is the right one. It appears to agree with all the other experimental data, whereas the idea of the distorted co-ordinates fits only some results.

The preferred departure directions at all four places are between the home direction and west (see vectors in Figure 2). If one adds all the headings together, the distribution is significantly different from random, and the mean vector points to a little north of west.

Two more examples may illustrate the kind of interference between the two tendencies (Figure 3). At four places, each about 150 km distant from home, inexperienced pigeons from two different lofts were released alternately. The mean vectors show that they vanished in quite different directions. The overall mean of the Wilhelmshaven birds points a little south of east. The consanguineous Nordenham birds, whose loft was located 27 km away, preferred the north-west. It is remarkable, however, that these birds changed their direction towards home, at least at one point, when the difference between the generally preferred compass direction and home direction became greatest (western release point). At another place with an equal difference between the two directions, only the scatter increased (northern release point). Even the Wilhelmshaven birds, although heading predominantly in easterly directions at all places, showed an obvious relationship to the locality of their loft. The mean vectors deviate always from the general mean to the home site, and in the east, where both directions are nearly opposite, the vector is shortest, i.e. the scatter is greatest. At this point, more birds vanished in the western half of the compass than at the other places.

It is possible to demonstrate the reality of the two components as well as the relations between them by different correlations. One of them is shown in Figure 4. It contains the scatter-values of cross-releases with pigeons of four different lofts in connection with the angular difference between the overall mean of the respective population and the home direction. If both directions coincide the mean vectors are long, i.e. the pigeons fly well-directed, and if the directions are opposite to each other, the vectors are short, i.e. the pigeons fly widely scattered.

The relative strength of the two components may vary so that in the pigeons of one loft, goal-directed flying is more conspicuous, while in the pigeons of another loft, flying in parallel directions predominates. In the latter case the pigeons behave in a fashion similar to that observed in several wild birds (Griffin & Gold-

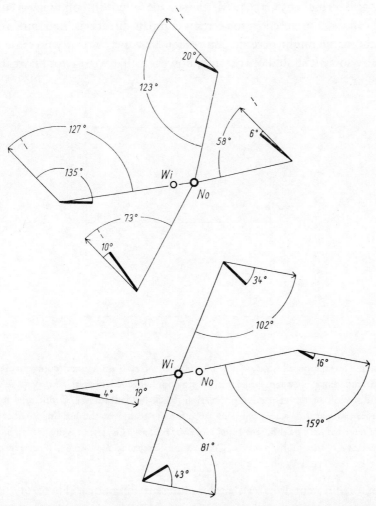

FIGURE 3. Directional tendencies in first-flight pigeons of two lofts, Nordenham (top) and Wilhelmshaven (bottom).—Thick lines indicate the mean vectors resulting from the initial headings at the respective release sites (number of birds ranging from 29 to 32); the length of the arrows represents $\bar{a} = 1$. The arrows themselves indicate the two preferred compass directions of the two populations. They are calculated from the total of the headings (below), and from the headings at the northern and the southern place (above) respectively. (The mean direction of the Nordenham birds at all four places together is indicated by the short lines to the right of the arrows.) (From Wallraff, 1967.)

smith, 1955; Bellrose, 1958, 1963; Matthews, 1961, 1963a). Following Matthews, one could call these preferences for certain compass directions 'nonsense' orientation. Yet this name might give the impression that there is really no sense in this kind of behaviour. It should only imply, however, that we do not know its sense at the present.

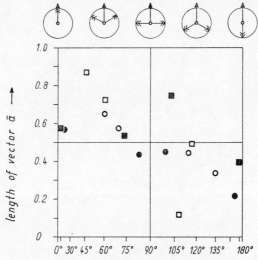

FIGURE 4. Correlation illustrating the interference of two directional components.— Abscissa: difference between home direction (double-headed arrow) and average departure direction of the respective population (black-headed arrow). Ordinate: length of the mean vector $\bar{a}$ as a reciprocal measure for the scatter of the headings. Different symbols refer to birds of different lofts (Ho, Wi, No, and $Os_1$; see Figure 1). Each dot represents 23–40 first-flight pigeons. Correlation coefficient $r = -0.65$, chance probability $p < 0.01$. (From Wallraff, 1967.)

Pigeons of different lofts can prefer different directions. Three of the four populations analysed in north-western Germany preferred north-western directions; only the Wilhelmshaven birds showed a strong tendency to ESE. It is not yet clear whether homing pigeons within a wider area generally tend to prefer the NW–SE axis. There might well be a very broad pattern showing different but consistent directional tendencies in different geographical regions. This is suggested by the fact that in North America in three quite different areas pigeons with no or little experience tended to prefer directions between west and south-west (Graue & Pratt, 1959; Graue, 1965; Schmidt-Koenig, 1963b, 1966). But the data do not yet permit definite conclusions.

Our knowledge about one-directional tendencies in pigeon homing is not entirely new (Wallraff, 1959b, 1960b; Schmidt-Koenig, 1963b). But formerly it was not possible to get a clear picture of these phenomena, especially with regard to the interrelationship between the two components acting on the initial orientation. There are two reasons for this. One is that many of the former experiments were done with more or less experienced birds, and it is shown below that experience influences the directions chosen by displaced pigeons. The other reason is that many of the former experiments were done at short distances, and distance also plays some role in the homing process. This is shown in the next section.

*The Role of Distance*

It was suggested by Matthews (1955, 1963b), that home orientation becomes better with increasing distance. His experimental data were not very convincing, but his conclusions were right. This was shown by Schmidt-Koenig (1966) who conducted a great series of releases at various distances in the four main compass directions (Figure 5). The average curve of the so-called home component is high at very short distances, declines between 15 and 40 km, and rises again slowly until reaching an apparent constant level at about 200 km. The dissociation of the curves for different directions in the middle range again suggests some inter-ference of home tendencies with one-directional tendencies. But the picture may be complicated by the experience of the birds, and no other criteria of the head-ings have been published. Thus, for a more detailed analysis a less complete series may be used.

In general, Figure 6 shows for first-flight pigeons of the Wilhelmshaven loft similar trends to those just demonstrated in experienced birds of the Durham loft. The different curves for different directions are easy to understand with our know-ledge about directional components. In releases from the west there are no changes worth mentioning with increasing distance. In fact, they are hardly to be expected because the loft-specific preferred direction and home direction roughly coincide, and with no conflicting impulses the birds' performances are optimal in any case. In the opposite direction, however, there is a considerable dependence on the distance of displacement. At 4 km most pigeons flew more or less in the home direction. But at 22 km, they followed purely their directional tendencies with no relationship to the home direction. With increasing distance, the mean direction remained unchanged but the scatter increased, thus demonstrating that the in-fluence of the homeward component was growing. At the southern points, the change occurred in another way, namely, the scatter remained nearly constant, but the mean direction shifted more and more to the direction of home.

In general, if we were to neglect the direction of displacement we would get a quite confusing picture, showing good home orientation at short distances and poor orientation at much longer distances.

It was shown that there is a minimum of home-directedness at about 20 km in inexperienced and at about 40 km in very experienced pigeons. Matthews

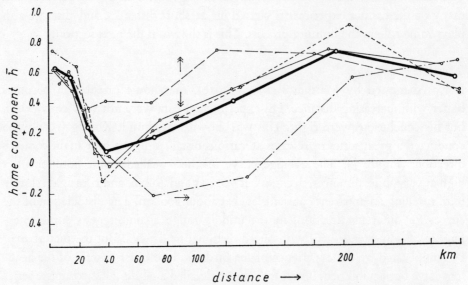

FIGURE 5. Home-directedness of headings as a function of distance.—Very experienced pigeons were released at eight distances in each of the four main compass directions around their loft at Durham, N.C., USA. The thick line connects the average values of all four directions, the thin lines refer to different home directions as indicated by the double-headed arrows. Each small dot represents 38–40 bearings. For an illustration of the home component $\bar{h}$ see Figure 6. (Modified from Schmidt-Koenig, 1966.)

(1955, 1963b) suggested that at still shorter distances the birds can find their loft by landmark recognition. There are indeed arguments supporting this interpretation (see also Wallraff, 1967), and so far no data have been published contradicting it. According to the clock-shifting experiments of Graue (1963) at very short distances, the time-dependent location of the sun seems to be included in the system of familiar 'landmarks'.

Thus we can assume that the investigator of bird navigation should mainly be interested in the rising curve with increasing distance. One may conclude from it, that the process of navigation needs a minimum distance from home before coming into play, and that its efficiency increases to a distance of about 200 km. A distance effect of such a kind can be expected in any system of bi-coordinate navigation, because the difference between the respective parameters at home and at the release point should increase with increasing distance.

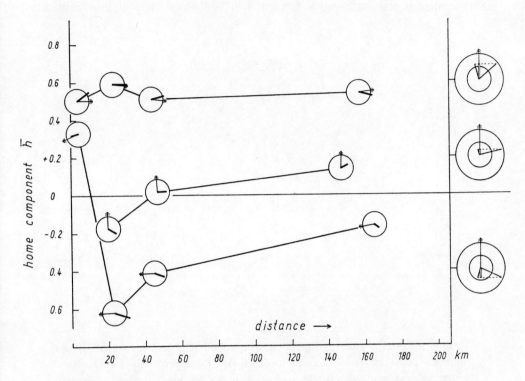

FIGURE 6. Initial orientation of first-flight pigeons at various distances and various directions from their loft at Wilhelmshaven.—The double-headed arrows indicate the home direction. The radius of the small circles indicates the vector length $\bar{a} = 0.5$. Each circular diagram represents 32–147 birds.—At the right, examples are shown illustrating the relation between the length $\bar{a}$ of a mean vector (solid lines) and its home component $\bar{h}$ (vertical white line). Smaller values of $\bar{h}$ can be caused either by a great scatter ($\bar{a}$ being small), or by a great deviation of the mean direction from the axis running through home. (Modified from Wallraff, 1967.)

*The Role of Experience*

It is well known that the homing performance of pigeons increases with the number of preceding flights (Wallraff, 1959a; Schmidt-Koenig, 1963a). Not only homing speed and homing success are influenced by experience, however, but also the initial headings. The experience of only one flight is sufficient to determine the headings of the next flight, as shown in Figure 7. At a point 160 km distant from home, pigeons with no experience at all and pigeons with experience of one preceding flight were released simultaneously. The inexperienced birds vanished in the south-east as is normal in Wilhelmshaven pigeons (compare

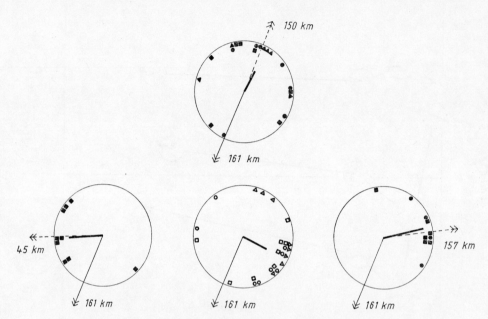

FIGURE 7. Influence of a previous flight on the distribution of headings.—Solid arrows point to the actual direction of home, dotted arrows to the respective home direction at the first release. Open symbols refer to first-flight pigeons, black symbols to second-flight pigeons (first release 1–7 weeks ago). Symbols of the same shape indicate coinciding release days. Mean vectors as in Figure 2.

Figure 3). The mean vectors of the other birds, however, coincide exactly with the home direction of their first release.

This result is a rather extreme one. In most cases the effect is smaller. Another example shows only slight deviations between two groups of second-flight birds whose first release had been from opposite directions (Figure 8). Some more examples are published elsewhere (Wallraff, 1959a).

If a single release can cause deflections of different amounts, it follows that a greater number of releases from different directions may result in still more unpredictable deflections. Graue (1965) has clearly shown the cumulative effect of several releases, and he also comes to the conclusion that 'the direction of the deflection but not the amount is predictable'. With other training patterns, even the sign of the deflection might be obscured.

It may be possible to minimize the disturbing effect of experience by releasing the pigeons many times at symmetrically distributed places. After passing through a phase of instability they may finally become a quasi-homogeneous material,

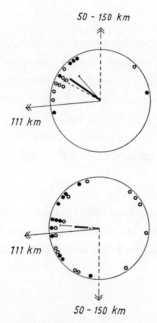

FIGURE 8. Headings of second-flight pigeons with preceding flights from opposite directions.—Arrows as in Figure 7. Different symbols refer to two different release sites, 14 km apart from each other (exact distances to the loft at Osnabrück 104 and 118 km). The pigeons were released at both places simultaneously during 3 hours.

being now less liable to be affected by single releases. It is not yet known, however, whether a steady state can be reached, and if so, at what stage of experience.

In any event, we can expect that experience will change the original inter-relationship between home orientation and preference for a certain compass direction. There are indications suggesting a change in the preferred compass direction not only if training acts asymmetrically, as it does inevitably in the Wilhelmshaven area, but also if the releases are conducted in a symmetrical pattern (Schmidt-Koenig, 1966). On the whole, symmetrical experience seems to change the proportion between one-directional tendency and homeward tendency in favour of the latter (indirect conclusions from the data of Schmidt-Koenig, 1963a, 1966).

As a general conclusion, experience constitutes a third component influencing the initial orientation of pigeons. The interference between all three components is rather complicated and has not yet been studied in detail.

## Variations in Time

It has been known for a considerable time that even at the same release site pigeons do not always behave in the same manner. There are obvious day-to-day fluctuations in homing performances as well as in departure directions which cannot be explained by overt weather conditions. Furthermore, there is a marked annual cycle, but only in homing performance and so far only shown at short distances (Wallraff, 1959b). It was possible to correlate the homing behaviour of the pigeons with some meteorological parameters, but the kind of connection is still obscure (Wallraff, 1960a).

The variability of homing behaviour in time has not been in the focus of research during recent years, and therefore it is mentioned here just for completeness. However, it might well be worth re-analysing this variability against the background of our recent knowledge about the interference between different directional components.

## The Role of the Sun

Fifteen years ago Matthews (1951, 1953) demonstrated poor initial orientation under overcast skies. The significance of these results was doubted because of the considerable fluctuations of the headings even in bright sunshine, and because in some instances pigeons were well orientated at departure when the sky was overcast (for references see Wallraff, 1966b). A re-examination of this question under better controlled conditions, however, showed that with dense cloud cover the distribution of the headings indeed approached randomness (Wallraff, 1966b).

This suggests that the sun plays some role in the process of orientation, and the assumption is supported by the clock-shifting experiments of Schmidt-Koenig (1958, 1961). He kept groups of pigeons in an artificial light–dark cycle for several days producing phase-shifts in the physiological clock by 6 hours forwards, 6 hours backwards, and by 12 hours respectively. The summarizing diagram in Figure 9 shows that the pigeons deviated in the same manner from untreated controls as time-shifted birds do when using their well-known

# Status of our knowledge about pigeon homing

sun-azimuth compass (Hoffmann, 1954, 1960; Schmidt-Koenig, 1958, 1961). This strongly suggests that displaced pigeons make use of their sun compass.

Although the deviation of the pigeons with shifted clocks was always in the

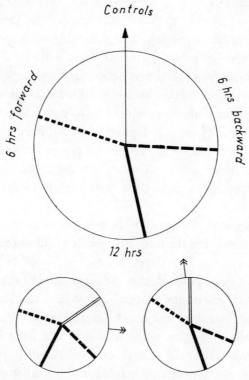

FIGURE 9. Effect of shifting the circadian clock on the headings of displaced pigeons.— Above: Mean directions calculated from many releases at many places. The reference direction (uppermost) is obtained by superposition of the mean directions of the control birds at the single releases. The total of each of the three shifting-groups is between 200 and 260 bearings.—Below: True compass directions (north being uppermost) at release sites 44 km west (left) and 70 km south (right). The double line indicates the mean direction of the controls, the other lines refer to time-shifted birds as in the diagram above. (Modified from Schmidt-Koenig, 1961.)

expected direction, the amount of deflection was different at different release sites, as shown by the two lower examples in Figure 9. It might well be that these differences have something to do with the several components acting on the headings. In view of this, the results with time-shifted pigeons should be reconsidered.

345

# Hans G.Wallraff

Not only the differences between experimental and control groups should be taken into account, as was mainly done so far, but also the relationships to the compass directions and to the home site should be evaluated.

## The Role of Topography

For completeness, we should briefly refer to one further factor. Topographical features could have either a guiding or a deflecting influence on the directions taken by homing birds. Actually, they seem to have both.

As mentioned above (p. 340), at very short distances the pigeons orient themselves probably with the help of familiar landmarks. The radius of countryside with which they are acquainted may perhaps increase with an increasing number of returns after displacement (compare Figures 5 and 6). Furthermore, it is difficult to exclude landmark recognition in experienced pigeons even at greater distances, although local experience seems to affect the directional choices only when based on several repeated releases at the same site (Wallraff, 1959a; Matthews, 1963b).

In unknown country, topography cannot help home orientation (except under special conditions), but the birds may either avoid or prefer certain features as coasts, hills, valleys, woods, villages, towns, etc., or other structures less conspicuous to man. It is quite probable that the flight paths of the pigeons are indeed influenced by the local environment, but in most cases this influence seems to be of minor importance (see, e.g., Hitchcock, 1952; Pratt & Wallraff, 1958; Graue & Pratt, 1959; Wallraff, 1959b). Otherwise it would have been impossible to deduce consistent rules about the orientational behaviour in respect to direction, distance, experience, etc. On the other hand, some smaller deviations from the expected directions at certain places may well be caused by topographical factors. Thus, if reality does not exactly coincide with the idealized rules, this may, at least partially, be due to disturbing effects of the landscape.

## Conclusion

All the preceding sections were concerned with the simple question: In which directions do displaced pigeons fly? It should have become clear that it is not possible to give an answer of equal simplicity. There is a variety of factors acting on the directions of flight which must all be taken into account when homing behaviour is analysed. Although essential parts of the navigational mechanism and important causal connections are still unknown, it seems possible to sketch the outlines of the orientational system at least in a descriptive way. This will be done by an attempt at summarizing and in some degree interpreting the results mentioned above:

The basic pattern of pigeon orientation is characterized by two directional tendencies. One of them is the *tendency towards home*, which increases with increasing *distance*. The other tendency points to a *certain compass direction* which is specific for a certain loft site or perhaps for a certain area. It can be changed or superimposed by 'second order' directional tendencies depending on the *experience* of the individual gained during previous flights. The initial orientation of pigeons can always be interpreted as a compromise between one-directional component(s) and the homeward component. Only in very extreme cases one of them may approach zero.

The orientational behaviour of pigeons shows considerable *variability in time*. It seems to be connected in some way with certain *meteorological factors*. At least for the determination of compass directions the pigeons make use of the *sun* and of their *physiological clock*.

The described rules are not or only partially valid at very short distances when *landmark recognition* comes into play. Even in unknown country *topographical features* can exert some influence on the flight paths, but this influence is usually slight.

## EXPERIMENTS VARYING THE ENVIRONMENTAL CONDITIONS AT THE HOME SITE

Up to the present, the possibilities of influencing the navigational system experimentally have been and are rather limited. A major reason for this is that it has not been possible so far to get sufficient information about the orientation of pigeons in a space restricted enough for experimental operations, as it would be, for instance, in a cage with a diameter of at most a few metres. Hence it has hardly been possible to make any artificial changes of the environment at the displacement site. It was fortunate, therefore, that Kramer (1959 a, b) was able to influence the homing behaviour of pigeons by varying the environmental conditions at the home site. These experiments with shielded aviaries, which continued for several years after Kramer's death (Wallraff, 1966a), will be the subject of the following pages.

This section deals exclusively with aviary pigeons. These are birds which have been living in cages of wire netting for several months from just leaving the nest until the day of displacement and release. Twelve years ago Kramer & Saint Paul (1954) could demonstrate clear homeward tendencies even in such pigeons

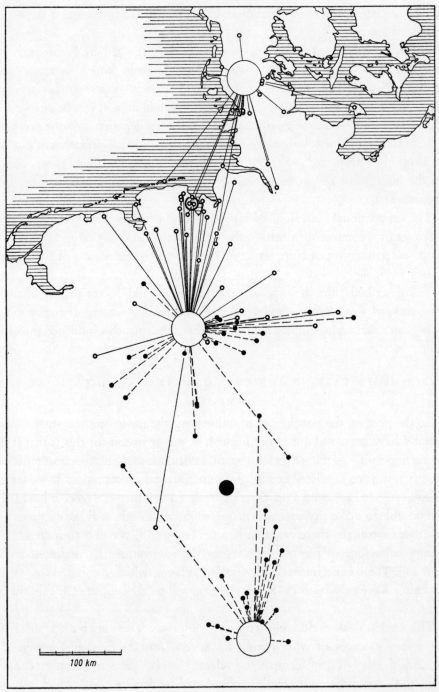

FIGURE 10

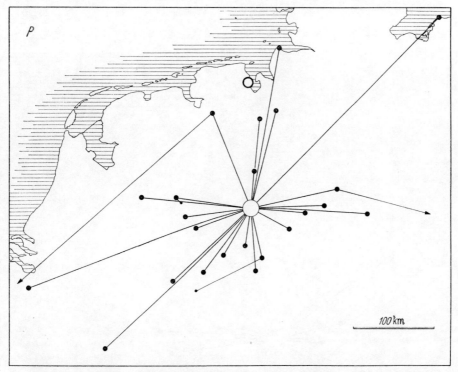

FIGURE 11. Recoveries of pigeons raised in aviaries surrounded by a wooden palisade and released about 150 km south of their loft. (From Wallraff, 1966a.)

with an extremely restricted home range. Later, it could be confirmed by displacements in opposite directions as well as by releases of pigeons from different home sites at the same place that true goal orientation is involved, and that it was not just simulated by the preference for a certain compass direction (Figure 10; see also Figure 2).

Kramer (1959 a, b) could show that home orientation disappeared when the aviary was surrounded by a wooden wall a little higher than the aviary itself. The recoveries of the so-called 'palisade pigeons' were not noticeably related to the home site (Figure 11). The same was true if there was a broad gap in the wooden

FIGURE 10. Recoveries of pigeons raised in unscreened aviaries at Wilhelmshaven (thick circle at the coast) and near Giessen (large black dot). The birds were released at a common place between the two home sites, and at places in the opposite direction from the respective loft. White dots and solid lines refer to recoveries of Wilhelmshaven birds, black dots and dotted lines to recoveries of Giessen birds. (From Wallraff, 1967. Note: The release sites of the Wilhelmshaven pigeons are the same as in the following figures.)

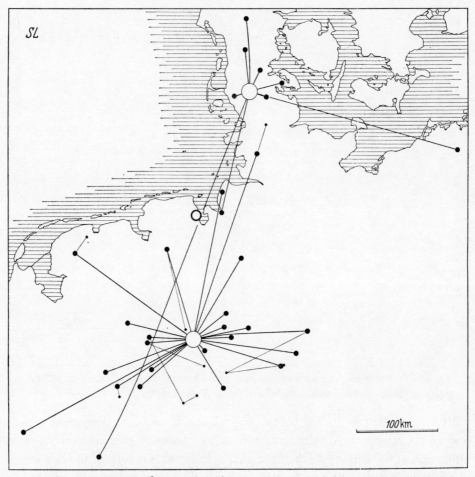

FIGURE 12. Recoveries of pigeons raised in aviaries surrounded by a wooden palisade with a southern gap. (From Wallraff, 1966a.)

wall either in the north or in the south allowing the pigeons to view nearly a whole semi-circle. Figure 12 shows the widely scattered recoveries of birds from the palisade with a southern gap.

The next step was to replace the upper part of the wooden wall by glass (Figure 13). Sitting on the perch, the pigeons had the same view around as they had in an open aviary without any palisade. After release, their recoveries were much more scattered than the recoveries of birds from unscreened aviaries (Figure 14). Concerning the relation to the home site, the difference is highly significant, while the difference between these birds and the birds kept in the wooden palisade is not

FIGURE 13. The 'glass palisade'. (From Wallraff, 1966a.)

FIGURE 15. The 'roofed palisade'. At the left, one of the nine flaps, by which the slit can be closed, is being manipulated. (From Wallraff, 1966a.)

statistically significant. These results obtained with the so-called glass palisade suggest that the main factor that is changed or blocked off by surrounding walls is not optical in nature.

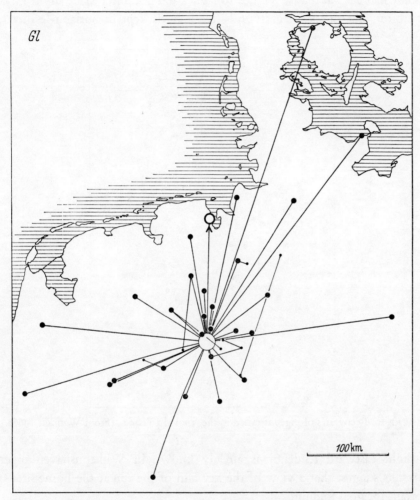

FIGURE 14. Recoveries of pigeons raised in the 'glass palisade'. (From Wallraff, 1966.)

A last kind of cage screening, the 'roofed palisade', is shown in Figure 15. A wooden roof covered the whole aviary, the sides being screened except for a narrow slit at the height of the perch. Thus, this kind of palisade was complementary to the first-mentioned kind: the horizon as well as the lowest parts of the sky were visible while by far the greater part of the sky was blocked off. In addition, a direct view of the sun was never possible, because the slit was closed during the morning and evening hours when the sun was low.

Most of the recovered pigeons raised in this aviary came nearer to their loft than they had been at release (Figure 16). They did not differ markedly from open aviary birds, but differed significantly from birds kept in horizon-less aviaries.

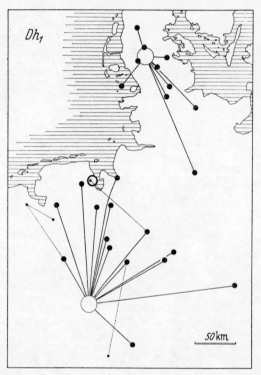

FIGURE 16. Recoveries of pigeons raised in the 'roofed palisade'. (From Wallraff, 1966a.)

The slight eastward tendency is already known in Wilhelmshaven pigeons. The results suggest that a view of the sky and of the sun at the home site is not important for goal finding.

## THEORETICAL ASPECTS

The main purpose of this paper is to review our present knowledge about pigeon homing. I have tried to do this in the preceding sections by describing the results of empirical research. This last section is merely a fragmentary appendix, containing opinions and suggestions, but no solutions and no well-rounded theories.

# Status of our knowledge about pigeon homing

There is a rather limited number of navigation hypotheses, and in my opinion it looks as if none of them is the right one. This supposition cannot be substantiated in detail in only a few words, but it should be stressed that it would be extremely difficult to interpret the described phenomena by either an inertial navigation system (Barlow, 1964; see also Wallraff, 1965), or a mechanism using the magnetic field of the earth and the coriolis force (Yeagley, 1947; see also Matthews, 1955), or a system of pure sun-navigation or other celestial navigation of any kind (Matthews, 1953, 1955; Pennycuick, 1960; see also Hoffmann, 1965; Schmidt-Koenig, 1965).

All the hypotheses brought forward so far have had a common starting point: in each it has been considered which of the known physical parameters or systems of parameters could enable an animal to find its way from one place on the earth to a certain other place. It was a reasonable starting point, and I think it was the natural one. But so far this approach has not led to success. Therefore, I think we should try another line of approach, starting from two general assumptions.

The first assumption is that most of the empirical data described in this paper are consequences necessarily following from the orientational mechanism. At present, we cannot with certainty distinguish between essential and accidental phenomena. But if we were to assume that most of the experimental results are not in causal connection with the mechanism of goal finding, we might as well stop investigating the matter any further.

The second assumption is that our speculations may reckon with any arbitrary parameter, and need not be confined by our present knowledge about the physical world. Thus, we should try to deduce the characters of the factors involved in bird navigation from the analysis of the homing behaviour. Afterwards we may search for actual parameters which could fit the theoretical demands derived from the empirical results.

With these two assumptions in mind we can develop theoretical systems which are able to explain the typical features of pigeon homing without at first considering their bases in concrete physical factors. In my opinion hypothetical models of such a kind are more than just academic games, because they may give rise to concrete questions and thus suggest lines for future research. This may be exemplified by some speculations.

One of the most conspicuous phenomena described above is the fact that displaced pigeons tend to fly in certain compass directions. This peculiar behaviour could make sense if the preferred direction coincided roughly with the direction of the *gradient* of an informative parameter, and if the difference between the values of this parameter at home and at the release site were too small for perception. The difference would either remain too small, telling the animal that it is on this line not far from home, or the difference between the values would increase as rapidly as possible until reaching a measurable amount and telling the animal now that it has to turn back. A second parameter could announce displacements lateral to the direction of the gradient resulting, for instance, in turning commands, either right or left. The second parameter need not be necessarily connected with a second substrate. Let us assume that the gradient has a punctiform centre at a certain place on the earth, but not at the poles, and an imaginary substrate of information extends uniformly therefrom in all directions. Two co-ordinates could then be derived from it. One could be, for instance, the intensity, decreasing with distance from the centre. The other could be the angle between the direction of the gradient and the north–south axis, or in other words the compass direction of the gradient. If this were the case, compass directions would be essential as reference directions, and the sun compass would be used as an integral part of the navigational system even for the determination of position, not only as an additional aid as it was thought of in Kramer's (1953, 1957) concept of map and compass.*

Although such speculations should not be taken too seriously in their details, some suggestions for future research can be derived from them, as for instance the following questions. Are the preference directions of inexperienced pigeons within a wide region, for example in central Europe, all on about the same axis? In another region, e.g. in North America, is another axis preferred? Do all the axes of preference intersect in one area, or are there several points of intersection, or is there no system at all? Is there an upper limit of distance for homing ability, or are pigeons able to point homeward at any place on the globe, even in trans-continental displacements? Furthermore, a thorough analysis might show whether there are any typical differences in the behaviour of pigeons displaced along their axis of preference and those displaced perpendicularly to this line.

Another question concerns the role of the sun-compass. If it were necessary

---

* It should be mentioned here that a gradient system exists which in principle could be used in the described manner, that is the magnetic field of the earth. It would make extremely high demands on the precision of the mechanism, however, because the magnetic poles are not very eccentric with respect to the axis of the earth, and in most regions declination changes only little with changes in position (in central Europe about 1° per 100 km E–W). Furthermore, the results of the palisade experiments would hardly be explicable if the navigational system were based on magnetism. Nevertheless, we should not ignore the magnetic field.

for measuring small differences in the direction of a certain parameter, a small shift of the internal clock should cause considerable errors in the determination of position. If, on the other hand, it is only a question of a choice of a certain compass direction, such small shifts would be of small influence. It might well be that normally both demands occur simultaneously, and the results of clock-shifting experiments could be complicated by this in different ways not to be discussed here. Some unexplained peculiarities of former experiments could perhaps be based on such complications.

These examples should show how speculative considerations can help to develop a framework for empirical research. As long as we have no realistic navigation hypothesis we should try to minimize the possible number of theoretical models, and I believe that by this means the models themselves can stimulate the experimental approach.

### SUMMARY

Inexperienced homing pigeons released at places unfamiliar to them usually depart in directions which can be understood as the resultants of two components: one component is the direction to the home loft, the other is a preferred compass direction which is specific for the pigeons of a certain loft, and which can be different for consanguineous populations settled only 20–30 km apart from each other. The relative strength of the two components can vary over a wide range, so that in one case the compass component and in another case the homeward component predominates. In general, the initial headings become better oriented to the home loft with increasing distance from it.

The departure directions in later flights are influenced by the directions of displacement in former flights. Thus, in the headings of experienced pigeons a third component is involved.

The variability of the homing behaviour in time as well as the role of topographical features are briefly mentioned.

It is almost certain that displaced pigeons normally make use of the sun, because their departure diagrams show much more scatter under overcast skies than in sunny conditions. Furthermore, shifting of their circadian clock influences the departure headings in a way which is similar to the influence of such shifts on the direction choices in sun-compass training experiments.

Navigation, i.e. home orientation without searching at random and without use of known landmarks, can be demonstrated even in pigeons which have been kept in aviaries all the time before the experimental release. This is true only if the aviary was in a relatively open site and consisted mainly of wire mesh. There was no evidence of a connection between the movements of the displaced pigeons and the home loft if the aviary was surrounded by a wooden wall. Nor were the preferences improved if a gap was left either in the north or in the south of the wooden 'palisade'. Even if the upper part of the wall was made of glass, so that the birds could look in all directions when sitting on a perch, these birds were significantly more poorly oriented than the pigeons of the unscreened control aviaries. If, on the other hand, the aviary was covered by a roof and the pigeons could see only the lowest parts of the sky, these birds were well oriented to the home loft, although they had never seen the sun before release.

The theoretical aspects of pigeon homing are discussed. In the author's opinion none of the hypotheses brought forward up to the present is able to explain satisfactorily all the phenomena of homing behaviour which have been found in experimental studies. Suggestions are given for further considerations and investigations.

## ACKNOWLEDGEMENTS

I am much indebted to Dr H.Mittelstaedt for valuable discussions and to Professor H.C.Howland as well as to the editor, Dr D.W.Snow, for correcting the English manuscript.

## REFERENCES

BARLOW J.S. (1964) Inertial navigation as a basis for animal navigation. *J. Theor. Biol.* **6,** 76–117.

BELLROSE F.C. (1958) Celestial orientation by wild Mallards. *Bird-Banding* **29,** 75–90.

BELLROSE F.C. (1963) Orientation behavior of four species of waterfowl. *Auk* **80,** 257–289.

GRAUE L.C. (1963) The effect of phase shifts in the day-night cycle on pigeon homing at distances of less than one mile. *Ohio J. Science* **63,** 214–217.

GRAUE L.C. (1965) Experience effect on initial orientation in pigeon homing. *Anim. Behav.* **13,** 149–153.

GRAUE L.C. & PRATT J.G. (1959) Directional differences in pigeon homing in Sacramento, California and Cedar Rapids, Iowa. *Anim. Behav.* **7,** 201–208.

GRIFFIN D.R. & GOLDSMITH T.H. (1955) Initial flight directions of homing birds. *Biol. Bull.* **108,** 264–276.

HITCHCOCK H.B. (1952) Airplane observations of homing pigeons. *Proc. Amer. Phil. Soc.* **96,** 270–289.

HOFFMANN K. (1954) Versuche zu der im Richtungsfinden der Vögel enthaltenen Zeitschätzung. *Z. Tierpsychol.* **11,** 453–475.

HOFFMANN K. (1960) Experimental manipulation of the orientational clock in birds. *Cold Spring Harbor Symp. Quant. Biol.* **25,** 379–387.

# Status of our knowledge about pigeon homing

HOFFMANN K. (1965) Clock-mechanisms in celestial orientation of animals. In *Circadian Clocks*, pp. 426–441. Ed. J.Aschoff. North-Holland Publishing Co., Amsterdam.

KRAMER G. (1953) Wird die Sonnenhöhe bei der Heimfindeorientierung verwertet? *J. Ornith.* **94,** 201–219.

KRAMER G. (1957) Experiments on bird orientation and their interpretation. *Ibis* **99,** 196–227.

KRAMER G. (1959a) Über die Heimfindeleistung unter Sichtbegrenzung aufgewachsener Brieftauben. *Verh. Dtsch. Zool. Ges. Frankfurt a.M. 1958,* pp. 168–176.

KRAMER G. (1959b) Recent experiments on bird orientation. *Ibis* **101,** 399–416.

KRAMER G. (1961) Long-distance orientation. In *Biology and Comparative Physiology of Birds*, vol. II, pp. 341–371. Ed. A.J.Marshall. Academic Press, New York and London.

KRAMER G. & SAINT PAUL U. v. (1954) Das Heimkehrvermögen gekäfigter Brieftauben. *Ornith. Beob.* **51,** 4–12.

MATTHEWS G.V.T. (1951) The experimental investigation of navigation in homing pigeons. *J. exp. Biol.* **28,** 508–536.

MATTHEWS G.V.T. (1953) Sun navigation in homing pigeons. *J. exp. Biol.* **30,** 243–267.

MATTHEWS G.V.T. (1955) *Bird Navigation.* University Press, Cambridge.

MATTHEWS G.V.T. (1961) 'Nonsense' orientation in Mallard *Anas platyrhynchos* and its relation to experiments on bird navigation. *Ibis* **103a,** 211–230.

MATTHEWS G.V.T. (1963a) 'Nonsense' orientation as a population variant. *Ibis* **105,** 185–197.

MATTHEWS G.V.T. (1963b) The orientation of pigeons as affected by the learning of landmarks and by the distance of displacement. *Anim. Behav.* **11,** 310–317.

PENNYCUICK C.J. (1960) The physical basis of astro-navigation in birds: theoretical considerations. *J. exp. Biol.* **37,** 573–593.

PRATT J.G. & WALLRAFF H.G. (1958) Zwei-Richtungs-Versuche mit Brieftauben: Langstreckenflüge auf der Nord-Süd-Achse in Westdeutschland. *Z. Tierpsychol.* **15,** 332–339.

SCHMIDT-KOENIG K. (1958) Experimentelle Einflussnahme auf die 24-Stunden-Periodik bei Brieftauben und deren Auswirkungen unter besonderer Berücksichtigung des Heimfindevermögens. *Z. Tierpsychol.* **15,** 301–331.

SCHMIDT-KOENIG K. (1961) Die Sonne als Kompass im Heim-Orientierungssystem der Brieftauben. *Z. Tierpsychol.* **18,** 221–244.

SCHMIDT-KOENIG K. (1963a) Neuere Aspekte über die Orientierungsleistungen von Brieftauben. *Ergebn. Biol.* **26,** 286–297.

SCHMIDT-KOENIG K. (1963b) On the role of the loft, the distance and site of release in pigeon homing (the 'cross-loft experiment'). *Biol. Bull.* **125,** 154–164.

SCHMIDT-KOENIG K. (1965) Current problems in bird orientation. *Adv. Study Behav.* **1,** 217–278.

SCHMIDT-KOENIG K. (1966) Über die Entfernung als Parameter bei der Anfangsorientierung der Brieftaube. *Z. vergl. Physiol.* **52,** 33–55.

WALLRAFF H.G. (1959a) Über den Einfluss der Erfahrung auf das Heimfindevermögen von Brieftauben. *Z. Tierpsychol.* **16,** 424–444.

WALLRAFF H.G. (1959b) Örtlich und zeitlich bedingte Variabilität des Heimkehrverhaltens von Brieftauben. *Z. Tierpsychol.* **16,** 513–544.

WALLRAFF H.G. (1960a) Über Zusammenhänge des Heimkehrverhaltens von Brieftauben mit meteorologischen und geophysikalischen Faktoren. *Z. Tierpsychol.* **17,** 82–113.

# Hans G. Wallraff

WALLRAFF H.G. (1960b) Does celestial navigation exist in animals? *Cold Spring Harbor Symp. Quant. Biol.* **25**, 451–461.

WALLRAFF H.G. (1965) Über das Heimfindevermögen von Brieftauben mit durchtrennten Bogengängen. *Z. vergl. Physiol.* **50**, 313–330.

WALLRAFF H.G. (1966a) Über die Heimfindeleistungen von Brieftauben nach Haltung in verschiedenartig abgeschirmten Volieren. *Z. vergl. Physiol.* **52**, 215–259.

WALLRAFF H.G. (1966b) Über die Anfangsorientierung von Brieftauben unter geschlossener Wolkendecke. *J. Ornith.* **107**, 326–336.

WALLRAFF H.G. (1967) Über die Flugrichtungen verfrachteter Brieftauben in Abhängigkeit vom Heimatort und vom Ort der Freilassung. (In preparation.)

YEAGLEY H.L. (1947) A preliminary study of a physical basis of bird navigation. *J. Appl. Phys.* **18**, 1035–1063.

# Report of the Standing Committee on Ornithological Nomenclature of the International Ornithological Congress, 1963–66

The present members of the Standing Committee on Ornithological Nomenclature of the International Ornithological Congress (s.c.o.n.) were elected in March 1963 by the Permanent Executive Committee in correspondence with the President of the Congress. The s.c.o.n. now consists of Professor Jean Dorst, Muséum National d'Histoire Naturelle, Paris; Mr Eugene Eisenmann, The American Museum of Natural History, New York; Dr Finn Salomonsen, Universitetets Zoologiske Museum, Copenhagen; Professor Dr Karel Voous, Zoölogisch Museum, Amsterdam, and Dr Charles Vaurie (Chairman), American Museum of Natural History, New York. This committee has merely advisory functions. The power to decide nomenclatural questions and to interpret and modify the application of the Code of Zoological Nomenclature is vested in the International Commission for Zoological Nomenclature.

The first action of the s.c.o.n. was to publish an announcement in the leading ornithological journals that it was ready to function. Ornithologists were invited to submit proposals for advice before they were forwarded for action to the International Commission on Zoological Nomenclature, and to request any other help or advice on nomenclatural questions. The key sentence of the announcement was that 'the Standing Committee endorses the principle of the Preamble of the Code of Zoological Nomenclature that well-established names should be preserved'.

The second action of the s.c.o.n. was to redraft and submit again to the International Commission certain proposals reported at the International Ornithological Congress at Helsinki, which had been submitted to the Commission by the then chairman of the s.c.o.n., Dr Salomonsen, but which had not been acted upon by the International Commission:

(a) Suppression for all nomenclatural purposes of the 1758 edition of Moehring's *Geslachten der Vogelen*.

(b) Validation of four specific names (long in general use) in Tunstall's *Ornithologia Britannica*, 1771: *Falco peregrinus, Falco aesalon, Alauda rubescens* (currently used in the combination *Anthus spinoletta rubescens*) and *Motacilla cinerea*.

At present writing action has not yet been taken by the International Commission, but we believe these proposals will be approved.

The Secretariat of the International Commission has sent to the s.c.o.n. for comment various proposals dealing with the nomenclature of birds submitted to the Commission.

A somewhat controversial proposal, relating to various names of tanagers, including the family name, had been submitted by Drs Mayr, Stresemann, Miller and Storer, in substitution for a previous proposal discussed, and in part vigorously opposed, at the Congress in Helsinki, which had been submitted by an earlier s.c.o.n. (see *Proc. XII Internat. Orn. Congr.* 1960, pp. 30, 43).

The present s.c.o.n. unanimously recommended approval of the latest application, with the exception of one item. The items recommended for approval were:

1. Suppression of the generic names *Tanagra* Linnaeus, 1764 and *Tanagra* Linnaeus, 1766, because of their different applications, and because of the confusing similarity to *Tangara* Brisson, 1760, a genus in the same family. The suppression of *Tanagra* Linnaeus, 1764 would validate and restore the synonym *Euphonia* Desmarest, 1806, long used for this genus.

2. Placing the family name Thraupidae Wetmore and Miller, 1926 on the Official List of Family Names and suppressing the name Tanagridae Bonaparte, 1838, placing it on the Official Index.

3. Placing the specific names *Tanagra ornata* Sparrman, 1789 (currently used in the combination *Thraupis ornata*) and *Tanagra episcopus* Linnaeus, 1766 (currently used in the combination *Thraupis episcopus*) on the Official List of Specific Names, and rejecting the action of Gyldenstolpe in 1945, as first reviser, in preferring *Loxia virens* Linnaeus, 1766 to the long-used *Tanagra episcopus* Linnaeus, 1766 of the same publication.

The s.c.o.n. opposed so much of the application as sought to place the specific name *Euphonia olivacea* Desmarest, 1806 on the Official List, replacing the specific name *Euphona minuta* Cabanis, 1849 (currently used in the combination *Tanagra minuta*), which latter specific name has been universally employed in all ornithological literature for over 30 years. The s.c.o.n. asked instead (as had its predecessor s.c.o.n.) that the International Commission exercise its plenary power to place the specific name *Euphona minuta* on the Official List and *Euphonia olivacea* on the Official Index of Specific Names.

A proposal introduced by Drs Mayr, Serventy and Keast requesting exercise of the plenary power to validate *Cacatua* Brisson, 1760, replacing *Kakatoe* Cuvier, 1800, was submitted to the s.c.o.n. The s.c.o.n., after elaborate investigation, found that considerable current competing usage existed as between the names *Cacatua* and *Kakatoe*, that during most of the nineteenth century the prevailing name had been *Cacatua*, with authorship usually credited to Vieillot, 1817, that *Cacatua* was not in fact a generic name in Brisson's *Ornithologie* and the International Commission had repeatedly held that of the names in that work only the 115 expressly designated as genera were available. The s.c.o.n. concluded that to give Brissonian generic status to the name *Cacatua* would create a dangerous precedent, for many other names long ago rejected had equivalent Brissonian origin.

In an effort to settle the conflict of usage in a manner that would avoid upsetting other names, the s.c.o.n. suggested that *Cacatua* Vieillot, 1817 be adopted as a *nomen conservandum*. This was approved both by the proponents of the Brissonian name and by vote of the Royal Australasian Check-list Committee, which had long been the chief supporter of *Kakatoe* Cuvier. An application to this effect was made to the International Commission.

None of the applications mentioned pending before the International Commission, some for more than 3 years, have yet been the subject of published decision.

Shortly before his death, Dr James P. Chapin filed an application to validate the generic name *Turacus* Cuvier, 1800 and to suppress *Tauraco* Kluk, 1779. In view of the fact that this proposal is more controversial than most, and that some ornithologists had expressed opposition, the s.c.o.n. requested and obtained deferment of consideration by the International Commission until after the matter could be discussed by interested ornithologists at this Congress. (See Postscript, p. 363.)

The s.c.o.n., represented by Vaurie and Eisenmann, participated in the open meetings of the International Committee and at the Section on Nomenclature of the International Zoological Congress, held at Washington in August 1963. The Congress adopted an amendment to the new Code, introduced by the s.c.o.n., which changed Article 31 to a recommendation, deleted Article 31(a) and amended Article 32, thereby eliminating the Code provision requiring species-group names based on human names to have specified genitive endings and compelling emendation if they did not. This amendment preserved long-established usage and avoided the need of much futile emendation in ornithology.

The new Code of Nomenclature has effected important changes in regard to family-group names, greatly altering ornithological usage. Contrary to past practice, priority is to apply to family-group names (i.e. names of superfamilies, families, subfamilies and tribes); these are deemed co-ordinate and are available even if introduced with an ending different from that now conventional. Moreover, while family-group names are based on the generic name of the type-genus, a change of name of the type-genus because of the substitution of a senior synonym after 1960 will not work a change in the family-group name [Article 40]. In the interest of conservation the Code provides: (1) that where the application of priority to a family-group name 'would upset general usage' application shall be made for decision to the International Commission (presumably without need for invoking the plenary power) [Article 23(d) (ii)]; and (2) that where a family-group name was changed prior to 1961 to correspond with a change of name of the type-genus and such change has won general acceptance, the changed family-group name is to be maintained [Article 40(a)].

The S.C.O.N. proposed to prepare a list of generally accepted family-group names in ornithology to submit for inclusion in the Official List of Family Names maintained by the International Commission, so as to avoid nomenclatural upsets consequent on the application of priority to family names. Determining such priority presents a very difficult bibliographic problem, because it has not been customary to list family-group synonymies in ornithology and because there are a great number of old names for suprageneric groups, introduced without modern conventional endings, that may possibly rank as family-group names under the new Code, Article 11(e). The priority of names, and even more often of authorship and date, may be affected. Article 23(b) of the Code, the statute of limitations, helps in eliminating names wholly unused in the past 50 years, but ascertaining that fact itself involves bibliographic work and often nomenclatural interpretation. Moreover, the Secretariat of the International Commission has apparently been of the view that family-group names to qualify for inclusion on the Official List must be supported by an application including data as to authorship and earliest publication of the name.

The members of the S.C.O.N. are not in a position to undertake personally the extensive bibliographic research needed for ensuring correct first authorship and date. The S.C.O.N. is of the view that, to conform with the purpose of the Code provisions, the International Commission should accept some simplified method for placing on the Official List as *nomina conservanda*, generally accepted family-group names, regardless of who may ultimately be credited as the earliest author and what may be the earliest date. Meanwhile, considering the Code provisions mentioned, the S.C.O.N. strongly recommends that, absent some controlling action by the International Commission, ornithologists should continue to employ the well-established family-group names and should decline to adopt individual proposals for change of such names which are based merely on supposed priority. The Code plainly contemplates that for family-group names adopted before 1961, general usage, rather than priority, is the primary consideration.

The terms of the present members of the S.C.O.N. expire upon the close of the present Congress, but they can be reappointed if that is desirable. The present S.C.O.N. was appointed by the current President of the Congress, pursuant to power delegated by the Executive Committee at the last Congress at Ithaca. The previous S.C.O.N. was elected at Helsinki by the members of the Congress attending the session on nomenclature at which the predecessor S.C.O.N. reported.

Respectfully submitted,

Standing Committee on Ornithological Nomenclature of the International Ornithological Congress

JEAN DORST                     FINN SALOMONSEN
EUGENE EISENMANN          KAREL VOOUS
            CHARLES VAURIE (Chairman)

POSTSCRIPT

At the meeting on nomenclature of the XIV International Ornithological Congress, on July 25, 1966, at Oxford, England, at which Eugene Eisenmann acted as Chairman, the matter of using the plenary power to substitute *Turacus* Cuvier, 1800 for *Tauraco* Kluck, 1799 was fully discussed. It was the almost unanimous opinion of the workers on African birds that in view of the general current use of *Tauraco*, the interest of stability required denial of the application to exercise the plenary power. After this meeting the S.C.O.N. voted unanimously to recommend to the International Commission that the application to place *Tauraco* on the Official Index be denied and that said name be placed on the

# Report on Ornithological Nomenclature

Official List. Dr Vaurie, who was not present, had previously submitted a memorandum, read at the meeting, expressing this view.

There was also considerable discussion of the effect of the new Code of Zoological Nomenclature on family-group names in ornithology. It was the unanimous consensus that in view of the policy to preserve established family-group names expressed in the Code and the lack of synonymies of such names in ornithology, the International Commission should be urged to place family-group names on the Official List on the basis of some simplified method not requiring the bibliographic research needed to trace the first author and publication of a family-group name for the taxon.

The matter of the many years delay by the International Commission in acting on the several ornithological proposals was discussed. Suggestions were made as to methods by which action on such proposals might be accelerated. One speaker urged that the Secretariat be required to comply with the rules of the Commission as to sending out matters for early vote, which he said had been disregarded.

EUGENE EISENMANN
Acting Chairman, S.C.O.N.

# Proposal for an internationally agreed world list of birds

In opening a discussion on this subject on July 28, Dr Lack said that any ornithologist who is not a taxonomist must be bewildered at the present time by the great variations found in different ornithological publications in regard to nomenclature, sequence and taxonomic status; families, subfamilies, genera and species are all affected. Hence there is a real need among biologists, among editors of journals and local lists, among authors of bird books on particular regions, among museum workers and among amateur ornithologists generally, for a stable reference list. Peters's *Check-List*, which would otherwise have served, is only in part published, while the early volumes are well known to be out of date; and no other list has more than individual authority and none refers to the whole world. Dr Lack therefore proposed that the International Congress should set up a committee to consider publishing an internationally agreed world list of birds, including the orders, families, subfamilies, genera and species, but not the subspecies.

Three questions, he said, need discussion. First, do we really want such a world list, and if so, of what general kind? Secondly, do we want it in any way authorized by the Congress, and if so how? Thirdly, if these points are sufficiently agreed, how do we elect a committee to draw up the list?

He continued that classification is always in large part arbitrary and conventional, however sound the biological background. This applies especially to the sequence in which the species are listed, and also to the treatment of the inevitable intermediate cases at every taxonomic level. The vast majority of ornithologists do not mind what sequence is used provided that it is reasonably stable. At the same time, classification should so far as possible denote affinities, hence periodic change is essential. This means that, if a list committee is set up, it must be kept in being to bring out periodic revisions. Also, if such a list is to be effective, it must be produced (and later revised) speedily and cheaply. Hence it should include only the essential minimum information. The work could be considerably accelerated if sections of the list could be treated by regional or other committees. For instance, a committee of the Seabird Group has recently proposed some sensible changes in the nomenclature of the Procellariiformes. Again, no European would wish to interfere with American views on exclusively American families.

365

# Proposal for a world list of birds

The project necessarily involves considerable difficulties. Two of them are: (1) the relationship of such a list to Peters's *Check-List* and (2) the present existence of two main alternative sequences for the passerine families. Given good will, but only with expansive good will, can these be overcome. But those taxonomists who feel heated on either side of the current schism concerning the sequence of passerine families ought to have regard to the 99 per cent of other ornithologists who do not mind which sequence is used provided that it is the same one. Similar considerations hold for the three very different sequences recently published for the species in the family Turdidae, by Ripley, Vaurie and White respectively. In ways such as this, Dr Lack said that he thought the taxonomists were letting other ornithologists down badly, and that it should be realized that almost the whole of these and similar disputes concern arbitrary convention, not biological principles. Where biological principles are at stake, all are agreed that taxonomic changes are not merely inevitable but are to be welcomed, but this does not apply to most of the differences found between the different published lists of birds in current use, especially those relating to sequence, for which, moreover, no justification has usually been published.

The problem of the authorization of a world list is very difficult. Without some form of international backing, it is almost certain that such a list would not be accepted sufficiently widely to justify the immense work involved. At the same time, if the authorization were too strong, there would be danger of freezing nomenclature, or at least of too conservative an approach, while none of us wish to be 'authorized' into accepting bad nomenclature. Dr Lack concluded that in his view the biggest single difficulty is the enormous amount of work that would be entailed, which would certainly not be worth undertaking unless or until public ornithological opinion were strongly behind such a scheme.

Many ornithologists took part in the subsequent discussion, from which it became clear that there was a considerable divergence of views. In particular, while many, though not all, of those present welcomed the idea of a world list, a much smaller proportion accepted the need that it should be 'authorized', and the general view was probably that, if the Congress set up a committee to publish what might be called simply a 'World List', this would be sufficient. (With this point, Dr Lack agreed.) The chief opponents of the scheme were various North American taxonomists and systematists, but in this connection it has to be kept in mind that most of the world's taxonomists now work in North America; and there were various taxonomists from other regions who agreed with them. Hence, in part the division came between working taxonomists, who felt that we do not yet have sufficient knowledge to justify such a list, and other ornithologists, who are badly in need of it; and though these other ornithologists are in the great majority, they require taxonomists to help in the list's preparation. There was widespread agreement on two details of the form that such a list should take if it were published, namely that it should include an extremely brief statement of the range of each species, and that space should be left for the usual vernacular name, so that it could be added if the list were published in different languages.

Through lack of time, the discussion had to be closed when many others still wished to speak. In conclusion Dr Lack felt that there did not yet seem to be sufficiently strong or wide agreement to justify putting a resolution to the Congress to urge the preparation of such a list now. He hoped, however, that seeds had been sown and that the subject would come up for discussion in a later congress. It was subsequently learned that, in part stimulated by the inconclusive termination of this discussion, various leading European ornithologists were making proposals for an agreed European list, and that in this connection they were entering into correspondence with the editors of the North American checklist.

# International Ornithological Committee

At the meeting of the International Ornithological Committee on July 29, 1966 on the occasion of the Fourteenth International Congress at Oxford, it was decided to replace not only those members who had expressed a desire to withdraw but also those who had not attended the last two Congresses except in those cases where attendance was made impossible by illness, etc.

Consequently the composition of the Committee is now as given below. Names in italics are those of new members of the Committee; names in parentheses are those of members of the 1962–66 Committee who have now been replaced; those with an * in addition have been replaced by a representative of another country.

ARGENTINA    Navas J.R., Mus. Arg. de Ciencias Nat., Buenos Aires
Olrog C.Chr., Instituto Miguél Lillo, S.M. de Tucumán

AUSTRALIA    Marshall A.J., Dept. of Zoology and Comparative Physiology, Monash University, Clayton, Victoria
Serventy D., C.S.I.R.O., University of W. Aust., Nedlands, W. Australia
(Frith H.J.)
*Keast J.A.*, Dept. of Biology, Queen's University, Kingston, Ontario, Canada

AUSTRIA    Bauer K., Naturhistorisches Museum, P.O. Box 417, A 1014 Vienna
Rokitansky G., A 1130 Wien 13, Jodlgasse 7/7

BRAZIL    Sick H., Museu Nacional, Quinta da Bôa Vista, Rio de Janeiro

CANADA    Godfrey W.E., Curator of Ornithology, National Museum of Canada, Ottawa, Ontario
Lloyd H., 582 Mariposa Avenue, Rockliffe Park, Ottawa 2, Ontario

CHILE    Philippi R.A., Tobalaba 157, Santiago

COLOMBIA    Borrero J.I., Inst. de Ciencias Nat., Univ. Nac. de Colombia, Bogotá

CZECHOSLOVAKIA    Černý W., Viničná 7, Praha 2, Charles-University, Faculty of Science, Dept. of Vertebčatá Zoology, Č.S.S.R.

# International Ornithological Committee

DENMARK      Løppenthin B., Torvevej 14, Skovlunde
Paludan K., Jagt-og Skovbrugsmuseet, Hörsholm
Salomonsen F., Zoologisk Museum, Universitetsparken 15, Copenhagen Ø

FINLAND      von Haartman L., Dept. of Zoology, Univ. of Helsinki, Helsinki
*Hilden O.*, Dept. of Zoology, Univ. of Helsinki, Helsinki

FRANCE      Berlioz J., Muséum National d'Histoire Naturelle, 55 Rue de Buffon, Paris V$^e$
Dorst J., Muséum National d'Histoire Naturelle, Mammifères et Oiseaux, 55 Rue de Buffon, Paris V$^e$
Etchécopar R-D., C.R.M.M.O., 55 Rue de Buffon, Paris V$^e$
Jouanin C., Muséum National d'Histoire Naturelle, Laboratoire d'Ornithologie, 55 Rue de Buffon, Paris V$^e$
Prévost J., Muséum National d'Histoire Naturelle, Laboratoire d'Ornithologie, 55 Rue de Buffon, Paris V$^e$
Roux F., Muséum National d'Histoire Naturelle, Mammifères et Oiseaux, 55 Rue de Buffon, Paris V$^e$
(Bourlière F.B.)
(Hue F.)
(Heim de Balzac H.)
*Blondel J.*, Station biologique de La Tour du Valat, 13 Le Sambuc
*Ferry C.*, 25 Place Darcy, 21 Dijon
*Erard C.*, C.R.M.M.O., Muséum National d'Histoire Naturelle, 55 Rue de Buffon, Paris V$^e$

GERMANY      Aschoff J., Max-Planck-Inst. f. Verhaltensphysiologie, 8131 Erling-Andechs/Oberbayern
Drost R., Danziger Str. 25, Wilhelmshaven
Goethe F., 294 Wilhelmshaven, Vogelwarte Helgoland, Kirchreihe 19B
Kuhk R., Vogelwarte Radolfzell, 7761 Schloss Möggingen bei Radolfzell
Löhrl H., Max-Planck-Inst. f. Verhaltensphysiologie, Vogelwarte Radolfzell, 7761 Möggingen
Meise W., Hamburg 13, Von-Melle-Park 10, Zool. Staatsinstitut und Museum
Niethammer G., 53 Bonn, Koblenzerstr. 162
Schüz E., 714 Ludwigsburg, Paulinenstr. 39
Stresemann E., Berlin 45, Kamillen-Str. 28
(Koehler O.)
*Immelmann, K.*, Zool. Inst., Pockelsstr. 10a, Braunschweig

GREAT BRITAIN      Barclay-Smith, Miss P., 51 Warwick Avenue, London, W.9

# International Ornithological Committee

Fisher J., Ashton Manor, Northants
Lack D., Edward Grey Institute, Botanic Garden, High Street, Oxford
(MacDonald J.D.)
Moreau R., Michaeldene, Sutton St Nicholas, Hereford
Mountfort G., Plovers Meadow, Possingworth Park, Blackboys, Sussex
Nicholson E.M., 13 Upper Cheyne Row, Chelsea, London, S.W.3
Scott P., The Wildfowl Trust, Slimbridge, Glos
Thomson A.L., 42 Girdwood Road, Southfields, London, S.W.18
Thorpe W.H., 9 Wilberforce Road, Cambridge
Wynne-Edwards V.C., Marischal College, University of Aberdeen,
Aberdeen
*Tinbergen N.*, Dept. of Zoology, Parks Road, Oxford

HUNGARY
Keve A., Hungarian Institute of Ornithology, Madartani Intezet, Budapest II, Garas u.14

ICELAND
Gudmundsson F., Museum of Natural History, P.O. Box 532, Reykjavik

INDIA
Abdulali H., c/o Faiz and Co., 75 Abdul Rehman Street, Bombay 3
Ali S., 33 Pali Hill, Bandra, Bombay 50
Biswas B., Zoological Survey of India, Indian Museum, Calcutta 13

INDONESIA
*Somadikarta S.*, Museum Zoologicum Bogoriense, Bogor

ITALY
Frugis S., Belfiore 11, Milano
Moltoni E., Museo Civico di Storia Naturale di Milano, Corso Venezia 55,
Milano

JAPAN
Kuroda Nagahisa, Yamashina Inst. for Ornithology, 49 Nanpeidai-machi,
Shibuya-ku, Tokyo
Yamashina Y., 49 Nanpeidai-machi, Shibuya-ku, Tokyo
(Kuroda Nagamichi)*

KENYA
*North M.E.W.*, Box 8225, Nairobi, Kenya
(Williams J.G.W.)

MALAYA
(Loke)

NETHERLANDS
Bierman W., 18 Lorentzplein, Haarlem
Brouwer G.A., de Genestetlaan 32, Bilthoven
Kluyver H.N., Van Goghstraat 11, Arnhem
Voous K.H., c/o Zoologisch Museum, Plantage Middenlaan 53, Amsterdam C

# International Ornithological Committee

NEW ZEALAND     Falla R.A., Dominion Museum, Private Bag, Wellington
(Gibb J.A.)
*Kinsky F.*, c/o Dominion Museum, Private Bag, Wellington

NORWAY     Holgersen H., Stavanger Museum, Stavanger
(Hagen Y.)*

PERU     Koepcke M., Casa Humboldt, Casilla 5129, Miraflores, Lima

PHILIPPINES     Rabor D.S., Dept. of Biology, Silliman University, Dumaguete City, Negros Oriental

POLAND     *Rydzewski W.*, Laboratory of Ornithology, Wrocław, Sienkiewicza 21

RHODESIA     Smithers R.H.N., National Museums Administration, P.O. Box 8540, Causeway

S. AFRICA     Niven C., Amanzi, Uitenhage, C.P.
Vincent J., I.C.B.P., c/o I.U.C.N., 1110 Morges, Switzerland

SPAIN     Bernis F., Castellana 80, Madrid 6
Valverde J.A., Estación Biológica de Doñana, Paraguay 1, Sevilla

SWEDEN     Curry-Lindahl K., Zoological Dept., Nordiska Museum und Skansen, Stockholm
Horstadius S., Zoological Institute, Uppsala
Rudebeck G., Zoologiska Institutionen, Lund

SWITZERLAND     Géroudet P., Avenue de Champel 37, 1206 Genève
Schifferli A., Schweiz. Vogelwarte, 6204 Sempach
(Hoffman L.)
*Glutz von Blotzheim U.*, Schweiz. Vogelwarte, 6204 Sempach
*Sutter, E.*, Naturhistorisches Museum, Augustinergasse 2, 4000 Basel

U.S.A.     Amadon D., American Museum of Natural History, Central Park West, New York, N.Y., 10024
Deignan H.G., Boulevard de la Forêt 24A, 1012 Lausanne/Pully, Switzerland
Delacour J., American Museum of Natural History, Central Park West, New York, N.Y. 10024
Lowery G.H., Museum of Natural Sciences, Louisiana State University, Baton Rouge 3, Louisiana
Mayr E., Museum of Comp. Zoology, Cambridge, Mass. 02138

# International Ornithological Committee

Peterson R.T., Neck Road, Old Lyme, Connecticut

Rand A.L., Chicago Natural History Museum, Roosevelt Road & Lake Shore Drive, Chicago Illinois 60605

Ripley S.D., Smithsonian Institution, Washington 25, D.C.

Sibley C.G., Peabody Museum of Natural History, Yale University, New Haven, Connecticut

Storer R.W., Museum of Zoology, University of Michigan, Ann Arbor, Michigan 48104

Wetmore A., Smithsonian Institution, Washington D.C. 20560 (Chapin)

Friedmann H., Los Angeles Co. Museum., Los Angeles 7, California (Miller)

*Eisenmann E.*, American Museum of Natural History, Central Park West, New York, N.Y. 10024

*Farner D.S.*, Dept. of Zoology, Univ. of Washington, Seattle, Washington 98105

U.S.S.R.

Dementiev G., University Zoological Museum, Herzenstr. 6, Moscow K-9

Gladkov N.A., Univ. Zool. Museum, Herzenstr. 6, Moscow K-9

Ivanov A.I., Zoological Inst. of the Academy of Sciences, Leningrad B-164

*Portenko L.*, Leningrad P-79, Zoologischesky Perevlok 1, App 28

VENEZUELA

Phelps W.H., Colección Ornitológica Phelps, Apartado 2009, Caracas

# Official Delegates

ARGENTINA
Asociación Ornitológica del Plata: Prof. C.C.Olrog
Instituto Miguel Lillo, Tucumán: Prof. C.C.Olrog

AUSTRALIA
Australian Museum and Royal Zoological Society of New South Wales:
Mr J.Disney
Department of Fisheries and Fauna, West Australia: Mr H.Shugg
National Museum of Victoria: Mr A.McEvey
Royal Australasian Ornithologists' Union: Prof. Allen Keast

AUSTRIA
Natural History Museum, Wien: Dr G.Rokitansky
Österreichische Vogelwarte: Dr K.Bauer

BELGIUM
Société d'Études ornothologiques 'AVES', Liège: Mr P.Collette
Société d'Études ornithologiques 'AVES', Bruxelles: Mr P.Devillers
Ornitologia Rondo Esperantlingua: Mr Antoon De Roo

BRAZIL
Museu de Biologia Prof. Mello Leitão: Prof. Augusto Ruschi
Museu Nacional 'do Brasil', Rio de Janeiro: Prof. Augusto Ruschi

CANADA
National Museum of Canada, Ottawa: Mr W.Earl Godfrey
Canadian Wildlife Service, Prairie Migratory Bird Research Centre: Mr
A.Dzubin, Dr W.W.H.Gunn
The Federation of Ontario Naturalists: Mrs D.J.Speirs, Dr J.M.Speirs
The Margaret Nice Ornithological Club: Mrs D.J.Speirs, Dr J.M.Speirs
National Research Council of Canada: Dr W.W.H.Gunn
Province of Quebec Society for the Protection of Birds, Inc.: Hon.
Justice G.H.Montgomery
Redpath Museum: Mr Henri Ouellet

CENTRAL AFRICA
Tervuren Museum of Central Africa: Mr Antoon De Roo

CZECHOSLOVAKIA
Charles University, Prague: Dr Walter Černý
Czechoslovak Academy of Sciences: Dr Karel Hudec

DENMARK
Dansk Ornithologisk Forening: Prof. Finn Salomonsen
Vildtbiologisk Station, Kalø: Mr A.H.Joensen

ENGLAND
Avicultural Society, London: Miss Phyllis Barclay-Smith
'British Birds': Mr I.J.Ferguson-Lees

# Official Delegates

British Broadcasting Corporation Natural History Unit: Mr J.Boswall

British Ornithologists' Union, London: Sir Hugh Elliott, Prof. V.C. Wynne-Edwards

British Trust for Ornithology, Tring: Mr R.C.Homes, Mr K.Williamson, Mr D.Wilson

The Edward Grey Institute of Field Ornithology, Oxford: Dr David Lack, Dr C.M.Perrins

I.C.B.P.: Prof. W.H.Thorpe

The Ministry of Agriculture: Dr R.K.Murton, Mr E.N.Wright

The Norfolk Naturalists' Trust: Mr Philip Wayre

The Ornamental Pheasant Trust, Witchingham: Mr Philip Wayre

The Royal Society for the Protection of Birds, Sandy: Mr P.Conder, Mr F.Hamilton, Mr D.Lea, Mr P.Olney

The Severn Wildfowl Trust, Slimbridge: Dr Janet Kear, Mr Peter Scott, Dr G.V.T.Matthews

FINLAND

Finnish Ornithological Society: Dr Lars von Haartman

Zoological Museum, Bird Ringing Department, Helsinki: Mr G.Nordström

FRANCE

Centre d'études ornithologiques de Bourgogne: Dr C.Ferry, Mr B.Frochot

C.R.M.M.O.: Mr A.R.Dupuy, Dr R-D.Etchécopar

I.N.R.A.: Dr Jean Prévost

Ligue Française pour la Protection des Oiseaux: MMe M.Avery de la Salle, Baron Antoine Reille

Muséum National d'Histoire Naturelle, Paris: Prof. Jacques Berlioz, Prof. Jean Dorst, Dr Jean Prévost

Société des Sciences Naturelles de l'Ouest de la France: Dr S.Kowalski

Société Ornithologique de France: Mr C.Jouanin

GERMANY

Deutsche Demokratische Republik: Dr Burkhard Stephan

Deutscher Bund für Vogelschutz e-V, Frankfurt am Main: Dr H.Bruns, Dr S.O.Pfeifer

Deutsche Ornithologen-Gesellschaft: Prof. Erwin Stresemann

Institut für Vogelforschung, Wilhelmshaven: Dr Friedrich Goethe

Max-Planck Institut f. Verhaltensphysiologie: Mr E.Gwinner

Museum A. Koenig, Bonn: Prof. Günther Niethammer

Niedersächsisches Landesmuseum, Hannover: Prof. Fritz H.Steiniger

Ornithologische Gesellschaft in Bayern, München: Prof. Walter Wüst

Senckersberg-Museum, Frankfurt: Dr Joachim Steinbacher

Senckenbergische Naturforschende Gesellschaft, Frankfurt: Dr Joachim Steinbacher

Staatliche Museum für Naturkunde in Stuttgart: Prof. Dr Ernst Schüz

# Official Delegates

Vogelschutzstation Braunschweig: Dr R.Berndt
Vogelschutzwarte Frankfurt/Main: Dr S.O.Pfeifer
Vogelschutzwarte für Hessen, Rheinland-Pfalz und Saarland: Dr Werner Keil
Vogelschutzwarte Niedersachsen, Hannover: Dr Rudolph Berndt
Vogelwarte Radolfzell: Dr Rudolph Kuhk, Dr Gerhardt Zink
Zoologisches Institut der Universität Erlangen, Nürnberg: Dr Erwin Tretzel
Zoologisches Staatsinstitut und Zoologisches Museum, Hamburg: Dr Günther Timmermann

HUNGARY     The Academy of Sciences, Budapest: Dr Peter Szöke

ICELAND     Museum of Natural History, Reykjavik: Dr Finnur Gudmundsson

INDIA     The Government of Orissa: Mr S.Jayakar, Dr Helen Spurway

IRELAND     Department of Lands, Game and Wildlife Branch, Dublin: Mr Fergus O'Gorman
Irish Society for the Protection of Birds: Mr J.Temple Lang
Ulster Museum: Mr C.D.Deane

ITALY     Museo Civico di Storia Naturale di Milano: Dr Edgardo Moltoni

INDONESIA     National Biological Institute, Bogor: Dr S.Somadikarta

NETHERLANDS     Institute for Ecological Research, Department of Bird Migration: Mr Anton Cavé, Dr. A.C.Perdeck
*International Council for Bird Preservation, Netherlands Section: Mr Karel Bezemer
*Nederlandse Ornithologische Unie: Dr Willem Bierman
Rivon, States Institute for Nature Conservation Research: Dr M.Bijleveld, Mr Jan Rooth
Royal Netherlands Air Force: Mr Hans Blokpoel
The University of Groningen: Prof. G.Baerends
Zoölogische Museum, Amsterdam: Mr Jan Wattel

NEW ZEALAND     Ornithological Society of New Zealand, Inc.: Mr F.C.Kinsky, Mr L.W.McCaskill
Royal New Zealand Forest and Bird Protection Society: Mr L.W. McCaskill

NIGERIA     Nigerian Ornithologists' Society: Mr C.H.Fry

# Official Delegates

| | |
|---|---|
| NORWAY | Stavanger Museum: Mr H.Holgersen |
| POLAND | Polish Academy of Sciences, Warsaw: Dr Jan Pinowski, Prof. W.Rydzewski |
| RHODESIA | The Rhodesian Ornithological Society: Mr Rudyerd Boulton |
| RUMANIA | The Academy of the R.S.R., Bucharest: Dr Ludwig Rudescu |
| SCOTLAND | Royal Scottish Museum, Edinburgh: Mr Ian Lyster<br>Scottish Ornithologists' Club, Edinburgh: Dr Ian Pennie |
| SOUTH AFRICA | The Percy Fitzpatrick Institute of African Ornithology, Cape Town: Mrs Mary K.Rowan, Prof. J.M.Winterbottom<br>South African Ornithological Society: Mrs Cecily K.Niven |
| SWEDEN | Naturhistoriska Museet, Slottsskogen, Göteborg: Mr S.H.Mathiasson<br>Nordiska Museet und Skansen, Stockholm: Dr Kai Curry-Lindahl<br>Ottenby Bird Station: Dr R.Edberg<br>Sveriges Ornitologiska Förening, Stockholm: Prof. Sven Hörstadius, Dr G.Rudebeck<br>Sveriges Radio and T.V.: Mr Jan Lindblad<br>Swedish Bird Ringing Office, Stockholm: Mr Sten Österlöf<br>University of Stockholm, Ethological Department: Mr Jan Lindblad |
| SWITZERLAND | International Council for Bird Preservation, Morges: Colonel Jack Vincent<br>Ornithologische Gesellschaft of Zürich: Mr W.Gubler<br>Société romande pour l'étude et la protection des oiseaux: Dr Paul Géroudet<br>Schweizerische Vogelwarte, Sempach and Government of Switzerland: Dr A.Schifferli |
| U.S.S.R. | Academy of Sciences, Estonia: Prof. Dr. Eric Kumari |
| U.S.A. | Alaska Department of Fish and Game: Dr. R.Weeden<br>The Academy of Natural Sciences of Philadelphia: Mr James Bond<br>The American Museum of Natural History: Dr Dean Amadon, Mr Stuart Keith<br>American Ornithologists' Union: Dr Dean Amadon, Miss Hazel Philbrick<br>Audubon Naturalist Society of the Central Atlantic States, Inc.: Miss S.Briggs<br>Bureau of Sport Fisheries and Wildlife, U.S. Dept. of the Interior: Dr John Aldrich |

# Official Delegates

Carnegie Museum: Dr Kenneth C.Parkes
California Academy of Sciences: Dr Robert T.Orr
Chicago Natural History Museum: Dr A.L.Rand, Mr M.A.Traylor
Chicago Ornithological Society: Mrs Isabel B.Wasson
The Conservation Foundation, Washington: Dr F.Fraser Darling
Cornell University Laboratory of Ornithology: Dr D.A.Lancaster, Col.
   D.McChesney, Dr O.S.Pettingill
Earlham College, Dept. of Biology, Indiana: Dr Cameron E.Gifford
Federation of New York State Bird Clubs, Inc.: Miss Margaret Rusk
Golden Gate Audubon Society: Miss Aileen Pierson
Hawk Mountain Sanctuary Association: Dr Maurice Broun
Iowa Ornithologists' Union: Dr Robert F.Vane
Kent State University: Dr R.W.Dexter
Linnaean Society of New York: Mr Eugene Eisenmann
Maryland Ornithological Society: Mrs R.D.Cole
Massachusetts Audubon Society: Mr James Baird, Mrs W.Kellogg,
   Mr A.H.Morgan
Michigan Audubon Society: Dr Charles T.Black
Michigan Department of Conservation: Dr Geoge A.Ammann
Moore Laboratory of Zoology, Occidental College: Dr J.W.Hardy
National Academy of Sciences—National Research Council: Dr Ernst
   Mayr, Dr Donald S. Farner.
National Audubon Society: Mr R.C.Clement
New Jersey Agricultural Experimental Station: Dr P.Granett
New Jersey Audubon Society: Dr Betty Carnes
Northeastern Bird Banding Association: Dr. Charles E. Huntington,
   Mr E.A.Bergstrom
Nuttall Ornithological Club, Cambridge, Mass.: Mr Osborne Earle
Ohio State University: Dr Milton Trautman
Onondaga Audubon Society, Inc.: Miss Margaret Rusk
Peabody Museum, Salem: Miss Dorothy E.Snyder
Peabody Museum, New Haven: Mr A.Stickney Jr.
San Diego Natural History Museum: Dr R.C.Banks
San Diego State College: Prof. James Crouch, Mr G.Collier
St. Paul Audubon Society, Minnesota: Mr Thomas Savage
SCAR Biology Working Group's Committee on Antarctic Banding:
   Dr William J.L.Sladen
The Smithsonian Institution: Dr Philip S. Humphrey, Dr Alexander
   Wetmore
Society of Vertebrate Zoology: Dr Pierce Brodkorb
U.S. National Museum: Dr G.E. Watson, Dr Richard Zusi
The University of Michigan, Museum of Zoology: Prof. Robert W.Storer,
   Dr H.B.Tordoff

# Official Delegates

The University of Kansas: Dr Robert M.Mengel

Virginia Society of Ornithology: Mr Willard Rothery

Western Bird Banding Association: Mrs Enid K.Austin

Wilson Ornithological Society: Dr Roger Tory Peterson, Mr C.Chandler Ross

Wisconsin Conservation Department: Dr Frederick Hamerstrom

Woods Hole Oceanographic Institution: Mr Paul Willis

World Nature Club: Mr Orville Crowder

World Wildlife Fund of U.S.A.: Mr Richard H.Pough

Yale University: Prof. Charles G.Sibley

VENEZUELA

Ministerio de Agricultura y Cria: Mr Ramon Aveledo Hostos, Mr William H.Phelps

Ministerio de Educación: Mr Ramon Aveledo Hostos, Mr William H.Phelps

Museo de Ciencias Naturales de Caracas: Mr Ramon Aveledo Hostos, Mr William H.Phelps

Sociedad Venezolana de Ciencias Naturales: Mr Ramon Aveledo Hostos, Mr William H.Phelps

# Members of the XIV International Ornithological Congress

A  Associate Member      *  Member not present at the Oxford Meeting

Abdulali, Dr Humayun, 75 Abdul Rehman Street, Bombay 3, India

Abs, Dr Michael, Institut f. Allg. Zoologie, Ruhr-Universität Bochum, Friederikastr. 11, 463 Bochum, Germany

*A Abs-Wurmbach, I. (Mrs Michael)

Acland, Miss Clemence M., 2 Orchard Close, Banstead, Surrey, England

Adams, Dr James, 15 Oakwood Avenue, Gatley, Cheadle, Cheshire, England

Adkisson, Miss Kathryn E., 3519 Martha Custis Drive, Alexandria, Virginia, U.S.A.

A Adler, Mr Barry P.

Adler, Dr Helmut E., Department of Animal Behaviour, The American Museum of Natural History, Central Park West and 79th Street, New York, N.Y. 10024, U.S.A.

A Adler, Leonore L. (Mrs Helmut)

* Ahlen, Docent Ingemar, Zoological Institute, Lund, Sweden

Airey, Mr Alan F., St Margarets, Coast Road, Berrow, Burnham-on-Sea, Somerset

Aldrich, Dr John W., Bureau of Sport Fisheries and Wildlife, U.S. Department of the Interior, Washington, D.C., U.S.A.

A Aldrich, Mrs John W.

Alexander, Mr Horace G., 26 Bon Accord Road, Swanage, Dorset, England

A Alexander, Mrs Horace G.

Ali, Dr Salim, 33 Pali Hill, Bandra, Bombay 50, India

Allen, Dr Ted, Jacksonville University, Jacksonville, Florida, U.S.A.

Allsopp, Enid (Mrs Keith)

Allsopp, Mr Keith, 81 Uplands Road, Oadby, Leicestershire, England

Amadon, Dr Dean, American Museum of Natural History, Central Park West, New York, N.Y. 10024, U.S.A.

A Amadon, Mrs Dean

Ammann, Dr George A., Game Division, Michigan Department of Conservation, Lansing, Michigan, U.S.A.

Andrew, Mr Ian G., Department of Scientific and Industrial Research, Palmerston North, New Zealand

A Anoz, Mrs Lydia, Conde Rodezno 13-7°, Pamplona, Spain

Armstrong, Rev. Edward, St Mark's Vicarage, Cambridge, England

* Arn-Willi, Mr Hans, Wildbachstrasse 19, 4500 Solothurn, Switzerland

A Aschoff, Hilde (Mrs Jürgen)

Aschoff, Mr Jürgen, 8131 Erling-Andechs/Oberbayern, Germany

Ash, Dr John, The Game Research Association, Fordingbridge, Hampshire, England

Ashforth, Mr David, 209 Main Road, Claremont, Capetown, South Africa

A Ashmole, Myrtle J. (Mrs. Philip), 86 Heloise Street, Hamden, Connecticut, U.S.A.

# Members of the XIV International Ornithological Congress

Ashmole, Dr N. Philip, Division of Vertebrate Zoology, Peabody Museum of Natural History, Yale University, New Haven, Conn. 06520, U.S.A.

A Auber, Clotilde (Mrs. Lewis)

Auber, Dr Lewis, 28 Windsor Place, Portobello, Edinburgh 15, Scotland

A Austin, Elizabeth S. (Mrs Oliver)

Austin, Mrs Enid K., 1116 Mandana Boulevard, Oakland, California 94610, U.S.A.

Austin, Dr Oliver L., Florida State Museum, University of Florida, Gainesville, Fla. 32601, U.S.A.

Austin, Mr William, Glaston, Albert Road, Dumfries, Scotland.

* Autgaerden, Dr Susan, 14 Place Dauphine, Paris 1$^{er}$, France.

Auzinger, Dr Helene, Hoelzlweg 22, 81 Garmisch-Partenkirchen, Germany

Aveledo, Mr Ramon, Coleccion Ornitologica Phelps, Apartado 2009, Caracas, Venezuela

Avery de la Salle, Mrs Monica, 19 Avenue Franklin D. Roosevelt, Paris 8, France

A Bacon, Mr Raymond, 1613 Autry Way, Knoxville, Tenn. 37919, U.S.A.

Baerends, Dr Gerard P., Zoological Laboratory, Rijkstraatweg 78, Haren (Gron), Holland

A Baerends, Mrs Gerard

Bailey, Mr Richard, 1107 High Court, Berkeley 8, California, U.S.A.

Bailey, Mr Roger S., British Trust for Ornithology, Beech Grove, Tring, Hertfordshire, England

A Bailey, Jane (Mrs Roger), 24 Mill View Road, Tring, Hertfordshire, England

Baillie, Mr James L., Department of Ornithology, Royal Ontario Museum, University of Toronto, 100 Queen's Park, Toronto 5, Ontario, Canada

Bainbridge, Miss Moira V. 138 Long Hill Road, Ovingdean, Brighton, Sussex, England

Baird, Mr James, Massachusetts Audubon Society, South Great Road, Lincoln, Massachusetts, U.S.A.

A Baird, Mrs James

Balát, Dr František, Department of Ornithology, Institute of Vertebrate Zoology, (Czechoslovak Academy of Sciences), Drobného 28, Brno, Czechoslovakia.

Banks, Dr Richard C., Bird and Mammal Laboratories, U.S. National Museum, Washington, D.C., U.S.A.

Barclay-Smith, Miss Phyllis, 51 Warwick Avenue, London W.9., England

Barkalow, Dr Frederick S., Jr, 3439 Bradley Place, Raleigh, North Carolina 27607, U.S.A.

Barlow, Dr Jon C., Department of Ornithology, Royal Ontario Museum, University of Toronto, 100 Queen's Park, Toronto 5, Ontario, Canada

A Barlow, Judith B. (Mrs Jon C.)

A Barnes, Mr Egbert C., Hungerdown House, Seagry, Chippenham, Wiltshire, England.

Barnes, Ruth G. (Mrs Egbert)

Bartholomew, Dr George A, Department of Zoology, University of California, Los Angeles, Calif. 90024, U.S.A.

A Bassett, June (Mrs Terence), 1106, 7th Avenue South, Lethbridge, Alberta, Canada.

Bassett, Dr Terence, Purity Dairy Building, Lethbridge, Alberta, Canada

Bateman, Mr John V., 8 Kincora Avenue, Belfast 4, N. Ireland

Bauer, Dr Kurt, Naturhistorisches Museum, P.O. Box, A 417 Vienna, Austria

Bayramoglu, Prof. Dr (Mrs) Saadet, Taksim, Sehitmuhtar cad. 33/6, Istanbul, Turkey

Beeskow, Mr Adolf, Hahnenstr. 30, 3 Hannover, Germany.

Belcher, Miss Margaret, University of Saskatchewan, Regina Campus, Regina, Saskatchewan, Canada

Bell, Mr Benjamin, 33 Sneyd Avenue, Westlands, Newcastle-under-Lyme, Staffordshire, England.

Bellrose, Mr Frank, Illinois Natural History Survey, Havana, Illinois 62644, U.S.A.

Belterman, Dr Theo, Zoologisch Laboratorium der Universiteit van Amsterdam, Plantage Doklaan 44, Amsterdam (C), Holland

Bendell, Dr James, Department of Zoology, University of British Columbia, Vancouver 8, British Columbia, Canada

Benson, Mr C. W., Department of Zoology, Downing Street, Cambridge, England.

* Berger, Mr Daniel D., 510 E. MacArthur Road, Milwaukee, Wis. 53217, U.S.A.

Bergstrom, Mr E. Alexander, 37 Old Brook Road, West Hartford, Conn. 06117, U.S.A.

A Bergstrom, Mrs E. Alexander

Berlioz, Prof. Jacques, Muséum National d'Histoire Naturelle, 55 rue de Buffon, Paris 5$^e$, France

Berndt, Dr.rer.nat. Rudolf, Vogelschutzstation Braunschweig, Thielemannstr. 1, 33 Braunschweig, Germany

Bernis, Prof. Francesco, Castellana 80 (Museo), Madrid 6, Spain.

A Bernis, Mrs Francesco

Bernrieder, Miss Catherine, 55 Petworth Road, Courts Cottage, Haslemere, Surrey, England

Berthold, Dr Peter, Staatl. Museum f. Naturkunde, Schloss Rosenstein, 7000 Stuttgart, Germany

Beschnidt, Mr Ernst, Dresdenstrasse 27, 33 Braunschweig, Germany

Bezemer, Mr Karel, Groot Hoefijzerlaan 67, Wassenaar, Holland

Bezzel, Dr Einhard, Staatl. Vogelschutzwarte, Gsteigstr. 43, 81 Garmisch-Partenkirchen, Germany

A Bierman, Elisabeth (Mrs Willem)

Bierman, Dr Willem, 18 Lorentzplein, Haarlem, Holland

Bijleveld, Dr Maarten, Laan van Beek en Royen 40–41, Zeist, Holland

Biswas, Mr Biswamoy, Zoological Survey of India, Indian Museum, Calcutta 13, India

Black, Dr Charles T., Rose Lake Wildlife Research Station, RT.1, East Lansing, Michigan 48823, U.S.A.

Blaker, Mr David, Percy Fitzpatrick Institute of African Ornithology, University of Cape Town, Rondebosch, South Africa

Blokpoel, Mr Hans, van Heutzstr. 15A, Den Haag, Holland

Blondel, Mr Jacques, Station biologique de La Tour du Valat, 13–Le Sambuc, France

Blume, Mr Carl-Adolph, 10 Sct. Markus Plads, Copenhagen V, Denmark

Bock, Dr Walter J., Department of Biological Sciences, Columbia University New York, N.Y. 10027, U.S.A.

*A Boellard-van Heeckeren, Mrs A. (Mrs Willem)

* Boellard, Mr Willem, Kloosterend, de Bilt (u), Holland.

Boeson, Mr Brian W., P.O. Box 30, Carterton, New Zealand

Boev, Mr Nikolai, Inst. of Zoology, Bulgarian Academy of Sciences, Bul. Ruski 1, Sofia, Bulgaria

Böhr, Dr Hans-Joachim, Huttenstr. 5, 35 Kassel, Germany

Bolle, Miss Germaine, 11 chemin des Floralies, 1216 Cointrin/Genève, Switzerland

Bond, Mr James, 721 Davidson Road, Philadelphia, Pa. 19118, U.S.A.

A Bond, Mrs James

Bondesen, Dr Poul, Natural History Museum, University of Århus, Århus C., Denmark

Borodoulina, Mrs Tatiana Leonidovna, Institute of Animal Morphology, Academy of Sciences of the U.S.S.R., Lenin Avenue 33, Moscow W-71, U.S.S.R.

Boswall, Mr Jeffery, Natural History Unit, British Broadcasting Corporation, Whiteladies Road, Bristol 8, England

A Boulton, Louise (Mrs Rudyerd)

Boulton, Mr Rudyerd, Atlantica Ecological Research Station, P.O. Box 8305, Causeway, Salisbury, Rhodesia

Bourne, Dr W.R.P., c/o 70 Ashby Road East, Stanhope Bretby, Burton on Trent, England

Bowen, Mrs Ursula, 20 Winchester Road, Oxford

Boyd Watt, Mrs Winifred, San Simeon, 52 Wimborne Road, Bournemouth, Hamphire, England

* Brauen, Dr Albert, Ermitage 28, Neuchatel, Switzerland

Breckenridge, Dr Walter J., Minnesota Museum of Natural History, University of Minnesota, Minneapolis, Minnesota 55455, U.S.A.

A Breckenridge, Mrs Walter J.

Brémond, Mr Jean-Claude, Laboratoire de Physiologie Acoustique, 78 Jouy-en-Josas, France

Bridgman, Mr Charles, 'Kantara', 36 Esmead, Monkton Park, Chippenham, Wiltshire, England

Briggs, Miss Shirley A., 7605 Honeywell Lane, Bethesda, Maryland 20014, U.S.A.

* Brodkorb, Dr Pierce, Department of Zoology, University of Florida, Gainesville, Florida 32603, U.S.A.

* Brooke, Mr Richard Kendall, P.O. Box 8081, Causeway, Rhodesia

Broun, Dr Maurice, Strawberry Hill Farm, R.D.1, New Ringgold, Penna. 17960, U.S.A.

A Broun, M. Irma (Mrs Maurice)

A Browne, Miss Eleanor L., 34 Malone Park, Belfast 9, N. Ireland

* Brun, Mr Einar, Department of Zoology, Tromsö Museum, Tromsö, Norway

Brunel, Mr Jean, B.P. 418, Bouaké, Rep. de Côte d'Ivoire

A Brunel, Mrs Jean

Bruns, Dr. rer.nat. Herbert, Ilsenweg 11, 2 Hamburg 68, Germany

Brush, Dr Alan H., Department of Zoology, University of Connecticut, Storrs, Connecticut, U.S.A.

Bruun, Dr Bertel, 317 West 83rd Street, New York, N.Y. 10024, U.S.A.

* Bryan, Dr Burton, Box 2, Adamsville, Rhode Island, U.S.A.

Bugalho, Mr João F.F., Rua Borges Carneiro 31-1°, Lisboa, Portugal

Bull, Mr John, Department of Ornithology, American Museum of Natural History, Central Park West at 79th Street, New York, N.Y. 10024, U.S.A.

A Bull, Edith (Mrs John)

Bulmer, Dr Ralph N.H., Department of

Anthropology, University of Auckland, Box 2175, Auckland, New Zealand

Burnier, Dr med. Jacques, 34 av. Jacques-Martin, 1224 Chêne-Bourgeries/Genève, Switzerland

Burton, Mr Philip, 54 Albany Park Road, Kingston, Surrey, England

Butt, Mr David, Sandy Hollow, Renwick Park, West Runton, Norfolk, England

Buxton, Mr E. John M., Cole Park, Malmesbury, Wiltshire, England

Cabot, Mr David, Department of Zoology, University College, Galway, Ireland

Cadbury, Mr James, c/o 11 Boutport Street, Barnstaple, N. Devon, England

A Cadbury, Joy (Mrs James)

* Callegari, Dr Pier-Francesco, via Barbiani 8, Ravenna, Italy

Cameron, Mrs Edith, Canadian Army Staff College, Kingston, Ontario, Canada

Campbell, Dr Bruce, Hordley, Woodstock, Oxfordshire, England

A Campbell, Margaret (Mrs Bruce)

Carleton, Mr Geoffrey, 55 E. 87 Street, New York, N.Y. 10028, U.S.A.

A Carleton, Mrs Geoffrey

Carnes, Dr Betty (Mrs Herbert E.) 11801 Sundown Drive, Scottsdale, Arizona, U.S.A.

* Caroni, Mrs Mary, Via Solaria, 6648 Minusio, Ticino, Switzerland

Catchpole, Mr Clive, 33 Sneyd Avenue, Westlands, Newcastle-under-Lyme, Staffordshire, England

Cavé, Mr Anton, Vogeltrekstation, Kemperbergerweg 11, Arnhem, Holland

Černý, Dr Walter, Department of Vertebrate Zoology, Faculty of Science, Charles-University, Viničná 7, Praha 2, Č.S.S.R.

Chapin, Mrs Ruth Trimble, 419 West 119 St., Apt. 9E, New York, N.Y. 10027, U.S.A.

* Clark, Dr Goerge C., 110 Medical Arts Building, Port Arthur, Ontario, Canada

*A Clark, Mary (Mrs George)

Clarke, Mr Gordon, 2 Mountain View, Queens Road, Kendal, Westmorland, England

Clay, Dr Theresa, British Museum (Natural History), Cromwell Road, London S.W.7, England

Clement, Mr Roland C., 1130 Fifth Avenue, New York, N.Y. 10028, U.S.A.

Cohen, Mr Edwin, Hazelhurst, Sway, Lymington, Hampshire, England

Cohn, Jean W. (Mrs Theodore J.) 4787 Beaumont Drive, La Mesa, Calif. 92041, U.S.A.

A Cohn, Dr Theodore J.

* Coldewey, Mr Constant Jan, Van der Feltzweg 5, Gorssel, Holland

Cole, Mrs Richard D., 625 Valley Lane, Towson, Maryland 21204, U.S.A.

Collette, Mr Pierre, 52 av. E. Digneffe, Liege, Belgium

Collias, Dr Nicholas E., Department of Zoology, University of California, Los Angeles, California 90024, U.S.A.

A Collias, Dr Elsie C. (Mrs Nicholas E.), Los Angeles County Museum, Exposition Park, Los Angeles, California, U.S.A.

Collier, Mr Gerald, Department of Zoology, San Diego State College, San Diego, California 92115, U.S.A.

A Collier, Mrs Gerald

# Members of the XIV International Ornithological Congress

Collins, Dr Charles T., Department of Ornithology, American Museum of Natural History, New York 24, New York, U.S.A.

Combier, Mr Jacques, 64 Quai de la Fosse, Nantes 44, France

Conder, Mr Peter, The Royal Society for the Protection of Birds, The Lodge, Sandy, Bedfordshire, England

Constant, Mr Pierre, Laboratorre de Biologie Animale, Faculté des Sciences, 2 Place Pasteur, 35 Rennes, France

Coombs, Dr C.J. Franklin, Greenwith Place, Perranwell, Truro, Cornwall, England

Coombs, Mrs C.J.F.

A Cooper, Mr Eric S., 75 Dobie Avenue, Town of Mount Royal, Montreal 16, P.Q., Canada

Cooper, Ruth (Mrs Eric S.)

Cope, Prof. James, Earlham College, Richmond, Indiana, U.S.A.

Corbin, Dr Kendall W., Department of Biology, Kline Biology Tower, Yale University, New Haven, Connecticut 06520, U.S.A.

A Corbin, Mrs Kendall W.

Cornwallis, Mr Lindon, Department of Biology, Pahlavi University, Shiraz, Iran

Cornwallis, Mr Richard K., Bleasby Grange, Legsby, Market Rasen, Lincolnshire, England

Coulson, Dr John, Department of Zoology, Durham University, South Road, Durham City, England

Cowdy, Mrs Susan, The Lee, Great Missenden, Buckinghamshire, England

Cowles, Mr Graham S., Bird Section, British Museum (Natural History), Cromwell Road, London S.W.7

Cramp, Mr Stanley, 32 Queen Court, London W.C.1.

Craw, Mr Henry A., Greenways, Sutton Place, Abinger Hammer, Dorking, Surrey, England

A Craw, Gillian L.A. (Mrs Henry A.)

Crook, Dr John Hurrell, Psychology Department, Bristol University, Bristol 8, England

Crouch, Prof. James, San Diego State College, San Diego, Calif. 92115, U.S.A.

A Crouch, Mary (Mrs James)

Crowder, Mr Orville, Harpers Ferry, W.Va. 25425, U.S.A.

Cullen, Dr J. Michael, Department of Zoology, Parks Road, Oxford

Cunningham, Mr Josias, Silversprings, Templepatrick, Co. Antrim, N. Ireland

A Cunningham, Isobel (Mrs Josias)

Curry-Lindahl, Dr Kai, Zoological Department, Nordiska Museum und Skansen, Stockholm, Sweden.

Cusa, Dr Noel William, River House, Letheringsett, Holt, Norfolk, England

D'Alessandrio, Dr med. Pietro, 6762 Faido (TI), Switzerland.

A D'Alessandrio, Mrs Pietro

Dare, Dr Peter John, Fisheries Experiment Station, Castle Bank, Conway, Caernarvonshire, U.K.

Darling, Mr Louis, R.F.D. 2, Old Lyme, Connecticut 06371, U.S.A.

A Darling, Lois (Mrs Louis)

Davis, Mr L. Irby, 1122 E. Polk, Harlingen, Texas 78550, U.S.A.

A Davis, Mrs L. Irby

Deane, Mr C. Douglas, Ulster Museum, Stranmillis, Belfast, Northern Ireland

Deignan, Mr Herbert G., Boulevard de la Forêt 24A, 1012 Lausanne/Pully, Switzerland

# Members of the XIV International Ornithological Congress

A  Deignan, Stella L. (Mrs Herbert G.)

Delacour, Mr Jean, American Museum of Natural History, Central Park West at 79th Street, New York, N.Y. 10024, U.S.A.

De Maerschalk, Mr Jules, Kapellestraat 44, Denderbelle, Belgium.

De Naurois, Prof. René, Institut Catholique, 31 Rue de la Fonderie, 31 Toulouse, France

de Reyher, Miss Adèle, 8 Chemin de Fantaisie, 1009 Pully, Switzerland

de Reyher, Miss Jeanne, 69 Route de Berne, 1010 Lausanne, Vaud, Switzerland

De Roo, Mr Antoon E.M., Kon Museum Midden-Afrika, Tervuren, Belgium

A  De Roo, Mrs Anton

Desfayes, Mr Michel, 1913 Saillon, Valais, Switzerland

Devillers, Mr Pierre, 11 av. de l'Oiseau bleu, Bruxelles 15, Belgium

De Worms, Dr Charles, Three Oaks, Shore's Road, Woking, Surrey, England

Dexter, Dr Ralph W., Dept. of Biological Sciences, Kent State University, Kent, Ohio 44240, U.S.A.

A  Dexter, Mrs Ralph W.

Di Carlo, Dr Elio Augusto, Cantalupo Sabino (Rieti), Italy.

Dickinson, Mr H. John, Paston, North Walsham, Norfolk, England

Dircksen, Prof. Dr Rolf, Sielerweg 173, 4904 Enger (Westf.), Germany

A  Dircksen, G. (Mrs Rolf)

Disney, Mr H. John de S., Australian Museum, College Street, Sydney, New South Wales, Australia

Dixon, Dr Keith L., Department of Zoology, Utah, State University, Logan, Utah 843321, U.S.A.

Dobinson, Mr Humphrey M., The Old

Barn, Sonning Common, Reading, Berkshire, England

Donchev, Mr Stefan, Inst. of Zoology, Bulgarian Academy of Sciences, Bul. Ruski 1, Sofia, Bulgaria

Dorst, Prof. Jean, Muséum National d'Histoire Naturelle, 55 rue de Buffon, Paris 5$^e$, France

Dorward, Dr Douglas F., Department of Zoology, Monash University, Clayton, Victoria, Australia

A  Drury, Mary C. (Mrs William H.)

Drury, Dr William H., Codman Road, Lincoln, Mass. 01733, U.S.A.

Dunham, Dr David W., Zoölogisch Laboratorium, Rijksuniversiteit te Leiden, Leiden, Holland

Dunn, Miss Erica, 49 Elm Street, Wellesley, Mass. 02181, U.S.A.

Dunnet, Dr George M., Culterty Field Station, The University of Aberdeen, Newburgh, Aberdeenshire, Scotland.

Dupuy, Mr André-Roger, 48 Avenue Victor Hugo, Paris 16$^e$, France.

Dusenberry, Miss Niña Jay, 446 Ocean Avenue, Brooklyn, N.Y. 11226, U.S.A.

Dyck, Mr Jan, Danish Defence Research Board, Østerbrogades Kaserne, Copenhagen, Denmark

A  Dyck, B. (Mrs Jan)

* Dykstra, Mr Jay, University of Arkansas, Department of Zoology, Fayetteville, Arkansas 72701, U.S.A.

Dzubin, Mr Alexander, Canadian Wildlife Service, Prairie Migratory Bird Res. Center, Univ. of Saskatchewan Campus, Saskatoon, Sask. Canada

A  Dzubin, Dolores (Mrs Alexander)

Earle, Mr Osborne, 71 Appleton Street, Cambridge, Massachusetts, U.S.A.

A  Earle, Mrs Osborne

Earle, Mr Timothy K.

Eber, Dr (Miss ) Gisela, Vogelschutz-warte, Ägidiustrasse 94, 43 Essen-Bredeney, Germany

Edberg, Redaktör Ragnar, Långlöt, Runsten, Sweden

Edgar, Mr Robert D.M., 2 Reynolds Close, Hampstead Way, London N.W.11, England

Edgerton, Mr Dan E., Monson, Maine, 04464, U.S.A.

A Edgerton, Mrs Dan E.

Edwards, Mr Ernest P., Sweet Briar College, Sweet Briar, Virginia 24595, U.S.A.

A Edwards, Mrs Ernest P.

Eisenmann, Mr Eugene, American Museum of Natural History, New York, N.Y. 10024, U.S.A.

Elgood, Mr John, 11 Parkside Avenue, Littlehampton, Sussex, England

Elliott, Sir Hugh, 173 Woodstock Road, Oxford, England

Ellis, Mr Charles W.S., Firgrove, Netherend, Lydney, Gloucestershire, England

A Elofson, Eyvor (Mrs Olof)

Elofson, Dr Olof, Ludvigsbergsvägen 3, Sundsvall, Sweden

Ely, Dr Charles A., Pacific Ocean Biological Survey Program, Smithsonian Institution, Washington D.C. 20560, U.S.A.

A Ely, Mrs Charles A.

A Emlen, Katharine P. (Mrs Stephen T.)

Emlen, Dr Stephen T., Division of Biological Sciences, Section of Neurobiology and Behavior, Cornell University, Ithaca, New York, U.S.A.

Ennion, Dr Eric, Shalbourne Mill, Marlborough, Wiltshire, England

Erard, Mr Christian, C.R.M.M.O., Museum National d'Histoire Naturelle, 55 rue de Buffon, Paris 5e., France

Erickson, Dr Carl, Zoölogisch Laboratorium, Rijkstraatweg 78, Haren (Gr.), Holland

Erickson, Dr (Miss) Mary Erickson, Department of Biological Sciences, University of California, Santa Barbara, California 93106, U.S.A.

Estes, Mrs Josephine R., 939 S. Walnut St., West Chester, Pa. 19380, U.S.A.

* Erskine, Dr Anthony J.E., P.O. Box 180, Sackville, New Brunswick, Canada

*A Erskine, Mrs A.J.E.

Etchécopar, Dr Robert-Daniel, 55 rue de Buffon, Paris 5e., France

Evans, Dr Peter, Edward Grey Institute, Botanic Garden, Oxford, England

Falla, Mr Robert A., Dominion Museum, Private Bag, Wellington, New Zealand

A Falls, E. Ann (Mrs J. Bruce)

Falls, Dr J. Bruce, Department of Zoology, University of Toronto, Toronto 5, Canada

Farner, Prof. Donald S., Department of Zoology, University of Washington, Seattle, Washington 98105, U.S.A.

Faurion, Mr Jacques, 11 rue Lamartine, 71 Macon, France

A Ferdinand, Anni (Mrs Lorenz)

Ferdinand, Dr Lorenz, Jonstrupvangvej 4, Ballerup, Denmark

Ferguson-Lees, Mr I. James, 10 Merton Road, Bedford, England

* Ferrier, Miss Judith M., Otterden Place, Eastling, Faversham, Kent, England.

Ferry, Dr Camille, 25 place Darcy, 21 Dijon, France

Fisher, Mr James M. McC., Ashton Manor, Northampton, England

A Fitter, Maisie (Mrs Richard)

Fitter, Mr Richard S.R., Drifts, Chinnor Hill, Oxford, England

# Members of the XIV International Ornithological Congress

A Fleming, Dr Bethel H. (Mrs Robert L.)

Fleming, Dr Robert L., Shanta Bhawan Hospital, Kathmandu, Nepal

Flensburg, Fil. Lic. Tom, Fack, Stockholm 6, Sweden

Flower, Miss Winifred, 5 Airthrey Avenue, Glasgow, W.4, Scotland

Fogden, Miss Susan C.L., 13 Valley Road, Hunter's Ride, Henley-on-Thames, Oxon, England

Fookes, Miss Ursula, The Double House, Wiveton, Norfolk, England

Fordham, Dr Robin A., 146 Barnard Street, Wellington, New Zealand

Formon, Mr Aldin, Norges-le-bas, 21 Ruffey-les-Echirey, France

Forster, Miss Elizabeth, The Double House, Wiveton, Holt, Norfolk, England

Fraser, Bernice (Mrs George B.), 2937 University Terrace N.W., Washington, D.C. 20016, U.S.A.

Fraser Darling, Dr Frank, Shefford Woodlands House, Newbury, Berkshire, England

Frochot, Mr Bernard, C.E.O.B. Laboratoire de Zoologie, Faculté des Sciences, Bd. Gabriel, 21 Dijon, France

A Frugis, Mr Decio

Frugis, Dr Sergio, via Belfiore 11, Milano, Italy

Fry, Mr C. Hilary, Department of Zoology, Ahmadu Bello University, Zaria, Nigeria

Fuchs, Dr Hans, Dubochet 16, Clarens, Vd., Switzerland

A Fuchs, Ursula (Mrs Hans)

A Galbraith, Ebba (Mrs Ian)

Galbraith, Ian C.J., British Museum (Natural History), Cromwell Road, London S.W.7, England

Garavini, Dr Ettore, S. Pancrazio (Ravenna), Italy.

A Garavini, Mr Raffaele

Gaunt, Dr Abbot S., Dept. of Biology, Middlebury College, Middlebury, Vermont 05753, U.S.A.

A Gaunt, Sandra Louise L. (Mrs Abbot S.)

Géroudet, Dr Paul, 37 Av. de Champel, 1206 Genève, Switzerland.

A Géroudet, Mrs Paul

Gherardi, Miss Eliane, 23 chemin Vestpré, 1211 Conches, Genève, Switzerland

Gifford, Dr Cameron E., Department of Biology, Earlham College, Richmond, Indiana 47374, U.S.A.

Gillmor, Mr Robert, 58 Northcourt Avenue, Reading, Berkshire, England

Glutz von Blotzheim, Dr Urs, Schweiz. Vogelwarte, CH 6204 Sempach, Switzerland

A Glutz von Blotzheim, Mrs Urs

Godfrey, Mr W. Earl, National Museum of Canada, Ottawa, Canada

A Goethe, Elisabeth (Mrs Friedrich)

Goethe, Dr Friedrich, Vogelwarte Helgoland, 294 Wilhelmshaven, Germany

Gompertz, Miss Teresita, Woodway, Pinner Hill, Pinner, Middlesex, England

Goodwin, Mr Derek, 40 Frankfurt Road, Herne Hill, London S.E.24, England

Gould, Mr Patrick J., Department of Vertebrate Zoology, Smithsonian Institution, Washington D.C. 20560, U.S.A.

Granett, Dr Philip, Department of Entomology and Economic Zoology, Rutgers—The State University, New Brunswick, N.J. 08903, U.S.A.

Grant, Dr Peter R., Zoology Department, McGill University, Montreal, P.Q., Canada

# Members of the XIV International Ornithological Congress

*A  Grant, Rosemary (Mrs Peter)

*  Griffin, Dr Donald R., The Rockefeller University, New York, N.Y. 10021, U.S.A.

*A  Griffin, Dr Jocelyn Crane (Mrs Donald R.)

Grimeland, Mrs Anne-Marie, Lökkeveien 7, Oslo, Norway.

Groen, Miss Lena G., Bernhardlaan 2, Bedum, Holland

A  Gubler, Marcelle (Mrs Willy)

Gubler, Mr Willy, 97 Möhrlistrasse, 8006 Zürich, Switzerland

Gudmundsson, Dr Finnur, Museum of Natural History, P.O. Box 532, Reykjavik, Iceland

A  Gudmundsson, Mrs Finnur

A  Gunn, Anne F. (Mrs William, H.)

Gunn, Dr William W.H., 455 Meadow Wood Road, Clarkson, Ontario, Canada

Gustafson, Miss Ruth, Kungsklippan 11, Stockholm K, Sweden

Guthmann, Mr Elmar, Hüttenstr. 1, 506 Bensberg-Refrath, Germany

Guyomarc'h, Mr Jean-Charles, Laboratoire de Biologie Animale, Faculté des Sciences, Université de Rennes, Rennes 35, France

Gwinner, Mr Eberhard, Max-Planck-Institut f. Verhaltensphysiologie, 8131 Erling-Andechs, Obb., Germany

Gysels, Dr Henrik, Laboratorium voor Dierkunde-Systematiek, Rijksuniversiteit Gent, Ledeganckstraat 35, Ghent, Belgium

A  Gysels, Maria (Mrs Hendrik)

Hall, Dr Alan, 14 Linden Road, Bicester, Oxfordshire, England

Hall, Mrs Beryl P., Bird Room, British Museum (Nat. Hist.), Cromwell Road, London S.W.7.

Hall, Dr George A., Department of Chemistry, W. Virginia University, Morgantown, West Virginia, U.S.A.

A  Hall, Tanya (Mrs George A.)

Hall-Craggs, Mrs Joan, Little Holt, Woodcote, Reading, Berkshire, England

Hamerstrom, Dr Frances (Mrs Frederick)

Hamerstrom, Dr Frederick Jr., R.R.1, Plainfield, Wisconsin 54966, U.S.A.

Hamilton, Frank D., The Royal Society for the Protection of Birds, The Lodge, Sandy, Bedfordshire, England

*  Hancock, Mr James A., Coniston, Orchehill Avenue, Gerrards Cross, Buckinghamshire, England

Handmann, Dr Wolfgang, Postfach 187, 58 Gotha/Thür, Germany

Hardy, Dr John William, Moore Laboratory of Zoology, Occidental College, Los Angeles, California 90041, U.S.A.

Harrell, Dr Byron, Zoology Department, University of South Dakota, Vermillion, South Dakota, 57609, U.S.A.

A  Harrell, Joyce (Mrs Byron)

*  Harrison, Dr James M., Bowerwood House, St Botolph's Road, Sevenoaks, Kent, England

Hartley, The Rev. Peter, Badingham Rectory, Woodbridge, Suffolk, England

A  Hartley, Mrs Peter

Hartmann-Müller, Mrs Bertha, 3504 Oberkaufungen-Kassel, Am Rossgang 3, Germany

*  Hatch, Mr Jeremy, Department of Zoology, Duke University, Durham N.C. 27706, U.S.A.

Havlín, Ing. Jiří, Institute of Vertebrate Zoology, Czechoslovak Academy of Sciences, Drobného 28, Brno, Czechoslovakia.

Hawkins, Mr Desmond, B.B.C., Broadcasting House, Bristol 8, England

Heimerdinger, Dr Mary A., Carnegie Museum, Pittsburgh, Pennyslvania 15213, U.S.A.

Hekstra, Drs Gerrit P., Zacharias Jansestraat 58, Vatergrafsmeer, Amsterdam, Holland

Henderson, Miss Mary, 44 Higher Bebington Road, Bebington, Wirral, Cheshire, England

Henning, Mr Gustav Adolf, Fontenay 1 D, 2 Hamburg 36, Germany

Herbert, Kathleen Green (Mrs Richard A.) R.D.2, Middletown, Delaware, U.S.A.

Hill, Mrs Janet Lyman, Van Houten Fields, West Nyack, New York, U.S.A.

Hinde, Prof. Robert A., Sub-Dept. of Animal Behaviour, High Street, Madingley, Cambridge, England

A  Hofslund, Elaine (Mrs Pershing), 4726 Jay St., Duluth, Minnesota 55804, U.S.A.

Hofslund, Dr Pershing B., Biology Department, University of Minnesota, Duluth, Minnesota 55812, U.S.A.

Hold, Mr Trevor, Department of Music, University of Liverpool, 82 Bedford Street South, Liverpool 7, England

Holgersen, Mr Holger, Stavanger Museum, Stavanger, Norway

Hollands, Mr F. Gordon, F.R.C.S., Red Ley, Quarndon, Derbyshire, England

Hollom, Mr Philip A.D., Crastock Cottage, Woking, Surrey, England

Holmes, Dr Richard T., Department of Biology, Tufts University, Medford, Massachusetts 02155, U.S.A.

Homes, Mr Richard C., 5 Shelvers Way, Tadworth, Surrey, England

Hornby, Mr Richard J., Kingsland, Long Burton, Sherborne, Dorset, England

A  Hörstadius, Greta (Mrs Sven)

Hörstadius, Professor Sven, Zoological Institute, Uppsala, Sweden

Horvath, Dr L., Zoological Department, Hungarian Nat. Hist. Museum, Budapest VIII, Baross-utca 13, Hungary

Hosking, Mr Eric, 20 Crouch Hall Road, London N.8., England

A  Hosking, Mrs Eric

Houssay, Miss Jacqueline, Impasse Rosière d'Artois, 44 Nantes, France

Houston, Dr C. Stuart, 863 University Drive, Saskatoon, Sask., Canada

A  Houston, Mary I. (Mrs C. Stuart)

Howard-White, Mr F.B., Compton Hill, Farnham, Surrey, England

A  Howard-White, Mrs F.B.,

Howell, Dr Joseph C., 1613 Autry Way Knoxville, Tenn. 37919, U.S.A.

A  Howell, Dr Thomas R., Department of Zoology, Los Angeles, California 90024, U.S.A.

A  Howell, Mrs Thomas R.

Hublé, Prof. Dr Jan, Lab. Oecologie, Ledeganckstr. 35, Gent, Belgium

A  Hublé, Nadia (Mrs Jan)

Hudec, Dr Karel, Czechoslovak Academy of Sciences, Institute of Vertebrate Zoology, BRNO, Drobného 28, Czechoslovakia

Hughes, Mrs Angela, East Farm, Hammoon, Sturminster Newton, Dorset, England

Humphrey, Dr Philip S., Department of Vertebrate Zoology, U.S. National Museum, Washington D.C., U.S.A.

A  Humphrey, Mrs Philip S., 5718-9th Road North, Arlington, Virginia, U.S.A.

# Members of the XIV International Ornithological Congress

Huntington, Prof. Charles E., Department of Biology, Bowdoin College, Brunswick, Maine 04011, U.S.A.

A Huntington, Louise S. (Mrs Charles E.)

Hurrell, Mr Henry George, Moorgate, South Brent, Devon, England

A Hurrell, Mrs Henry G.

Ingolfsson, Mr Agnar, Akugerdi 38, Reykjavik, Iceland

Inozemtsev, Dr Alexander, Biological Laboratory, State Pedagogical Institute, Yaroslavska Street Korp. 5, Moscow 1, U.S.S.R.

Iribarren, Juan J., Circunvalacion 5–8°C, Pamplona, Spain

A Iribarren, Mrs J.

* Jany, Mr Joachim Eberhard, Potsdamer Str. 10, 1 Berlin 45, Germany

Jayakar, Mr Suresh D., Genetics and Biometry Laboratory, Government of Orissa, Bhubaneswar—3, Orissa, India

Jellis, Miss Rosemary E., Woodway, Pinner Hill, Middlesex

Jenkins, Dr David, The Nature Conservancy, 12 Hope Terrace, Edinburgh 9.

Jenni, Dr Donald A., Department of Zoology, University of Montana, Missoula, Montana, U.S.A.

Joensen, mag. scient. Anders Holm, Drejøgade 39, København Ø, Denmark

Johnsgard, Dr Paul, Department of Zoology and Physiology, University of Nebraska, Lincoln, Nebraska 68505, U.S.A.

Johnson, Mr Alfred William, c/o Katz Johnson & Co. Ltd., Casilla 327, Santiago de Chile, South America

A Johnson, Elsie (Mrs Alfred W.)

* Johnson, Mr Ernest David Hope,

Crabière Cottage, Route des Mielles, Saint Ouen, Jersey, Channel Islands

Johnson, Mr Robert A., R 1, Bloomington, Indiana, U.S.A.

Johnston, Prof. Richard F., Museum of Natural History, The University of Kansas, Lawrence, Kansas 66045, U.S.A.

Johnstone, Mr Gavin W., Natural History Department, Marischal College, Aberdeen University, Scotland

* Jordan, Mrs Helene J., American Museum of Natural History, 79th Street and Central Park West, New York, N.Y. 10024, U.S.A.

Jørgensen, Mrs Harriet I., Visbygade 10^{II}, København Ø, Denmark

Jouanin, Mr Christian, Laboratoire d'Ornithologie, 55 rue de Buffon, Paris 5^e, France

Kadlec, Dr John A., U.S. Bureau of Sport Fisheries and Wildlife, c/o Massachusetts Audubon Society, Lincoln, Massachussetts, U.S.A.

Kaila, Mr Leo, Bernhardinkatu 1, Helsinki 13, Finland

Kear, Janet (Mrs G.V.T. Matthews), Wildfowl Trust, Slimbridge, Glos., U.K.

Keast, Prof. Allen, Queen's University, Kingston, Ontario, Canada

Keil, Dr Werner, Steinauer Str. 44, 6 Frankfurt/M.—Fechenheim, Germany

Keith, Mr G. Stuart, American Museum of Natural History, Central Park West, New York, N.Y. 10024, U.S.A.

*A Keith, Mrs G. Stuart

Kellogg, Juliet R. (Mrs Waters), 59 Phillips Street, Andover, Mass., U.S.A.

Kemna, Dr Alwin, Krautstr. 59, 56 Wuppertal-Barmen, Germany

# Members of the XIV International Ornithological Congress

A Kemna, Herma (Mrs Alwin)

Kendall, Mr Michael, B.B.C. Natural History Unit, Broadcasting House, Whiteladies Road, Bristol 8.

Kendeigh, Dr S. Charles, Vivarium Building, University of Illinois, Wright & Healey Streets, Champaign, Illinois, U.S.A.

A Kendeigh, Mrs S. Charles

King, Dr James R., Department of Zoology, Washington State University, Pullman, Washington 99163, U.S.A.

Kinsky, Mr Frederick Charles, Dominion Museum, Private Bag, Wellington New Zealand

* Kliefoth, Dr Ilse, Kronsberg 15, 2057 Geesthacht-Krümmel, Germany

Kluyver, Dr Huybert N., van Goghstraat 11, Arnhem, Holland

A Kluyver, Maria (Mrs H.N.)

Kokshaysky, Dr Nikolai V., Institute of Animal Morphology, Academy of Sciences, of the U.S.S.R., Lenin Avenue 33, Moscow W-71, U.S.S.R.

König, Dr Claus, Staatliche, Vogelschutzwarte f. Baden-Württemberg, Favoritepark, 714 Ludwigsburg, Germany

Kowalski, Dr Stanislas, La Chapelle Basse-Mer, Loire-Atlantique, France

Kramer, Dr Helmut, Rheinweg 75, 53 Bonn, Germany

A Kramer, Mrs U. (Mrs Gustav)

Kruijt, Dr Jaap P., Zoological Laboratory, Rijkstraatweg 78, Haren (Gr.), Holland

Kruuk, Dr Hans, Tanzania National Parks, P.O. Box 3134, Arusha, Tanzania

Kuhk, Dr Rudolf, Vogelwarte Radolfzell, 7761 Schloss Möggingen bei Radolfzell, Germany

Kumari, Prof. Dr Erik, Institute of Zoology and Botany, Academy of Sciences of the Estonian S.S.R., 21 Vanemuise Street, Tartu, U.S.S.R.

Kumerloeve, Dr Hans, Hubert-Reissner-Strasse 7, 8032 Gräfelfing (München), Germany

Kunkel, Dr Peter, I.R.S.A.C., Lwiro, Bukavu, Rep. Dem. du Congo

A Kunkel, Irene (Mrs Peter)

* Kuroda, Dr Nagahisa, 2-Chome-17-10, Akasaka, Minato-ku, Tokyo, Japan

Kyllingstad, Mr Henry, Cairo American College, 40 Road 78, Maadi, Egypt

Lachner, Dr Rolf, Nr. 384, 4985 Dünne/Westfalen, Germany

Lack, Dr David, Edward Grey Institute, Botanic Garden, Oxford, England

A Lack, Elizabeth (Mrs David)

Lambourne, Mr George C., The Cottage Farm, Ipsley, Redditch, Worcestershire, England

* Lancaster, Dr Douglas A., Laboratory of Ornithology, Cornell University, Ithaca, N.Y. 14850, U.S.A.

A Lanyon, Vernia (Mrs Wesley E.)

Lanyon, Dr Wesley E., American Museum of Natural History, Central Park West at 79th Street, New York, N.Y. 10024, U.S.A.

Lavigne, Mrs Elizabeth, Les Tourterelles, Couëron (Loire Atlantique), France

A Lavigne, Miss Francoise

Lea, Mr David, The Lodge, Sandy, Bedfordshire, England

Le Brun, Mr Olivier, 17 rue Montmartre, 21 Dijon, France

Lehman, Mrs Claire, 55 rue de Buffon, Paris 5ᵉ, France

Leibbrand, Bib. Eduard, Im Geiger 84, 7 Stuttgart-Cannstatt, Germany

# Members of the XIV International Ornithological Congress

Lemon, Dr Robert, Department of Zoology, McGill University, Montreal, P.Q., Canada

Lersch, Mr Edwin, Sickingerstr. 14, 675 Kaiserslautern, Germany

Lévêque, Mr Raymond, 10 Chemin des Crêts, Petit Saconnex, 1211 Genève 19, Switzerland

A Lindblad, Camilla (Mrs Jan)

Lindblad, Mr Jan, Sandfjördsgatan 110, Johanneshov 7, Sweden

Lister, Mr Robert, 11115–84th Avenue, Edmonton, Alberta, Canada

Lister, Mrs Robert

\* Liversidge, Mr Richard, McGregor Museum, P.O. Box 316, Kimberley, South Africa

Lofts, Dr Brian, Department of Zoology, St Bartholomew's Hospital, Medical College, Charterhouse Square, London E.C.1., England

Löhrl, Dr Hans, Max-Planck-Institut f. Verhaltensphysiologie, Vogelwarte Radolfzell, 7761 Möggingen., Germany

Longfield, Miss Cynthia, The Park House, Castle Mary, Cloyne, Co. Cork, Eire

\* Lopez-Ross, Miss Anita, 14 Place Dauphine, Paris 1ᵉ, France

Løppenthin, Dr Bernt, Torvevej 14, Skovlunde, Denmark

A Løppenthin, Gudrun (Mrs Bernt)

A Løppenthin, Lars

Løppenthin, Viggo

A Lovejoy, Charlotte S. (Mrs Thomas E.)

Lovejoy, Mr Thomas E., Peabody Museum of Natural History, Yale University, New Haven, Connecticut 06520, U.S.A.

Lübcke, Dr Ursula, Pfitznerstr. 73, 2 Hamburg 50, Germany

Ludlow, Mr Alan R., 37 Gloucester Place Mews, London W.1, England

Lyster, Mr Ian H.J., Department of Natural History, Royal Scottish Museum, Edinburgh 1, Scotland

A McCaskill, Isobel Murray (Mrs Lancelot W.)

McCaskill, Mr Lancelot William, 50 Clifford Avenue, Christchurch 1, New Zealand

McChesney, Col. Donald, P.O. Box 591, Syracuse, New York, N.Y. 13201, U.S.A.

A McChesney, Mrs Donald

McEvey, Mr Allan R., Curator of Birds, National Museum of Victoria, Russell Street, Melbourne, Victoria, Australia

Maclean, Mr Gordon L., Zoology Department, Rhodes University, Grahamstown, C.P., South Africa

McManus, Mr Reid, Memramcook, New Brunswick, Canada

McNeice, Lady Yuen Peng, Pointe du Pré, St. Lawrence, Jersey, Channel Islands

Mainardi, Prof. Danilo, Department of Zoology, University of Parma, Parma, Italy

Manninen, Miss Hilkka, Saarijärvi, Finland

Marler, Dr Peter R., The Rockefeller University, New York, N.Y. 10021, U.S.A.

Marris, Mr David, Fairacres, St Leonards Hill, Windsor, Berkshire, England

Marshall, Mr Ian, 37 The Avenue, Durham City, England

Martin, Dr Elden W., Department of Biology, Bowling Green State University, Bowling Green, Ohio 43402, U.S.A.

A Martin, Mary A. (Mrs Elden W.)

# Members of the XIV International Ornithological Congress

Mason, Miss Dora, 21 Alpha House, Kendrick Road, Reading, Berkshire, England

Mathiasson, am. Sven H., Naturhistoriska museet, Slottsskogen, Göteborg 11, Sweden

Matthews, Dr Geoffrey V.T., The Wildfowl Trust, Slimbridge, Gloucestershire, England

Maxse, Miss Violet, Hatchetts, Westburton, Pulborough, Sussex, England

Mayer-Gross, Mr Henry, British Trust for Ornithology, Beech Grove, Tring, Hertfordshire, England

Mayr, Prof. Ernst, Museum of Comparative Zoology, Cambridge, Mass. 02138, U.S.A.

A Mayr, Margaret (Mrs Ernst)

Mead, Mr Christopher J., 4 Beaconsfield Road, Tring, Hertfordshire, England

A Meise, Eva (Mrs Wilhelm)

Meise, Dr Wilhelm, Zoologisches Staatsinstitut und Museum, von-Melle-Park 10, Hamburg 13, Germany

Mengel, Dr Robert M., Museum of Natural History, The University of Kansas, Lawrence, Kansas 66044, U.S.A.

A Mengel, Mrs Robert M.

Merkel, Prof. Dr Friedrich-Wilhelm, Zoologisches Institut der Universität, Siesmayerstr. 70, 6 Frankfurt/M., Germany.

Merkel, Ilse (Mrs Friedrich-Wilhelm)

Mertens, Mr Joseph A.L., Instituut voor Oecologisch Onderzoek, Kemperbergerweg 11, Arnhem, Holland

Messersmith, Dr Donald H., Department of Entomology, University of Maryland College Park, Maryland 20742, U.S.A.

Meyburg, Mr Bernd-Ulrich, Herberstr. 14, 1 Berlin 33 (Grunewald), Germany

*Meyerriecks, Dr Andrew J., Department of Zoology, University of South Florida, Tampa, Florida, 33620, U.S.A.

Middleton, Mr Alexander L.A., Department of Zoology, University of Guelph, Guelph, Ontario, Canada

Mills, Dr James Dewholm, The White House, Claremont Road, Seaford, Sussex, England

A Mills, May Campbell (Mrs James D.)

Moltoni, Dr Edgardo, Museu Civico di Storia Naturale, Corso Venezia 55, Milano, Italy

A Moltoni, Paola (Mrs Edgardo)

Monk, Mr James F., D.M., The Glebe Cottage, Goring-on-Thames, Reading, Berkshire, England

Montgomery, Hon. Just. George H., 4689 Westmount Avenue, Westmount 6, P.Q., Canada

A Montgomery, Mrs George H.

Moreau, Mr Reginald E., Michaeldene, Sutton St Nicholas, Hereford, England

A Morgan, Alice (Mrs Allen H.)

Morgan, Mr Allen H., Mass. Audubon Society, South Great Road, Lincoln, Massachusetts 01773, U.S.A.

Mougin, Mr Jean-Louis, Museum National d'Histoire Naturelle, Laboratoire de Zoologie, 55 rue de Buffon, Paris 5e, France

Mountfort, Mr Guy, Plovers Meadow, Possingworth Park, Blackboys, Sussex, England

A Mountfort, Mrs Guy

Moynihan, Dr Martin H., Smithsonian Tropical Research Institute, Box 2072, Balboa, Canal Zone

Mueller, Prof. Helmut C., Department of Zoology, University of North Carolina, Chapel Hill, North Carolina, U.S.A.

# Members of the XIV International Ornithological Congress

A Mueller, Dr Nancy (Mrs Helmut C.), 305 Mason Farm Road, Chapel Hill, North Carolina

Müller, Dipl.Ing. Günther, Herrenalberstr. 41, 75 Karlsruhe, Germany

Mulligan, Dr (Rev.) James A., St Louis University, Department of Biology, St. Louis, Missouri 63104, U.S.A.

Murton, Dr. Ronald K., Ministry of Agriculture, Fisheries and Food, Tangley Place, Worplesdon, Guildford, Surrey, England

Myres, Dr M. Timothy, Department of Biology, University of Calgary, Calgary, Alberta, Canada

Nattrass, Professor Frederick J., Little Cocklands, Burford, Oxford, England

A Nattrass, Helen B. (Mrs. Frederick J.)

Nearing, Mr C. Turner, 1400 W. Macon Street, Decatur, Ill. 62522, U.S.A.

A Nearing, Mrs C.

Nelson, Dr J. Bryan, Culterty Field Station, Newburgh, Aberdeenshire, Scotland

A Nelson, June (Mrs J. Bryan)

Newton, Dr Ian, Edward Grey Institute, Botanic Garden, Oxford, England

Nicholls, Mr Thomas, University of Minnesota, Museum of Natural History, Minneapolis, Minnesota 55455, U.S.A.

A Nicholls, Mrs Thomas

Nicholson, Mr E. Max, 13 Upper Cheyne Row, Chelsea, London S.W.3, England

Nieboer, Dr Ebel, Biological Laboratories, Free University, de Boelelaan 1087, Amsterdam (Buitenveldert), Holland

Niethammer, Prof. Günther, Koblenzerstr. 162, 53 Bonn, Germany

A Niethammer, Ruth (Mrs Günther)

Nieuwenhuijs, Miss Anna, Kastanjelaan 91, Winschoten, Holland

Nilsson, Fil. hand. Leif, Zoological Institute, Lund, Sweden

Nisbet, Mr Ian C.T., 24 Lorong University, Petaling Jaya, Selangor, Malaya

Niven, Cicely K. (Mrs J.P. Mackie), Amanzi, Uitenhage, Cape Province, S. Africa

A Niven, Mr. J.P. Mackie

Nolan, Mr Val, Jr., 1708 North Fee Lane, Bloomington, Indiana, U.S.A.

A Nolan, Mrs. Val

Nordström, Mr Göran, Zool. Museum, Bird Ringing Department, P. Rautatiek 13, Helsinki 10, Finland

A Nordström, Raili (Mrs Göran)

* Norris, Mr C. Anthony, Clent House, Clent, Worcestershire, England

* North, Mr Myles E. W., Box 8225, Nairobi, Kenya

Nottebohm, Mr Fernando, University of California, Department of Zoology, Berkeley, Calif. 94720, U.S.A.

O'Gorman, Mr Fergus, Game and Wildlife Branch, Department of Lands, Dublin 2, Ireland

Öhman, Mr Carl G., Backgatan 2, P.O. Box 98, Bankeryd, Sweden

A Öhman, Mr Erik

Olney, Mr Peter J.S., The Lodge, Sandy, Bedfordshire

Olrog, Prof. Claes Chr., Instituto Miguel Lillo, S.M. de Tucumán, Argentina

Orenstein, Mr Ronald, 14 High Point Road, Don Mills, Ontario, Canada

Oring, Dr Lewis W., Zoological Laboratory, Universitetsparken 15,

University of Copenhagen, Copenhagen, Denmark

A Oring, Mrs Lewis W.

* O'Rourke, Miss Mary, Memramcook, New Brunswick, Canada

A Orr, Dorothy B. (Mrs Robert T.)

Orr, Dr Robert T., California Academy of Sciences, San Francisco, California 94118, U.S.A.

Österlöf, Mr Sten, Djursholm, Sweden

Ouellet, Mr Henri, Redpath Museum, McGill University, Montreal 2, P.Q., Canada

Palmer, Dr Ralph S., N.Y. State Museum, Albany, N.Y. 12224, U.S.A.

Paludan, Dr Knud, Jagt-og Skovbrugsmuseet, Hörsholm, Denmark

* Park, Mr A. Wallace, Cross House, Norham-on-Tweed, Berwick, Northumberland, England

Parkes, Dr Kenneth C., Carnegie Museum, Pittsburgh, Pennsylvania 15213, U.S.A.

A Parkes, Mrs Kenneth C.

A Parrinder, Eileen D. (Mrs Eric R.)

Parrinder, Mr Eric R., 91 Weald Road, Sevenoaks, Kent, England

Patterson, Dr Ian J., Culterty Field Station, Newburgh, Aberdeenshire, Scotland

Payton, Mr Harold W., Lianda, Hill Close, Harrow on the Hill, Middlesex, England

Peal, Mr Ronald, 24 Creighton Avenue, London N.10, England

Peall, Doreen (Mrs Oscar), Hatfield Farm, Oare, Marlborough, Wiltshire, England

A Peall, Mr Oscar

* Peleaux, Mrs. Gloria M., Museum of Natural History, University of Minnesota, Minneapolis, Minnesota, 55455, U.S.A.

Penney, Dr Richard L., New York Zoological Society and Rockefeller University, New York, N.Y. 10021, U.S.A.

Pennie, Dr Ian D., The Hollies, Golspie, Sutherland, Scotland

A Pennie, Janet (Mrs Ian D.)

Pepperell, Ruth (Mrs David A.), The Waves, Ledge Road, Newport, Rhode Island, U.S.A.

Perdeck, Dr Albert C., Vogeltrekstation, Kemperbergerweg 11, Arnhem, Holland

Perrins, Dr Christopher M., Edward Grey Institute, Botanic Garden, Oxford

A Perrins, Mary (Mrs Christopher)

Petersen, Mr Bernhard, Heidestr. 1A, 295 Leer-Heisfelde, Germany

Peterson, Dr Roger T., Neck Road, Old Lyme, Conn., U.S.A.

A Peterson, Mrs Roger T.

Pettingill, Dr Olin Sewall, Jr., Laboratory of Ornithology, Cornell University, Ithaca, New York 14850, U.S.A.

* Pettitt, Mr Garth, 16 Chilberton drive, Merstham, Surrey, England

Pfeifer, Dir. Sebastian O., Vogelschutzwarte F.a.M., Steinauerstr. 33, 6 Frankfurt a.M.-Fechenheim, Germany

Phelps, Mr William H., Jr., Colección Ornitológica Phelps, Apartado 2009, Caracas, Venezuela

A Phelps, Kathleen D. (Mrs William H.)

Philbrick, Miss Hazel B., Apt. 201, 5630 Pershing, St Louis, Missouri, 63112, U.S.A.

* Phillips, Dr Allan R., Apartado Postal 19-138, México 19, D.F., México

Phillips, Mrs C. Ruth, 43 Oxford House, Little Waltham, Chelmsford, Essex

# Members of the XIV International Ornithological Congress

Pierson, Miss Aileen, 810 Gonzalez Drive, Apt. 12–A, San Francisco, California 94132, U.S.A.

Pikula, Mr Jiri, Czechoslovakia Academy of Sciences, Drobného 28, BRNO, Czechoslovakia

Pinowski, Dr Jan, Institute of Ecology of Polish Academy of Sciences, Nowy Swiat 72, Warsaw, Poland

Pollock, Miss Margaret, The Saltings, Castlerock, Co. Londonderry, N. Ireland

Pomeroy, Mr Derek, Dept. of Forestry and Natural Resources, University of Edinburgh, 10 George Square, Edinburgh 8, Scotland

Portenko, Prof. Leonid A., Zoologichesky Peruelok 1, App. 28, Leningrad 79, U.S.S.R.

Potts, Dr G. Richard, Department of Zoology, University of Durham, South Road, Durham City, England

A Pough, Moira F. (Mrs Richard H.)

Pough, Mr Richard H., 33 Highbrook Avenue, Pelham, N.Y. 10803, U.S.A.

Poulsen, Dr Holger, Zoological Garden, Copenhagen F, Denmark

A Preuss, Bodil (Mrs Niels)

Preuss, Mr Niels, Zoologisk Museum, Universitetsparken 15, Kobenhavn Ø, Denmark

Prévost, Dr Jean, Museum National d'Histoire Naturelle, Laboratoire d'Ornithologie, 55 rue de Buffon, Paris 5ᵉ, France

Preywisch, Mr Kurt, Asgarstr. 19, 347 Höxter, Germany

Price, Miss Katharine, 69 Jack Straw's Lane, Oxford, England

Prou, Miss Reine, 40 rue de Gigant, Nantes, Loire-Atlantique, France

Proud, Mrs Desirée, Milton House, Milton Damerel, Devon, England

*A Przygodda, Annemarie (Mrs Wilfried)

* Przygodda, Dr Wilfried, Agidiusstr. 94, 43 Essen-Bredeny, Germany

Putnam, Mrs Theresa, 36 Addington Road, Brookline, Mass. 02046, U.S.A.

Quilliam, Mrs Helen, R.R.1, Kingston, Ontario, Canada

Rabaey, Prof. Marcel L., Department of Ophthalmology, University of Ghent, Belgium

Radford, Dr (Mrs) Mary C., Ridgeway, Harberton Mead, Oxford, England

Rahne, Miss Ute Irmgard, Bundesallee 50, 3301 Braunschweig, Germany

Rand, Dr Austin L., Chicago Natural History Museum, Roosevelt Road and Lake Shore Drive, Chicago, Illinois 60605, U.S.A.

A Rand, Rheua M. (Mrs Austin)

Reille, Baron Antoine, 10 rue Eugène Labiche, Paris 16ᵉ, France

Rhodes, Miss Georgia, Hildersham Hall Cambridge, England

Richardson, Dr Frank, Department of Zoology, University of Washington, Seattle, Wash 98105, U.S.A

Richter, Mr Dieter, Walkürenring 54, 33 Braunschweig, Germany

A Ridgway, Margaret (Mrs Richard)

Ridgway, Mr Richard H., Rossmore, Mallow, Co. Cork, Eire

Ripley, Prof. S. Dillon, Smithsonian Institution, Washington D.C. 20560, U.S.A.

A Ripley, Mrs S. Dillon

Riska, Mr Sven, Över-Malax, Finland

Robbins, Mr Chandler S., Migratory Bird Populations Station, U.S. Bureau of Sport, Fisheries and Wildlife, Laurel, Maryland, U.S.A.

A Robbins, Eleanor, Mrs Chandler S.

Robbins, Mr John, 123b Parkgate Road, Coventry, Warwickshire, England

Roberts, Mr Kevin, 85 Elers Road, Ealing, London W.13, England

Rogge, Mr Einar, Box 24, c/o Lindgson, Staffansdorp, Sweden

Rokitansky, Dr Gerth, Jodlgasse 7/7, A 1130 Wien 13, Austria

Rooke, Dr Kenneth B., Cranborne, Wimborne, Dorset, England

Rooth, Mr Jan, RIVON, Laan van Beek en Royen 40–41, Zeist, Holland

Ross, Mr C. Chandler, 710 Wolcott Drive, Philadelphia, Pa. 19118, U.S.A.

Ross, Miss Rosamond H., 1720 Larch street, Ste. 202, Vancouver, British Columbia, Canada

Rossello, Mrs Isabel, 6 Port Noir, 1207, Genève, Switzerland

A Rothery, Lillian (Mrs Willard)

Rothery, Mr Willard A., 3629 Gunston Road, Alexandria, Virginia 22302, U.S.A.

Roux, Mr Francis, Laboratoire de Zoologie, Muséum National d'Histoire Naturelle, 55 rue de Buffon, Paris 5e, France

Rowan, Mrs Mary K., Percy Fitzpatrick Institute of African Ornithology, University of Cape Town, Rondebosch, Cape, South Africa

Royama, Mr Tomoo, Forestry Research Laboratory, P.O. Box 35, Sillery, Quebec B, Canada

Rudebeck, Dr Gustaf, Zoologiska Institutionen, Lund, Sweden

Rudescu, Mr Ludwig, Comisia Monumentelor Naturii a Academiei R.S.R., Splaiul Independentei 296, Bucharest, Rumania

Runnerström, Mr Bengt, E. Dahlbergsgat 16, Helsingborg, Sweden

Ruschi, Prof. Dr Augusto, Museu de Biologia Prof. Mello Leitao, Santa Teresa, E. E. Santo, Brazil

Rusk, Miss Margaret S., 805 Comstock Avenue, Syracuse, N.Y. 13210, U.S.A.

* Russell, Dr Stephen M., Department of Zoology, University of Arizona, Tucson, Arizona 85721, U.S.A.

*A Russell, Mrs Stephen

Rutschke, Dr E., Institut f. Zoologie, Allee nach Sanssouci, Villa Leignitz, Potsdam, East Germany

Rydzewski, Prof. Wladyslaw, Laboratory of Ornithology, Wroclaw, Seinkiewicza 21, Poland

Safriel, Mr Uriel, Department of Zoology, Hebrew University, Jerusalem, Israel

Salmon, Col. H. Morrey, 24 Bryngwyn Road, Cyncoed, Cardiff, Wales

A Salmon, Mrs H. Morrey

Salomonsen, Prof. Dr Finn, Zoological Museum, Universitetsparken 15, Copenhagen 15, Denmark

*A Salomonsen, Mrs Finn

Saltford, Mr Herb, 6 West Winding, Poughkeepsie, N.Y. 12601, U.S.A.

A Saltford, Mrs Herb

* Sanders, Miss K. Friel, Broadwater Point, Churchton, Maryland, U.S.A.

Sanger, Mrs M. Bartlett, P.O. Box 954, Winter Park, Florida, U.S.A.

Sarles, Mr John, Ste. 206, 1855 Balsam Street, Vancouver 9, B.C., Canada

Sauer, Dr E.G. Franz, Department of Zoology, University of Florida, Gainesville, Florida 32601, U.S.A.

A Sauer, Dr Eleonore M. (Mrs E.G. Franz)

Savage, Mr Thomas, Pine Bond, Route 1, South St Paul, Minnesota, U.S.A.

# Members of the XIV International Ornithological Congress

A Savage, Mrs Thomas

Schaefer, Dr Glen, Farriers Lodge, Walton-by-Kimcote, Rugby, Warwickshire, England

A Schaefer, Mary (Mrs Glen)

Schaefer, Mr Willard H., 132 Pandora Avenue North, Kitchener, Ontario, Canada

Schifferli, Dr Alfred, Schweiz. Vogelwarte, 6204 Sempach, Switzerland

Schifferli, Mrs Alfred

Schoennagel, Dr Erich, Am Meisenbrink 14, 325 Hameln, Germany

A Schoennagel, Stephanie (Mrs Erich)

* Schreiber, Mr Ralph W., 9 Coburn Hall, University of Maine, Orono, Maine 04473, U.S.A.

Schüz, Prof. Dr Ernst, Staatl. Museum für Naturkunde in Stuttgart, Schloss Rosenstein, 7 Stuttgart, Germany

Schüz, Hanna (Mrs Ernst)

Schwarz, Mr Martin, Elisabethenstrasse 24, CH-4000 Basel, Switzerland

Schymura, Dr Reinhard, Ernst-Platz-Str. 36, 8 München 54, Germany

Scott, Dr David, Department of Zoology, University of Western Ontario, London, Ontario, Canada

A Scott, Mr Peter Markham, New Grounds, Slimbridge, Gloucestershire

Seel, Dr David C., Department of Zoology, University College of Wales, Penglais, Aberystwyth, Cardiganshire, Wales

Serventy, Dr Dominic, C.S.I.R.O., Division of Wildlife Research, Clayton Road, Helena Valley, Western Australia

A Serventy, Gertrude (Mrs Dominic)

A Shannon, Edna (Mrs George)

Shannon, Mr George, Oak Tree House, Hythe Road, Willesborough, Ashford, Kent, England

Shiloh, Mrs Rebecca, Usishkin 56, Tel-Aviv, Israel

Short, Dr Lester L., Jr., American Museum of Natural History, Central Park W. at 79 St., New York, N.Y. 10024, U.S.A.

Shugg, Mr Harry B., Department of Fisheries and Fauna, 108 Adelaide Terrace, Perth, Western Australia

Sibley, Prof. Charles G., Peabody Museum of Natural History, Yale University, New Haven, Connecticut, U.S.A.

A Sibley, Frances L. (Mrs Charles G.)

Sick, Dr Helmut, Museu Nacional, Quinta da Bôa Vista, Rio de Janeiro, Brazil

A Sick, Marga (Mrs Helmut)

Simmons, Mr Kenneth E.L., Department of Psychology, University of Bristol, 8 Berkeley Square, Bristol 8, England

Singer, Mr Arthur, 30 Hightop Lane, Jericho, L.I., New York 11753, U.S.A.

* Skead, Mr Cuthbert J., 4 Maitland Road, King William's Town, C.P., Africa

Sladen, Dr William J.L., Johns Hopkins University, 615 N. Wolfe Street, Baltimore, Md. 21205, U.S.A.

* Slater, Miss H. Elizabeth, Broadwater Point, Churchton, Maryland, U.S.A.

Slater, Mr Peter J.B., Department of Zoology, University of Edinburgh, West Mains Road, Edinburgh 9, Scotland

* Slud, Mr Paul, Smithsonian Institution, United States National Museum, Washington, D.C. 20560, U.S.A.

*A Slud, Mrs Paul

* Smidt van Gelder, Mr H.E., Meester Enscedeweg 2, Aerdenhout, Holland

Smith, Charlotte E. (Mrs Charles L.),

75 Westland Road, Weston, Mass. 02193, U.S.A.

Smith, Mr Victor Wallace, Rosebery, Moffat, Dumfriesshire, Scotland

A Smith, Susan T. (Mrs W. John)

Smith, Dr W. John, Department of Biology, L.L., University of Pennsylvania, Philadelphia, Pa. 19104, U.S.A.

Smithers, Dr Don L., Music Department, Syracuse University, Syracuse, New York, U.S.A.

Smythies, Mr Bertram E, Lark Rise, San Diego, Apartado 3, Estepona (Malaga), Spain.

A Smythies, Mrs Bertram E.

Snow, Dr David W., British Trust for Ornithology, Beech Grove, Tring, Hertfordshire, England

Snyder, Miss Dorothy E., Peabody Museum, Salem, Mass., U.S.A.

Somadikarta, Dr Soekarja, Museum Zoologicum, Bogoriense, Bogor, Indonesia

Spaans, Drs Arie L., Oosterend 29, Post Hoorn, Terschelling, Holland

A Spaans-Scheen, Drs Marianne J. (Mrs Arie L.)

Spiers, Doris Huestis (Mrs J. Murray), Cobble Hill, R.R.2, Pickering, Ontario, Canada

Spiers, Dr J. Murray, R.R.2, Pickering, Ontario, Canada

Spencer, Mr Robert, Warwick House, Grove Road, Tring, Hertfordshire, England

Spofford, Dr Walter R., State University of New York, Medical Center, Syracuse, N.Y. 13210, U.S.A.

Spurway, Dr Helen, Genetics and Biometry Laboratory, Government of Orissa, Bhubaneswar 3, Orissa, India

A Stein, Alice P. (Mrs Robert C.)

Stein, Dr Robert C., Biology Department, State University College, Buffalo, New York, 14222, U.S.A.

A Steinbacher, Elfriede (Mrs Joachim)

Steinbacher, Dr Joachim, Senckenberg Museum, Senckenberg Anlage 25, Frankfurt, Germany

Steiniger, Prof. Dr Fritz, Niedersaechsisches Landesmuseum, Am Maschpark 5, 3 Hannover, Germany

Stephan, Dr Burkhard, Zool. Museum, Invalidenstr. 43, 104 Berlin, Germany

A Stephens, Mrs Darthula Davis, 2502 Keating Lane, Austin, Texas 78703, U.S.A.

Sternberg, Mr Helmut, Im Schapenkampe 11, 33 Braunschweig, Germany

Stettenheim, Dr Peter, Avian Anatomy Project, Dept. of Poultry Science, Anthony Hall, Michigan State University, East Lansing, Michigan 48823, U.S.A.

Stewart, Miss Susan A., Pendennis, 11 Oakley Hill, Wimborne, Dorset, England

Stickney, Mr Albert, Jr., Leetes Island, Guilford, Connecticut, U.S.A.

A Stickney, Mrs. Albert, Jr.

A Stickney, Mr Albert, III

A Stickney, Mr H. Herrick

Stingelin, Mr Albert, Neusatzweg 5, 4133 Pratteln, Switzerland

Stonehouse, Dr Bernard, Zoology Department, Canterbury University, Christchurch, New Zealand

Storer, Professor Robert W., Museum of Zoology, The University of Michigan, Ann Arbor, Michigan 48104, U.S.A.

A Storer, Mrs Robert W.

A Stortenbeker, Ank (Mrs Claus)

Stortenbeker, Mr Claus, Institute for

# Members of the XIV International Ornithological Congress

Biological Field Research, Kemperbergerweg 11, Arnhem, Holland

Stresemann, Prof. Erwin, 28 Kamillen-Str., Berlin 45, Germany

Stresemann, Vesta (Mrs Erwin)

Strömberg, Giv. ing. Gunnar, Nya Skeppsbrogatan 1, Karlskrona, Sweden

A Strömberg, Fil.mag. Maj Lis (Mrs Gunnar)

Strosnider, Miss Ruth C., 4115 Wisconsin Ave. N.W., Washington, D.C. 20016, U.S.A.

Summers, Mr Derick D.B., Gallinula, Longmoor Road, Greatham, Liss, Hampshire, England

Summers-Smith, Dr J. Denis, Merlewood, Hutton Gate, Guisborough, Yorkshire, England

Suthers, Dr Roderick A., Department of Anatomy and Physiology, Indiana University, Bloomington, Indiana 47405, U.S.A.

Sutter, Dr Ernst, Naturhistorisches Museum, Augustinerstrasse 2, 4000 Basel, Switzerland

Swales, Mr Michael K., Denstone College, Uttoxeter, Staffordshire, England

Szijj, Dr Josef, Vogelwarte Radolfzell 7761 Möggingen, Germany

Szijj, Dr Laszlo J., California State Polytechnic College, Biology, Pomona, Calif. 91716, U.S.A.

A Szijj, Mrs Laszlo J.

Szöke, Mr Peter, Institute of Genetics of the Hungarian Academy of Sciences, Herman Otto ut 15, Budapest II, Hungary

* Taapken, Mr Jaap, Utrechtsweg 43, Hilversum, Holland

Täcklind Mrs Elisabeth, Skogsgatan 10, Katrineholm, Sweden

Tahvonen, Mr Eino, Teljäntie 9 A 9, Helsinki, Finland

A Tahvonen, Mrs Eino

Tamisier, Mr Alain, La Tour du Valat, le Sambuc, Bouches du Rhône, France

Tanner, Prof. James T., Department of Zoology, University of Tennessee, Knoxville, Tenn. 37916, U.S.A.

A Tanner, Mrs James

Tate, Mr Peter, Half Acre, Rooks Hill, Loudwater, Rickmansworth, Hertfordshire, England

Taylor, Mrs John B., 7326—118-A Street, Edmonton, Alberta, Canada

A Taylor, Philip

Temple Lang, Mr John, Hermaness, Hainault Road, Foxrock, Co. Dublin, Ireland

Thiede, Dr Walter, Lissingstr. 30, 2 Hamburg 22, Germany

Thielcke, Dr Gerhard, Vogelwarte Radolfzell, 7761 Möggingen, Germany

Thomson, Sir A. Landsborough, 42 Girdwood Road, Southfields, London S.W.18, England

A Thomson, Lady

Thorpe Prof. William H., 9 Wilberforce Road, Cambridge, England

A Thorpe, W. Mary (Mrs. William)

Timmermann, Dr habil. Günter, Zoologisches Museum, von-Melle-Park 10, 2 Hamburg 13, Germany

Tinbergen, Prof. Niko, Department of Zoology, Parks Road, Oxford, England

A Tinbergen, Lies (Mrs Niko)

A Tipton, Dr Isabel H. (Mrs Samuel R.)

Tipton, Dr Samuel R., Department of Zoology and Entomology, The University of Tennessee, Knoxville, Tenn. 37916, U.S.A.

Todt, Dr Dietmar, Zoologisches In-

# Members of the XIV International Ornithological Congress

stitut, Katharinenstrasse 20, 78 Freiburg i B, Germany

\* Tongue, Mr Philip, Royal Schools of Music, P.O. Box 4224, Cape Town, S. Africa

Tordoff, Dr Harrison B., Museum of Zoology, University of Michigan, Ann Arbor, Michigan, U.S.A.

A Tordoff, Jean (Mrs Harrison B.)

Tornielli, Dr Annibale, Arola (Parma), Italy

\*A Tornielli, Marisa (Mrs Annibale)

Tousey, Miss Katharine, 22 Grand View Avenue, Somerville, Mass. 02143, U.S.A.

Trautman, Dr Milton B., Ohio State Museum, Columbus, Ohio 43210, U.S.A.

A Trautman, Dr Mary A. (Mrs Milton B.)

Traylor, Mr Melvin A., Field Museum of Natural History, Roosevelt Road and Lake Shore Drive, Chicago, Illinois 60605, U.S.A.

Tretzel, Dr Erwin, Zoologisches Institut, Universitätsstrasse 19, 852 Erlangen, Germany

A Tretzel, Mrs Erwin

Trumbull, Mr Fred W., 80 Main Street, Los Altos, California 94022, U.S.A.

A Trumbull, Virginia M. (Mrs Fred W.)

Turner, Dr Robert W., 7724–139 Street, Edmonton, Alberta, Canada

A Turner, Mrs Robert W.

Turtle, Mr Lancelot J., 17/21 Castle Place, Belfast 1, N Ireland

\* Udvardy, Prof. Miklos D.F., Professor of Life Sciences, Sacramento State College, Sacramento, Calif. 95819, U.S.A.

Ulfstrand, Fil.lic. Staffan, Zoologiska Institutionen, Lund, Sweden

Upton, Mrs Rosemary, Park Lodge,

Margaretting, Ingatestone, Essex, England

Urban, Dr Emil K., Department of Biology, Faculty of Science, Haile Sellassie I University, P.O. Box 399, Addis Ababa, Ethiopia

Valverde, Dr José A., Estacion Biological de Doñana, Paraguay 1, Sevilla, Spain

van Balen, Mr Johan H., Institut voor Oecologisch Onderzoek, Kemperbergerweg 11, Arnhem, Holland

A van Balen, F.E. (Mrs Johan H.)

\* van den Anker, Mr Carel A., Diedenweg 117[II], Wageningen, Holland

Vane, Dr Robert F., 600 Dows Building, Cedar Rapids, Iowa 52401, U.S.A.

A Vane, Mrs Robert F.

van Geen, Baroness C.W., 3 Melchior Treublaan, Heemstede, Holland

van Hasselt, Mr Felix A.C.M., 26, Raadhuis Straat, Roosendaal, Holland

van Marle, Mr John G., Dam 27, Amsterdam, Holland

\* van Oosten, Mr Jan Roger, 1221 22nd East, Seattle, Washington 98102, U.S.A.

Vaucher, Mr Charles-André, Vieux Clos, 1223-Cologny, Genève, Switzerland

A Vetter, Gertrud (Mrs Walter)

Vetter, Fab. Walter, Im Geiger 25, 7 Stuttgart-Badcannstatt, Germany

Vincent, Col. Jack, I.C.B.P., c/o I.U.C.N., 1110 Morges, Switzerland

A Vincent, Mrs Jack

Viukari, Mrs Rauni, Luopioinen, Finland

\* Vleugel, Mr Dies A., A. de Haenstraat 53, The Hague 8, Holland

A von Haartman, Brita (Mrs Lars)

von Haartman, Dr Lars, Dept. of Zoology, University of Helsingfors, Finland

# Members of the XIV International Ornithological Congress

A Voous, H.C. (Mrs Karel)

Voous, Prof. Dr Karel H., Zoological Laboratory, Free University, de Boelelaan 1087 Amsterdam, Holland

Vuilleumier, Mr François, Museum of Comparative Zoology, Harvard University, Cambridge, Massachusetts 02138, U.S.A.

A Vuilleumier, Mrs François

Wahlberg, Major Sven, A 8 ing 5, Boden, Sweden

Wahlström, Dr Sten, Royal Inst. of Technology, Stockholm 70, Sweden

Walcott, Prof Charles, Department of Biology, Tufts University, Medford, Mass. 02155, U.S.A.

Wallace, Dr. George J., Department of Zoology, Michigan State University, East Lansing, Michigan 48823, U.S.A.

A Wallace, Martha (Mrs George J.), 517 Ann Street, East Lansing, Michigan 48823, U.S.A.

Wallraff, Dr Hans G., Max-Planck-Institut f. Verhaltenphysiologie, 8131 Seewiesen-u.-Starnberg, Germany

Walters, Mr Michael P., Osprey's Nest, 62 Mark Street, Portrush, Co. Antrim

Walters Davies, Mr. Peter, The Nature Conservancy, Plas Gogerddan, Aberystwyth, Cardiganshire, Wales

* Warner, Prof. Dwain, Museum of Natural History, University of Minnesota, Minneapolis, Minn. 55455, U.S.A.

A Wassenich, Cecile (Mrs Victor)

Wassenich, Mr Victor, 52 rue Jacquinot, Bettembourg, Gd. Duchy of Luxembourg

Wasson, Mrs Isabel B., 606 Thatcher Ave., River Forest, Illinois 60305, U.S.A.

Waterston, Mr George, Scottish Centre for Ornithology and Bird Protection, 21 Regent Terrace, Edinburgh 7, Scotland

Waterston, Irene (Mrs George)

Watt, Mr James P.C., 42 Grandview Crescent, Opoho, Dunedin, New Zealand

Watson, Dr Adam, Nature Conservancy Unit of Grouse and Moorland Ecology, Blackhall, Banchory, Kincardineshire, Scotland

Watson, Dr George E., Division of Birds, U.S. National Museum, Smithsonian Institution, Washington D.C. 20560, U.S.A.

Wattel, Mr Jan, Zoölogisch Museum, Plantage Middenlaan 53, Amsterdam C, Holland

Wayre, Mr Philip, Norfolk Wildlife Park and Ornamental Pheasant Trust, Great Witchingham, Norwich, England

A Weeden, Judith (Mrs Robert)

Weeden, Dr Robert, Box 425, College, Alaska, U.S.A.

A Weeks, Josephine (Mrs Mangum)

Weeks, Mr Mangum, 219 North Royal Street, Alexandria, Virginia, U.S.A.

Weidringer, Dr Wilhelm, Wagnerstr. 4/1, 8480 Weiden (Oberpfalz), Germany

Weil, Dr med. Clara, Solothurnerstrasse 8, 4600 Olten, Switzerland

Weismann, Mr Carl, Strødam, Hillerød, Denmark

Welty, Dr J. Carl, Rte. 1, Beloit, Wisconsin 53511, U.S.A.

A Welty, Mrs J. Carl

* Werth, Miss Irene, Department of Zoology, The University, Leeds 2.

Wetmore, Dr Alexander, Smithsonian Institution, Washington, D.C. 20560, U.S.A.

# Members of the XIV International Ornithological Congress

Weydt, Mrs Ursula, Wilhelm-Brandes-Str. 4, 334 Wolfenbüttel, Germany

Whitman, Mr Burton, Merepoint Road, Brunswick, Maine, U.S.A.

A Whitman, Mrs Burton

Williamson, Mr Kenneth, British Trust for Ornithology, Beech Grove, Tring, Hertfordshire, England

Willis, Mr Paul R., Woods Hole Oceanographic Institution, Woods Hole, Mass. 02543, U.S.A.

Wilson, Mr David R., British Trust for Ornithology, Beech Grove, Tring, Hertfordshire, England

Wiltschko, Mr Wolfgang, Zool. Inst. der Universität, Siesmayerstr. 70, 6 Frankfurt am Main, Germany

Wingate, Mr David B., P.O. Box 437, Hamilton, Bermuda

A Wingate, Mrs David B.

Winterbottom, Prof. John Miall, Percy Fitzpatrick Institute of African Ornithology, University of Cape Town, Rondebosch, C.P., South Africa

*A Winterbottom, Marjorie Grace (Mrs John M.)

Witts, Dr Kenneth J., 478A Ipswich Road, Colchester, Essex, England

* Wolk, Dr Robert G., Department of Biology, Adelphi University, Garden City, New York, 11530, U.S.A.

Won, Dr Pyong-Oh, Department of Biology, Kyung Hee University, Seoul, Korea

Woodcock, Mr Martin, 34 Hill Road, Theydon Bois, Essex, England

Woolfenden, Dr Glen E., Dept. of Zoology, University of South Florida, Tampa, Florida 33620, U.S.A.

Woolfenden, Mrs Glen, 8011 Cardinal Drive, Tampa, Florida 33610, U.S.A.

Wright, Mr Ernest N., Ministry of Agriculture, Tangley Place, Worplesdon, Guildford, Surrey, England

Wüst, Prof. Dr Walter, Hohenlohestr. 61, 8 München 19, Germany

A Wynne-Edwards, J.C. (Mrs. Vero C.)

Wynne-Edwards, Prof. Vero C., Marischal College, University of Aberdeen, Aberdeen, Scotland

Yakobi, Dr Vladimir E., Institute of Animal Morphology, U.S.S.R. Academy of Sciences, Vavilova Street 12 corp. 2, Moscow V-133, U.S.S.R.

Yamashina, Dr Yoshimaro, 49 Nampeidai-machi, Shibuya-ku, Tokyo, Japan

A Yamashina, Sugako (Mrs Yoshimaro)

Yapp, Mr Brunsdon, Dept. of Zoology and Comparative Physiology, The University, Birmingham 15, England

Yeatman, Mr Jammes Laurent, 11 Quai Voltaire, Paris 7e, France

Zastrov, Mr Mait, Skebokvarnsv. 265–9, Bandhagen, Sweden

Zim, Dr Herbert S., P.O. Box 34, Tavernier, Florida 33070, U.S.A.

A Zim, Sonia B. (Mrs Herbert S.), Plantation Key, Tavernier, Florida 33070, U.S.A.

Zink, Dr Gerhardt, 7761 Moeggingen bei Radolfzell, Germany

* Zink, Trude (Mrs. Gerhardt)

A Zusi, Luvia (Mrs Richard)

Zusi, Dr Richard, Division of Birds, U.S. National Museum, Washington, D.C., U.S.A.